D1273180

Fundamental Concepts of Higher Algebra

Fundamental Concepts of Higher Algebra

BY

A. ADRIAN ALBERT

Professor of Mathematics, The University of Chicago

THE UNIVERSITY OF CHICAGO PRESS

CHICAGO & LONDON

THE UNIVERSITY OF CHICAGO COMMITTEE ON PUBLICATIONS IN THE PHYSICAL SCIENCES

*

A. ADRIAN ALBERT
HORACE R. BYERS
EARL A. LONG
WARREN C. JOHNSON
JOSEPH E. MAYER
WILLIAM H. ZACHARIASEN

QA 155
.A5

INDIANA
UNIVERSITY
LIBRARY

NORTHWEST

Library of Congress Catalog Card Number: 56-5129

THE UNIVERSITY OF CHICAGO PRESS, CHICAGO & LONDON
The University of Toronto Press, Toronto 5, Canada

© *1956 by The University of Chicago. Published 1956. Fifth Impression 1963. Composed and printed by* THE UNIVERSITY OF CHICAGO PRESS, *Chicago, Illinois, U.S.A.*

Preface

The existence of the digital computer and other devices using binary digits has resulted in a renewal of interest in the mathematical theory of finite fields. The main exposition of the foundations of the subject was written over fifty years ago and has been out of print for many years. A new exposition using the modern theory of algebraic extensions of arbitrary fields seems very timely and is the principal reason for the preparation of the present text.

We give here a compact and self-contained exposition of the fundamental concepts of modern algebra which are needed for a clear understanding of the place of finite field theory in modern mathematics. In the first chapter we introduce the primitive concepts on which algebra is based and go on to a fairly complete exposition of the basic notions about finite groups, including the theory of composition series in general form.

In chapter ii we present the concepts of ring, ideal, difference ring, field, polynomials over a ring, and the simple cases of the integral domain of ordinary integers and of polynomials in one indeterminate over a field. The material of this chapter is then the foundation for the later theory of algebraic extensions.

A logical exposition of the theory of field extension is impossible without a preliminary exposition of the theory of vector spaces, linear mappings, and matrices. This is then the subject of chapter iii. All of the theory of matrices which seems to be appropriate is presented, including the theory of matrix equivalence over a polynomial ring and the theory of similarity. Since the theory of quadratic forms and orthogonal equivalence seems out of context, it is not presented.

In chapter iv we provide a substantial exposition of the theory of algebraic extensions of fields, including the Artin version of the galois theory. The chapter ends with a new and remarkably simple proof of the normal basis theorem for cyclic fields.

The real reason for the book is chapter v, in which we present a modern and improved exposition of the foundations of the theory of finite fields. Galois theory and group theory are used where they belong, and many proofs are improved thereby.

It is hoped that this new text will prove to be a valuable aid not only to those who wish to learn the basic theorems on finite fields but to those who wish to refresh their knowledge of modern algebra or to review a series of courses on modern algebra which they may have just completed. The text should also be usable as a first course in the subject, provided that it is recognized that the presentation is exceedingly compact and requires slow and careful classroom discussion.

The preparation of this text was supported by the Department of Defense. The author also wishes to acknowledge the very kind assistance of Drs. W. A. Blankinship and E. C. Paige, who proofread the original manuscript with great care.

A. ADRIAN ALBERT

Table of Contents

CHAPTER I

Groups

1. Sets and mappings. Abstract algebra is concerned with the study of certain mathematical objects called *algebraic systems*. Each system consists of a set of elements, one or more operations on these elements, and a number of assumptions (about the properties of the elements with respect to the operations) called the *defining postulates*. In this first section we shall introduce some of the elementary notions about sets which form the basis of the precise definitions which we shall present of several algebraic systems.

Let $\mathfrak{A}$ be a set whose elements $a, b, c, \ldots$, are *any objects whatever*, and let $\mathfrak{B}$ be a second set. Then we say that $\mathfrak{B}$ *is contained in* $\mathfrak{A}$, and write $\mathfrak{B} \subseteq \mathfrak{A}$, if every element of $\mathfrak{B}$ is in $\mathfrak{A}$. If $\mathfrak{B} \subseteq \mathfrak{A}$, we call $\mathfrak{B}$ a *subset* of $\mathfrak{A}$. We may also write $\mathfrak{A} \supseteq \mathfrak{B}$ and say that $\mathfrak{A}$ *contains* $\mathfrak{B}$. If $\mathfrak{A} \supseteq \mathfrak{B}$ and at least one element of $\mathfrak{A}$ is not in $\mathfrak{B}$, we say that $\mathfrak{B}$ is a *proper subset* of $\mathfrak{A}$ and write $\mathfrak{A} \supset \mathfrak{B}$ ($\mathfrak{A}$ *properly contains* $\mathfrak{B}$), or $\mathfrak{B} \subset \mathfrak{A}$ ($\mathfrak{B}$ is properly contained in $\mathfrak{A}$). The set having *no* elements is called the *empty* set.

The *intersection* of two sets $\mathfrak{A}$ and $\mathfrak{B}$ is the set of all elements which are in both $\mathfrak{A}$ and $\mathfrak{B}$. We designate this set by $\mathfrak{A} \cap \mathfrak{B}$. If $\mathfrak{C} \subseteq \mathfrak{A}$ and $\mathfrak{C} \subseteq \mathfrak{B}$, then $\mathfrak{C}$ is called a *common subset* of $\mathfrak{A}$ and $\mathfrak{B}$. Every common subset of $\mathfrak{A}$ and $\mathfrak{B}$ is a subset of $\mathfrak{A} \cap \mathfrak{B}$.

The *union* of $\mathfrak{A}$ and $\mathfrak{B}$ is the logical sum of $\mathfrak{A}$ and $\mathfrak{B}$. It consists of all elements which are either in $\mathfrak{A}$ or in $\mathfrak{B}$. We designate it by $\mathfrak{A} \cup \mathfrak{B}$.

The concepts of intersection and union may be generalized readily to several sets. Thus if $\mathfrak{A}_1, \ldots, \mathfrak{A}_n$ are sets, we define their intersection $\mathfrak{A}_1 \cap \mathfrak{A}_2 \cap \cdots \cap \mathfrak{A}_n$ to be the set of all elements which are simultaneously in every one of the sets $\mathfrak{A}_1, \ldots, \mathfrak{A}_n$. The union $\mathfrak{A}_1 \cup \mathfrak{A}_2 \cup \cdots \cup \mathfrak{A}_n$ consists of all the elements in all the sets $\mathfrak{A}_1, \ldots, \mathfrak{A}_n$. Note that the equation $(\mathfrak{A}_1 \cap \mathfrak{A}_2) \cap \mathfrak{A}_3 = \mathfrak{A}_1 \cap (\mathfrak{A}_2 \cap \mathfrak{A}_3) = \mathfrak{A}_1 \cap \mathfrak{A}_2 \cap \mathfrak{A}_3$ states that the set consisting of those elements in $\mathfrak{A}_1 \cap \mathfrak{A}_2$ which are also in $\mathfrak{A}_3$ is the same set as that consisting of those elements of $\mathfrak{A}_1$ which are in $\mathfrak{A}_2 \cap \mathfrak{A}_3$ and that this set is precisely the set of those elements which are in $\mathfrak{A}_1$, in $\mathfrak{A}_2$, and in $\mathfrak{A}_3$. Similarly, $(\mathfrak{A}_1 \cup \mathfrak{A}_2) \cup \mathfrak{A}_3 = \mathfrak{A}_1 \cup (\mathfrak{A}_2 \cup \mathfrak{A}_3) = \mathfrak{A}_1 \cup \mathfrak{A}_2 \cup \mathfrak{A}_3$.

A *mapping* S of a set $\mathfrak{A}$ *into* a set $\mathfrak{A}'$ is a set consisting of pairs designated as (a, aS), where S contains one and only one pair for every element a of the set $\mathfrak{A}$, and the elements denoted by aS are in $\mathfrak{A}'$. It is customary to represent the pairs of S by the symbol

$$S: \qquad a \rightarrow aS\,,$$

and we read $a \rightarrow aS$ as "a maps onto aS." The element aS is the second element of each pair of the set S. It is called the *image* of the arbitrary first element a of the set $\mathfrak{A}$. The set which consists of all image elements is a subset of $\mathfrak{A}'$ which we call the *image set.* We designate it by $\mathfrak{A}S$ and have $\mathfrak{A}S \subseteq \mathfrak{A}'$. If $\mathfrak{A}S = \mathfrak{A}'$, we say that S is a mapping of $\mathfrak{A}$ *onto* $\mathfrak{A}'$. When S is an onto mapping, every element a' of $\mathfrak{A}'$ is the image element $a' = aS$ of *at least* one element a of $\mathfrak{A}$.

A mapping S of $\mathfrak{A}$ into $\mathfrak{A}'$ is called a *one-to-one* mapping if S is a mapping of $\mathfrak{A}$ *onto* $\mathfrak{A}'$ and *every element* a' of $\mathfrak{A}'$ *is the image* of *exactly one* element of $\mathfrak{A}$. Then $aS = bS$ for a and b in $\mathfrak{A}$ if and only if $a = b$. In this case the mapping

$$S^{-1}: \qquad aS \rightarrow a$$

is defined. It is a one-to-one mapping of $\mathfrak{A}'$ onto $\mathfrak{A}$, called the *inverse* of the mapping S.

A mapping S of a set $\mathfrak{A}$ into itself is called a *transformation* of $\mathfrak{A}$. We call S a *non-singular* transformation of $\mathfrak{A}$ if S is a one-to-one mapping of $\mathfrak{A}$ onto $\mathfrak{A}$. Every non-singular transformation of $\mathfrak{A}$ has an inverse which is also a non-singular transformation of $\mathfrak{A}$. The transformation

$$I: \qquad a \rightarrow aI = a$$

is non-singular and is called the *identity* transformation of $\mathfrak{A}$.

A non-singular transformation of a finite set $\mathfrak{S}_n$ consisting of n elements is called a *permutation* (or a *substitution*). The permutations which interchange two elements of $\mathfrak{S}_n$ and leave all other elements fixed are called *transpositions*.

ORAL EXERCISES

1. Let $\mathfrak{E} = \mathfrak{E}'$ be the set of all ordinary integers and S be a mapping which maps each x of $\mathfrak{E}$ onto $2x$. What is $\mathfrak{E}S$? Is S a mapping into $\mathfrak{E}$ or onto $\mathfrak{E}$? Show that S is a one-to-one mapping of $\mathfrak{E}$ onto $\mathfrak{E}S$ and define S^{-1}.

2. Let $\mathfrak{A}$ be the set of students in a room, and let S map each student onto his first name. Describe the situation in the terms used in this section.

3. Let $\mathfrak{S}_n$ be a finite set, and let S map $\mathfrak{S}_n$ onto $\mathfrak{S}_n$. Show that S is a one-to-one mapping.

2. Products and operations. Let $\mathfrak{A}$, $\mathfrak{A}'$, $\mathfrak{A}''$ be sets, S be a mapping of $\mathfrak{A}$ into $\mathfrak{A}'$, and T be a mapping of $\mathfrak{A}'$ into $\mathfrak{A}''$. Then we can define a mapping ST of $\mathfrak{A}$ into $\mathfrak{A}''$ by

$$a \to a(ST) = (aS)T \,, \tag{1}$$

called the *product* of S and T.

Let S be a mapping of $\mathfrak{A}$ into $\mathfrak{A}'$, T be a mapping of $\mathfrak{A}'$ into $\mathfrak{A}''$, and U be a mapping of $\mathfrak{A}''$ into $\mathfrak{A}'''$. Then TU is a mapping of $\mathfrak{A}'$ into $\mathfrak{A}'''$, and $S(TU)$ maps $\mathfrak{A}$ into $\mathfrak{A}'''$. Similarly, ST maps $\mathfrak{A}$ into $\mathfrak{A}''$, and $(ST)U$ maps $\mathfrak{A}$ into $\mathfrak{A}'''$. But $(aS)(TU) = [(aS)T]U$ by equation (1) and $[a(ST)]U = [(aS)T]U$ for every a of $\mathfrak{A}$. It follows that

$$S(TU) = (ST)U \tag{2}$$

for all mappings S, T, U, and we say that *multiplication of mappings is associative.*

The product ST of a one-to-one mapping S of $\mathfrak{A}$ onto $\mathfrak{A}'$ and a one-to-one mapping T of $\mathfrak{A}'$ onto $\mathfrak{A}''$ is clearly a one-to-one mapping of $\mathfrak{A}$ onto $\mathfrak{A}''$. The product of two transformations S and T of a set $\mathfrak{A}$ is a transformation ST of $\mathfrak{A}$ which is non-singular if and only if S and T are both non-singular. If I is the identity transformation of $\mathfrak{A}$, the relations

$$SI = IS, \quad SS^{-1} = S^{-1}S = I \tag{3}$$

should be obvious.

If $\mathfrak{A}$ and $\mathfrak{B}$ are sets, we shall designate by $(\mathfrak{A}, \mathfrak{B})$ the set of *all* pairs (a, b) for a in $\mathfrak{A}$ and b in $\mathfrak{B}$. A mapping S of $(\mathfrak{A}, \mathfrak{B})$ into a set $\mathfrak{C}$ may then be designated by

$$S: \qquad (a, b) \to c \,,$$

and we shall refer to such a mapping as an *operation* on $(\mathfrak{A}, \mathfrak{B})$ to $\mathfrak{C}$.

The operations called "addition" and "multiplication" in elementary mathematics are examples of operations. For instance, let $\mathfrak{E}$ be the set consisting of all ordinary integers. Then addition is an operation on $(\mathfrak{E}, \mathfrak{E})$ to $\mathfrak{E}$. It is customary to write $a + b$ for the image of the pair (a, b) with respect to addition, that is, $(a, b) \to a + b$ under addition. Similarly, $(a, b) \to ab$ under the product operation of $\mathfrak{E}$. Thus we may write aOb for the image of (a, b) with respect to an operation on $(\mathfrak{A}, \mathfrak{B})$ to $\mathfrak{C}$. In discussing abstract sets where multiplication is not otherwise defined, it will be convenient to call an operation on $(\mathfrak{A}, \mathfrak{B})$ to $\mathfrak{C}$ the *product* operation and to write ab for the image of (a, b). It will also be convenient sometimes to call an operation the *addition* operation and to write $a + b$ for the image of (a, b).

We note that one example of a product operation has been mentioned already. Indeed, let $\mathfrak{M}$ be the set consisting of all transformations of a set. Then multiplication of transformations as described previously is an operation on $(\mathfrak{M}, \mathfrak{M})$ to $\mathfrak{M}$.

If O is an operation on $(\mathfrak{A}, \mathfrak{A})$ to $\mathfrak{A}$ and a and b are distinct elements of $\mathfrak{A}$, the pairs (a, b) and (b, a) are distinct and so may have distinct images aOb, bOa. If $aOb = bOa$ for every a and b of $\mathfrak{A}$, we call O a *commutative* operation.

EXERCISES

1. Show that addition and subtraction are operations on $(\mathfrak{R}, \mathfrak{R})$ to $\mathfrak{R}$ where $\mathfrak{R}$ is the set of all rational numbers. Describe division in these terms.

2. Let $\mathfrak{A}$ be the set of all even integers, $\mathfrak{B}$ be the set consisting of the integers $1, -1, 2, -2$. Describe division as an operation on $(\mathfrak{A}, \mathfrak{B})$ to $\mathfrak{C}$. What is $\mathfrak{C}$?

3. Give the details of the verification of equations (3).

4. There are six permutations of set consisting of three elements a, b, c. Write out these permutations $P_1 = I$, P_2, P_3, $P_4 = P_2P_3$, $P_5 = P_3^2$, $P_6 = P_2P_3$ explicitly. Obtain a six-by-six table in which the element in the ith row and jth column is the subscript k in $P_k = P_iP_j$. (*Hint:* Compute P_3P_2 and use the associative law and the fact that $P_2^2 = P_3^3 = I$.)

3. Relations. A relation R of a set $\mathfrak{A}$ is a mapping of $(\mathfrak{A}, \mathfrak{A})$ onto the set $\mathfrak{Q}$ consisting of two elements, one of which is called "*true*" and the other "*false*." We write aRb if the image of (a, b) is "true" and $a\not{R}b$ if the image of (a, b) is "false." We read the symbol aRb as "a is in the R relation to b" and the symbol $a\not{R}b$ as "a is not in the R relation to b."

A relation R of $\mathfrak{A}$ is said to be *reflexive* if aRa for every a of $\mathfrak{A}$. A relation R of $\mathfrak{A}$ is said to be *symmetric* if aRb implies that bRa. A relation R is said to be *transitive* if it is true that whenever aRb and bRc, then aRc. A relation is called an *equivalence* relation if it is reflexive, symmetric, and transitive. It is customary to write $a \cong b$ rather than aRb for equivalence relations.

If R is an equivalence relation of a set $\mathfrak{A}$, the set $\mathfrak{A}$ is the union of subsets called *equivalence classes*. Every element a of $\mathfrak{A}$ determines an equivalence class $\{a\}$ consisting of all elements in $\mathfrak{A}$ which are equivalent to a. Then a is in $\{a\}$. Also $\{a\}$ has an element in common with $\{b\}$ if and only if $\{a\} = \{b\}$, that is, $a \cong b$. If we represent an equivalence class as $\{a\}$, the element a which appears is called a *representative* of the class.

EXERCISES

1. Let $\mathfrak{G}$ be the set of all ordinary integers and define $a \equiv b \pmod{m}$ (read a is congruent to b modulo m) to mean that the positive integer m divides $a - b$. Show that congruence is an equivalence relation.

2. Let $\mathfrak{F}$ be the set of all pairs of integers (a, b) such that b is not zero. Define $(a, b) \cong (c, d)$ if $ad = bc$. Show that the relation so defined is an equivalence relation for $\mathfrak{F}$.

3. Let $\mathfrak{A}$ be the set of all real numbers and R be the relation $a \geq b$. Why is this relation *not* an equivalence relation?

4. Let $\mathfrak{F}$ be the set of all real numbers. We say that $a \cong b$ if $a - b$ is an integer. Show that this is an equivalence relation and that the equivalence classes are classes $\{r\}$, where $0 \leq r < 1$.

4. Properties of the integers. The set $\mathfrak{E}$ of all ordinary integers is an instance of a mathematical system which we shall discuss later and shall call a *ring*. Since some of the properties of $\mathfrak{E}$ will be used in our discussion of the more primitive systems called *groups*, we shall describe them now.

Let $\mathfrak{E}_p$ be the set of all *positive* integers. Every element a of $\mathfrak{E}_p$ then has a *successor* designated by $a + 1$. The *principle of mathematical induction* then states that if 1 is an element of a subset $\mathfrak{G}$ of $\mathfrak{E}_p$ and if $\mathfrak{G}$ contains the successor $a + 1$ of every element a of $\mathfrak{G}$, then $\mathfrak{G} = \mathfrak{E}_p$.

Another property of $\mathfrak{E}$ which is used frequently states that if $\mathfrak{G}$ is any non-empty set of integers $g \geq k$, where k is some fixed integer, then $\mathfrak{G}$ contains a least integer. This means that if every g of $\mathfrak{G}$ has the property $g \geq k$ (where k is fixed but need not be in $\mathfrak{G}$), there is then an integer r *in* $\mathfrak{G}$ such that every $g \geq r$.

If g is any integer, we define the absolute value $|g|$ of g to be g itself when $g \geq 0$, and to be $-g$ when $g \leq 0$.

Division Algorithm. *Let* f *and* g *be integers where* $g \neq 0$. *Then there exist unique integers* q *and* r *such that*

$$f = qg + r, \qquad 0 \leq r < |g| .$$

Assume, first, that $g > 0$. Consider the set $\mathfrak{M}$ of all integers $f - tg$ for t in $\mathfrak{E}$. Let $\mathfrak{G}$ be the subset consisting of the non-negative integers of $\mathfrak{M}$. Now $f - tg = |f|(g \pm 1) + g > 0$ if $t = -|f| - 1$, and so $\mathfrak{G}$ is not empty, $k \geq 0$ for every k of $\mathfrak{G}$. Then $\mathfrak{G}$ contains a least integer r, and $r = f - qg \geq 0$. The integer $f - (q + 1)g = r - g$ is in $\mathfrak{M}$ and is less than r. Hence $r - g$ is not in $\mathfrak{G}$, $r - g < 0$, and $g > r \geq 0$, as desired. If $g < 0$, we use the case just completed and can write $f = q_0(-g) + r$, where $0 \leq r < -g$. Then $f = qg + r$, where $q = q_0$, $0 \leq r < |g|$. Suppose, finally, that $f = qg + r = q_1 g + r_1$, where $0 \leq r < |g|$, $0 \leq r_1 < |g|$. Then $(q_1 - q)g = r - r_1$, $|q_1 - q||g| = |r - r_1|$. If $q_1 \neq q$, then $|r - r_1| = |q_1 - q||g| \geq |g|$, whereas $|r - r_1| < |g|$. Hence $q_1 = q$ and $r_1 = r$.

An integer a is said to be *divisible* by b if $a = bc$, where c is an integer. If a is divisible by b and b is divisible by a, then $a = bc$, $b = ad$, $a = a(cd)$

If $a \neq 0$, then $cd = 1$ and $d = c = 1$ or $d = c = -1$. If d divides f and g, we call d a *common divisor* of f and g. When $d > 0$ and every common divisor of f and g divides d, we call d the *greatest common divisor* (abbreviated g.c.d.) of f and g. It is *unique*. For if d and d_1 both have the required property, we see that d divides d_1 and vice versa. Then $d = \pm d_1$; by the foregoing argument, $d > 0$ and $d_1 > 0$ only if $d = d_1$. We now prove the *existence* of d.

LEMMA 1. *Let* f *and* g *be integers not both zero. Then there exists a positive divisor* $\mathrm{d} = \mathrm{af} + \mathrm{bg}$ *of both* f *and* g *where* a *and* b *are integers.*

For let $\mathfrak{G}$ consist of all integers of the form $xf + yg$ where x and y are in $\mathfrak{E}$. Since f, g, $-f$, and $-g$ are in $\mathfrak{G}$, the set $\mathfrak{G}_p$ of all positive integers of $\mathfrak{G}$ is not empty. Thus $\mathfrak{G}_p$ contains a least element $d = af + bg$, where a and b are in $\mathfrak{E}$. By the Division Algorithm, $f = qd + r$, where q is in $\mathfrak{E}$ and $0 \leq r < d$. Then $r = f - qd = (1 - qa)f + (-qb)g$ is in $\mathfrak{G}$, and $r < d$ implies that r is not in $\mathfrak{G}_p$, $r \leq 0$, and so $r = 0$. Hence d divides f. Similarly, d divides g, as desired.

Two integers f and g are called *relatively prime* (and we also say that f *is prime to* g) if their g.c.d. is unity. If f and g are relatively prime, we can write

$$af + bg = 1$$

for integers a and b. We use this fact to prove the following result:

LEMMA 2. *Let* f *divide* gh *and* f *be prime to* g. *Then* f *divides* h.

For $af + bg = 1$, $(ah)f + b(gh) = h$. But $gh = fq$, where q is in $\mathfrak{E}$, $h = (ah + bq)f$, as desired.

An integer p is called a *prime* if $p \neq 0, 1, -1$ and the only divisors of p are $1, -1, p, -p$. If $a \neq 0, 1, -1$ and if a is not a prime, we say that a is a *composite* integer. A divisor b of a is called a *proper divisor* of a if $|a| > |b| > 1$.

FUNDAMENTAL THEOREM OF ARITHMETIC. *Every integer* $\mathrm{a} > 1$ *is uniquely expressible as the product*

$$\mathrm{a} = \mathrm{p}_1^{e_1}\mathrm{p}_2^{e_2}\cdots\mathrm{p}_r^{e_r},$$

where the p_i *are positive primes and* $\mathrm{p}_1 < \mathrm{p}_2 < \cdots < \mathrm{p}_r$.

The result just stated is equivalent to the statement that every $a > 1$ is expressible as a product $a = p_1, \ldots, p_t$, where the p_i are unique positive primes and $p_1 \leq p_2 \leq \cdots \leq p_t$. This form of the result is clearly true if a is a prime and, in particular, if $a = 2$. Assume it true for all positive integers $b < a$. Let p_1 be the least positive divisor of a. Then $a = p_1a_1$, where $a > a_1 > 1$. If p_1 were composite, we would have $p_1 = q_1q_2$, where $p_1 > q_1 > 1$, and then $a = q_1(q_2a_1)$, contrary to hypothesis.

Hence p_1 is a prime. By the hypothesis of our induction, $a_1 = p_2 \cdots p_t$ for primes $p_2 \leq p_3 \leq \cdots \leq p_t$. Since p_2 divides a, we see that $p_1 \leq p_2$. If also $a = q_1 \cdots q_s$, where $q_1 = q_2 \leq \cdots \leq q_s$, then p_1 divides a, and Lemma 2 implies that p_1 divides one of the q_i. If $q_1 > p_1$, then every $q_i > p_1$, whereas the q_i are primes and p_i must equal one of the q_i. Hence $q_1 = p_1$, $a = p_1 a_1$, where $a_1 = p_2 \cdots p_t = q_2 \cdots q_s$. By the hypothesis of our induction, $s = t$ and $p_i = q_i$ for $i = 1, \ldots, t$ as desired.

EXERCISES

1. Consider the set $\mathfrak{C}_m$ of *residue classes* (equivalence classes with respect to congruence) modulo m. Define $\{a\} + \{b\} = \{a + b\}$ and $\{a\}\{b\} = \{ab\}$. Show that these definitions define operations on $(\mathfrak{C}_m, \mathfrak{C}_m)$ to $\mathfrak{C}_m$.

2. Let p be a prime. Show that the set $\mathfrak{C}_p^*$ of all classes $\{a\}$ with $a \neq 0$ has the product operation as an operation on $(\mathfrak{C}_p^*, \mathfrak{C}_p^*)$ to $\mathfrak{C}_p^*$.

5. Groups. Let $\mathfrak{G}$ be a non-empty set and O be an operation on $(\mathfrak{G}, \mathfrak{G})$ to $\mathfrak{G}$. Then $\mathfrak{G}$ is said to *form a group* with respect to O if:

I. *The associative law holds*, that is,

$$\mathrm{aO(bOc)} = \mathrm{(aOb)Oc} \tag{4}$$

for every a, b, c of $\mathfrak{G}$;

II. *For every* a *and* b *of* $\mathfrak{G}$ *there exist solutions* x *and* y *in* $\mathfrak{G}$ *of the equations*

$$\mathrm{aOx} = \mathrm{b}\,, \quad \mathrm{yOa} = \mathrm{b}\,. \tag{5}$$

The group is the *mathematical system* consisting of the set $\mathfrak{G}$, the operation O, and Postulates I and II. It is customary to designate the group by the same symbol $\mathfrak{G}$ as is used for the set of its elements. Thus we shall say that g is an element of the group $\mathfrak{G}$ when we mean that g is in the set $\mathfrak{G}$ of the mathematical system consisting of $\mathfrak{G}$, O, I, and II.

The notation used for the operation is *usually* unimportant and may be selected in any convenient way. When we use the symbol ab for aOb, we shall call $\mathfrak{G}$ a *multiplicative* group. In some cases $\mathfrak{G}$ will be a subset of a set $\mathfrak{A}$ for which multiplication is already defined, and the statement that $\mathfrak{G}$ is a multiplicative group will then mean that the product operation for $\mathfrak{A}$ induces an operation ab on $(\mathfrak{G}, \mathfrak{G})$ to $\mathfrak{G}$ such that $\mathfrak{G}$ is a group. When we write $a + b$ for the operation of $\mathfrak{G}$, we shall call $\mathfrak{G}$ an *additive* group.

DEFINITION. *A group* $\mathfrak{G}$ *is called a commutative* (or *abelian*) *group if* aOb = bOa *for every* a *and* b *of* $\mathfrak{G}$.

6. Elementary properties of groups. In deriving the elementary properties of groups it will be convenient to use the *product* notation for the *group operation.* Let $\mathfrak{G}$ be a group so that Postulate II implies that for every a of $\mathfrak{G}$ there exist elements e and f such that

$$ea = af = a . \tag{6}$$

Then $(ea)b = ab = e(ab)$ by Postulate I. If g is any element of $\mathfrak{G}$, there exists an element b by Postulate II such that $g = ab$. Then $eg = g$ for every g of $\mathfrak{G}$. Hence $ef = f = e$, and we have proved the existence of an element e in $\mathfrak{G}$ such that $eg = ge = g$ for every g of $\mathfrak{G}$. This element is unique, since if it is also true that $fg = gf = g$ for every g of $\mathfrak{G}$, then $fe = e = f$. However, e was an element such that $ea = a$ for some a. We have therefore shown that the *only* solution of *either* of the equations $xg = g$ or $gx = g$ is $x = e$. We have proved the first part of the following result.

THEOREM 1. *Every group $\mathfrak{G}$ has a unique identity element* e *such that*

$$\mathrm{g}O\mathrm{e} = \mathrm{e}O\mathrm{g} = \mathrm{g} \tag{7}$$

for every g *of $\mathfrak{G}$. The equations* $\mathrm{x}O\mathrm{g} = \mathrm{g}$ *and* $\mathrm{g}O\mathrm{y} = \mathrm{g}$ *in $\mathfrak{G}$ have the unique solution* $\mathrm{x} = \mathrm{y} = \mathrm{e}$. *Every* g *of $\mathfrak{G}$ has a unique inverse* g^{-1} *such that*

$$\mathrm{g}O\mathrm{g}^{-1} = \mathrm{g}^{-1}O\mathrm{g} = \mathrm{e} , \tag{8}$$

and the equations $\mathrm{x}O\mathrm{g} = \mathrm{h}$ *and* $\mathrm{g}O\mathrm{y} = \mathrm{h}$ *have the unique solutions*

$$\mathrm{x} = \mathrm{h}O\mathrm{g}^{-1}, \quad \mathrm{y} = \mathrm{g}^{-1}O\mathrm{h} . \tag{9}$$

To complete our proof, we write $xg = e$ and use Postulate II to obtain a solution x in $\mathfrak{G}$. Then $(gx)g = g(xg) = ge = g$. By Theorem 1 we see that $gx = e$. If $yg = e$, then $(yg)x = ex = x = y(gx) = ye = y$. Hence $x = g^{-1}$ is unique. The equation $xg = h$ has the solution $x = hg^{-1}$, since $(hg^{-1})g = h(g^{-1}g) = he = h$. But if $xg = h$, then $hg^{-1} = (xg)g^{-1} = x(gg^{-1}) = xe = x$, and so x is unique. Similarly, $y = g^{-1}h$ is the unique solution of $gy = h$. Note that $aa^{-1} = e$ implies that

$$(a^{-1})^{-1} = a . \tag{10}$$

When $\mathfrak{G}$ is an additive group, the identity element with respect to addition is usually called the *zero* element of $\mathfrak{G}$. The inverse of an element of $\mathfrak{G}$ is then usually indicated by $-g$ and the solutions of $g + x = h$ and $y + g = h$ by $x = -g + h$ and $y = h - g$.

Let us close by observing a converse of Theorem 1. Let $\mathfrak{G}$ be a set, O be an operation on $(\mathfrak{G}, \mathfrak{G})$ to $\mathfrak{G}$ such that the associative law, Postulate I, holds. Let $\mathfrak{G}$ contain an element e such that $eOg = gOe$ for every g of $\mathfrak{G}$. Suppose also that for every g of $\mathfrak{G}$ there is an element g^{-1} in $\mathfrak{G}$ such that $gOg^{-1} = g^{-1}Og = e$. Then $\mathfrak{G}$ is a group with respect to O.

EXERCISES

1. Show that the set Σ_3 of all permutations on the set of three elements is a group with respect to the operation of multiplication of mappings.
2. Show that the set $\mathfrak{E}_p^*$ defined in the exercises of Section 4 is a group.
3. Show that the set $\mathfrak{E}$ of all ordinary integers is a group with respect to addition. What are the identity and inverse elements?
4. Let a be any integer and define $xOy = x + y - a$. Show that the set $\mathfrak{E}$ of all integers forms a group with respect to this operation and that a is the identity element of this group. Find the inverse element.

7. Subgroups. A non-empty subset $\mathfrak{H}$ of a group $\mathfrak{G}$ is called a *subgroup* of $\mathfrak{G}$ if $\mathfrak{H}$ is a group with respect to the defining operation O of $\mathfrak{G}$. We then have the following result:

THEOREM 2. *A non-empty subset $\mathfrak{H}$ of a group $\mathfrak{G}$ is a subgroup of $\mathfrak{G}$ if and only if* aOb^{-1} *is in $\mathfrak{H}$ for every* a *and* b *of $\mathfrak{H}$.*

We take $\mathfrak{G}$ to be a multiplicative group. The condition is a necessary consequence of the definition of a group. Hence let ab^{-1} be in $\mathfrak{H}$ for every a and b of $\mathfrak{H}$. Then $\mathfrak{H}$ contains $aa^{-1} = e$, $ea^{-1} = a^{-1}$, and $a(b^{-1})^{-1} = ab$ for every a and b of $\mathfrak{H}$. But multiplication in $\mathfrak{G}$ is associative and so must be associative in $\mathfrak{H}$. By the converse of Theorem 1, $\mathfrak{H}$ is a group.

The foregoing argument implies:

THEOREM 3. *Let $\mathfrak{H}$ be a subgroup of $\mathfrak{G}$. Then the identity elements of $\mathfrak{H}$ and $\mathfrak{G}$ coincide. If* h *is in $\mathfrak{H}$, its inverses in $\mathfrak{G}$ and in $\mathfrak{H}$ coincide.*

If $\mathfrak{B}$ and $\mathfrak{C}$ are subsets of a multiplicative group $\mathfrak{G}$, we define $\mathfrak{B}\mathfrak{C}$ to be the set of all products bc for b in $\mathfrak{B}$ and c in $\mathfrak{C}$. If g is any element of $\mathfrak{G}$, we define $\mathfrak{B}g$ to be the set of all products bg for b in $\mathfrak{B}$. Similarly, we define $g\mathfrak{B}$ to be the set of all products gb for b in $\mathfrak{B}$. Multiplication of sets and elements is clearly associative.

If $\mathfrak{H}$ is a subgroup of $\mathfrak{G}$, we see that $\mathfrak{H}\mathfrak{H} = \mathfrak{H}$. Indeed, we have the following property:

LEMMA 3. *A non-empty subset $\mathfrak{H}$ of a group $\mathfrak{G}$ is a subgroup of $\mathfrak{G}$ if and only if $\mathfrak{H}$h $= \mathfrak{H}$ for every element* h *in $\mathfrak{H}$* (h$\mathfrak{H} = \mathfrak{H}$ *for every* h *of* $\mathfrak{H}$).

For if $\mathfrak{H}h = \mathfrak{H}$ and k is in $\mathfrak{H}$, there exists a solution x in $\mathfrak{H}$ of the equation $xh = k$. Then $x = kh^{-1}$ is in $\mathfrak{H}$ for every k and h of $\mathfrak{H}$, and $\mathfrak{H}$ is a subgroup of $\mathfrak{G}$ by Theorem 2. The converse follows from the fact that if $\mathfrak{H}$ is a subgroup, then $\mathfrak{H}\mathfrak{H} \subseteq \mathfrak{H}$, $\mathfrak{H}h \subseteq \mathfrak{H}$, $\mathfrak{H}h$ contains $(kh^{-1})h = k$ for every k of $\mathfrak{H}$, $\mathfrak{H}h \supseteq \mathfrak{H}$, $\mathfrak{H}h = \mathfrak{H}$, and $h\mathfrak{H} = \mathfrak{H}$ by symmetry.

EXERCISES

1. Show that the set of all even integers is a subgroup of the additive group $\mathfrak{E}$ of all integers.
2. Let $\mathfrak{E}_m$ be the set of all residue classes modulo m and $\mathfrak{G}_m$ be the set of

residue classes $\{a\}$, where a is prime to m. Show that $\mathfrak{G}_m$ is a group with respect to the operation $\{a\}\{b\} = \{ab\}$.

3. In Exercise 2 let $m = 12$, so that $\mathfrak{G}_{12}$ consists of $\{1\}, \{5\}, \{7\}, \{11\}$. Find all subgroups of $\mathfrak{G}_{12}$.

8. Cyclic and finite groups. *The order* of a group $\mathfrak{G}$ is the of number elements in the set $\mathfrak{G}$. When this number is finite, we call $\mathfrak{G}$ a *finite* group. Otherwise, $\mathfrak{G}$ is an *infinite* group, that is, a group of infinite order.

Let $\mathfrak{G}$ be a multiplicative group. Define $g^0 = e$ for every g of $\mathfrak{G}$ where e is the identity element of $\mathfrak{G}$. Define

$$g^\alpha = g^{\alpha-1}g \qquad (\alpha = 1, 2, \ldots). \tag{11}$$

We then have given a unique definition of g^α for all non-negative integers α. Define

$$g^{-\alpha} = (g^{-1})^\alpha \tag{12}$$

for all positive integers α. It should be clear that the associative law implies that

$$g^{-\alpha} = (g^\alpha)^{-1}, \quad g^\alpha g^\beta = g^{\alpha+\beta} \tag{13}$$

for all integers α and β. The set consisting of all integral powers of g is easily seen to be a subgroup of $\mathfrak{G}$, which we shall designate by $\{g\}$ and shall call the *cyclic group* generated by g. The order of this group is called the *order* (or *period*) of g.

THEOREM 4. *An element* g *has infinite order if and only if all powers of* g *with distinct exponents are distinct elements.*

If $g^\alpha = g^\beta$ only when $\alpha = \beta$, the group $\{g\}$ clearly has infinite order. Suppose, however, that $g^\alpha = g^\beta$, where $\alpha > \beta$. Then $g^{\alpha-\beta} = e$, where $\alpha - \beta > 0$. Let ν be the least positive integer such that $g^\nu = e$. Then every integer γ has the form

$$\gamma = \nu\lambda + \rho \qquad (0 \leq \rho < \nu), \tag{14}$$

and $g^\gamma = g^\rho$. Hence every element of $\{g\}$ is one of the elements

$$e, g, g^\nu, \ldots, g^{\nu-1}. \tag{15}$$

These elements are distinct, since if $g^\alpha = g^\beta$, where $\nu > \alpha > \beta$, then $\nu > \alpha - \beta > 0$, $g^{\alpha-\beta} = e$, contrary to the definition of ν. Hence $\{g\}$ has order ν.

The condition $g^\gamma = e$ implies that $g^\rho = e$ in equation (14), and the fact that the elements in expression (15) are distinct implies that $\rho = 0$. This yields the following result

THEOREM 5. *Let* g *be a group element of finite order* ν. *Then* $g^\gamma = e$ *if and only if* ν *divides* γ.

If $\mathfrak{G}$ is an additive group, the additive powers of an element g of $\mathfrak{G}$ are written as $\alpha \cdot g$ for all integers α. Thus $0 \cdot g = 0$ is the identity element zero of $\mathfrak{G}$; $\alpha \cdot g = (\alpha - 1) \cdot g + g$ for all positive integers α; and $(-\alpha) \cdot g = -(\alpha \cdot g) = \alpha \cdot (-g)$ for all positive integers α. Then $\{g\}$ is an *additive cyclic group*.

EXERCISES

1. Let $\mathfrak{G}$ be a cyclic group of order $n = mq$, where $m > 1$, $q > 1$, m is prime to q. Show that the subset $\mathfrak{H}$ of all elements of $\mathfrak{G}$ whose orders divide m is a subgroup of $\mathfrak{G}$.
2. Let $\mathfrak{E}_m$ be the set of residue classes of the set $\mathfrak{E}$ of all integers modulo m. Show that $\mathfrak{E}_m$ is a cyclic additive group.

9. Cosets and normal subgroups. If $\mathfrak{H}$ is subgroup of $\mathfrak{G}$, every element g of $\mathfrak{G}$ determines a subset $\mathfrak{H}g$, called a *left coset* of $\mathfrak{G}$ relative to $\mathfrak{H}$. The sets $g\mathfrak{H}$ are called the *right cosets* of $\mathfrak{G}$ relative to $\mathfrak{H}$.

DEFINITION. *A subgroup* $\mathfrak{H}$ *of a group* $\mathfrak{G}$ *is called a* normal *subgroup of* $\mathfrak{G}$ *if* $g\mathfrak{H} = \mathfrak{H}g$ *for every* g *of* $\mathfrak{G}$.

THEOREM 6. *A subgroup* $\mathfrak{H}$ *of a group* $\mathfrak{G}$ *is a normal subgroup of* $\mathfrak{G}$ *if* $g\mathfrak{H} \subseteq \mathfrak{H}g$ *for every* g *of* $\mathfrak{G}$.

For $g^{-1}\mathfrak{H} \subseteq \mathfrak{H}g^{-1}$, $g(g^{-1}\mathfrak{H})g = \mathfrak{H}g \subseteq g(\mathfrak{H}g^{-1})g = g\mathfrak{H}$, and so $g\mathfrak{H} = \mathfrak{H}g$.

The *intersection of two* subgroups $\mathfrak{H}$ and $\mathfrak{K}$ of $\mathfrak{G}$ *is easily* verified to be *a subgroup* of $\mathfrak{G}$. If $\mathfrak{H}$ is a normal subgroup of $\mathfrak{G}$ and $\mathfrak{K}$ is any subgroup of $\mathfrak{G}$, the *product* $\mathfrak{H}\mathfrak{K}$ *is* easily seen to be a subgroup of $\mathfrak{G}$.

THEOREM 7. *The intersection and the product of two normal subgroups* $\mathfrak{H}$ *and* $\mathfrak{K}$ *of* $\mathfrak{G}$ *are normal subgroups of* $\mathfrak{G}$.

For if $g\mathfrak{H} = \mathfrak{H}g$ and $g\mathfrak{K} = \mathfrak{K}g$, then $g(\mathfrak{H}\mathfrak{K}) = (\mathfrak{H}g)\mathfrak{K} = \mathfrak{H}(g\mathfrak{K}) = \mathfrak{H}(\mathfrak{K}g) = (\mathfrak{H}\mathfrak{K})g$. If $\mathfrak{D} = \mathfrak{H} \cap \mathfrak{K}$, then $g^{-1}\mathfrak{D}g \subseteq g^{-1}\mathfrak{H}g \subseteq \mathfrak{H}$, $g^{-1}\mathfrak{D}g \subseteq g^{-1}\mathfrak{K}g \subseteq \mathfrak{K}$, and $g^{-1}\mathfrak{D}g \subseteq \mathfrak{D}$ for every g of $\mathfrak{G}$. By Theorem 6 we see that $\mathfrak{D}$ is a normal subgroup of $\mathfrak{G}$.

We now study the properties of cosets.

THEOREM 8. *Two left cosets have an element in common if and only if they are the same set.*

Let k be in both $\mathfrak{H}g$ and $\mathfrak{H}g_1$. Then $k = hg = h_1g_1$, where h and h_1 are in $\mathfrak{H}$. But then $\mathfrak{H}h_1g_1 = \mathfrak{H}g_1 = \mathfrak{H}kg = \mathfrak{H}g$.

When $\mathfrak{G}$ is a finite group, we can express $\mathfrak{G}$ as the logical sum

(16) $$\mathfrak{G} = \mathfrak{H} \cup \mathfrak{H}g_2 \cup \cdots \cup \mathfrak{H}g_\mu$$

of the distinct cosets $\mathfrak{H}g_\alpha$ by Theorem 8. The integer μ is then called the *index* of $\mathfrak{H}$ under $\mathfrak{G}$ and will be designated by $[\mathfrak{G}:\mathfrak{H}]$.

THEOREM 9. *Let $\mathfrak{H}$ and $\mathfrak{K}$ be subgroups of a finite group $\mathfrak{G}$ such that $\mathfrak{H} \subseteq \mathfrak{K} \subseteq \mathfrak{G}$. Then*

$$[\mathfrak{G}:\mathfrak{H}] = [\mathfrak{G}:\mathfrak{K}]\,[\mathfrak{K}:\mathfrak{H}]\,. \tag{17}$$

Hence write $\mathfrak{G} = \mathfrak{K} \cup \mathfrak{K}g_2 \cup \cdots \cup \mathfrak{K}g_\lambda$ and $\mathfrak{K} = \mathfrak{H} \cup \mathfrak{H}k_2 \cup \cdots \cup \mathfrak{H}k_\mu$, where our definitions imply that $\lambda = [\mathfrak{G}:\mathfrak{K}]$ and $\mu = [\mathfrak{K}:\mathfrak{H}]$. Every element of $\mathfrak{G}$ then has the form $g = kg_\alpha$, where k is in $\mathfrak{K}$ and $\alpha = 1, \ldots, \lambda$. Here $g_1 = k_1 = e$ is the identity element of $\mathfrak{G}$. Now $k = hk_\delta$ for h in $\mathfrak{H}$, and so $g = hk_\beta g_\alpha$. It follows immediately that $\mathfrak{H}g = \mathfrak{H}hk_\beta g_\alpha = \mathfrak{H}k_\beta g_\alpha$, and so every left coset of $\mathfrak{G}$ relative to $\mathfrak{H}$ is one of the $\lambda\mu$ left cosets $\mathfrak{H}k_\beta g_\alpha$. If $\mathfrak{H}k_\beta g_\alpha = \mathfrak{H}k_\gamma g_\delta$, then $\mathfrak{K}g_\alpha \subseteq \mathfrak{K}g_\delta$, $\alpha = \delta$ by Theorem 8, $\mathfrak{H}k_\beta = \mathfrak{H}k_\gamma$, and $\beta = \gamma$. Hence there are $\lambda\mu$ distinct left cosets of $\mathfrak{G}$ relative to $\mathfrak{H}$, and equation (17) holds.

The order of a finite group $\mathfrak{G}$ is clearly $[\mathfrak{G}:\mathfrak{J}]$, where $\mathfrak{J}$ is the identity group. The following result is an immediate consequence of Theorem 9.

THEOREM 10. *The order of a subgroup $\mathfrak{H}$ of a finite group $\mathfrak{G}$ divides the order of $\mathfrak{G}$. In fact,*

$$[\mathfrak{G}:\mathfrak{J}] = [\mathfrak{G}:\mathfrak{H}][\mathfrak{H}:\mathfrak{J}]\,. \tag{18}$$

The order of an element g of a group $\mathfrak{G}$ is the order of the cyclic subgroup $\{g\}$ of $\mathfrak{G}$. By Theorem 10 we have

THEOREM 11. *The order of an element of a finite group $\mathfrak{G}$ divides the order of $\mathfrak{G}$.*

We close this section with the following observation about finite groups:

THEOREM 12. *Let $\mathfrak{H}$ be a non-empty subset of a finite group $\mathfrak{G}$. Then $\mathfrak{H}$ is a subgroup of $\mathfrak{G}$ if and only if $\mathfrak{H}\mathfrak{H} \subseteq \mathfrak{H}$.*

For when $\mathfrak{H}\mathfrak{H} \subseteq \mathfrak{H}$, it should be evident that h^α is in $\mathfrak{H}$ for all positive integers α. Since $\mathfrak{G}$ is a finite group, every h of $\mathfrak{H}$ has finite order ν. Then $h^\nu = e$ and $h^{\nu-1} = h^{-1}$ are both in $\mathfrak{H}$, so that $\mathfrak{H}$ is a subgroup of $\mathfrak{G}$ by Theorem 2.

If $\mathfrak{G}$ is a group whose elements are $g_1, g_2, \ldots, g_t$, we will sometimes write

$$\mathfrak{G} = (g_1, g_2, \ldots, g_t)\,.$$

We will also sometimes use the symbol 1 for the identity element of a group rather than e.

EXERCISES

1. Define the *right* index of $\mathfrak{H}$ under $\mathfrak{G}$ to be the number of right cosets $g\mathfrak{H}$. Show that if $\mathfrak{G}$ is a finite group, the right index is equal to the (left) index defined earlier.

2. Prove that every subgroup of an abelian group $\mathfrak{G}$ is a normal subgroup of $\mathfrak{G}$.

3. Let $[\mathfrak{G}:\mathfrak{H}] = 2$. Prove that $\mathfrak{H}$ is a normal subgroup of $\mathfrak{G}$.

4. Let $\mathfrak{G}_6 = (1, g, g^2, h, gh, g^2h)$, where $hg = g^2h$ and $h^2 = g^3 = 1$. Find all normal subgroups of $\mathfrak{G}_6$.

5. Show that every group of prime order is a cyclic group.

6. Determine all finite groups of order $n < 6$.

7. The *center* of a group $\mathfrak{G}$ is the set $\mathfrak{Z}$ of all elements z of $\mathfrak{G}$ such that $zg = gz$ for every g of $\mathfrak{G}$. Prove that $\mathfrak{Z}$ is a normal subgroup of $\mathfrak{G}$.

8. Let $\mathfrak{H}$ and $\mathfrak{K}$ be two normal subgroups of $\mathfrak{G}$ such that not every element of $\mathfrak{H}$ commutes with every element of $\mathfrak{K}$. Prove that the intersection of $\mathfrak{H}$ and $\mathfrak{K}$ contains at least two elements.

9. A non-cyclic group $\mathfrak{G}$ of order 10 has a normal subgroup of order 5. Give a multiplication table for $\mathfrak{G}$.

10. Let $\mathfrak{G}$ be a finite group not necessarily commutative and let $(xy)^n = x^ny^n$ for a fixed integer n and every x and y of $\mathfrak{G}$, where $n > 1$. Let $\mathfrak{G}_n$ be the set of all elements z of $\mathfrak{G}$ with $z^n = 1$, and $\mathfrak{G}^n$ be the set of all x^n for all x in $\mathfrak{G}$. Prove that $\mathfrak{G}_n$ and $\mathfrak{G}^n$ are normal subgroups of $\mathfrak{G}$ and that the order of $\mathfrak{G}^n$ is the index of $\mathfrak{G}_n$ under $\mathfrak{G}$.

10. Homomorphism. Let $\mathfrak{G}$ be a group with defining operation O and let $\mathfrak{G}'$ be a group with defining operation O'. Then a *homomorphism* S of $\mathfrak{G}$ into (onto) $\mathfrak{G}'$ is a mapping S of $\mathfrak{G}$ into (onto) $\mathfrak{G}'$ such that

$$(aOb)S = (aS)O'(bS) \tag{19}$$

for every a and b of $\mathfrak{G}$. A *one-to-one* homomorphism of $\mathfrak{G}$ onto $\mathfrak{G}'$ is called an *isomorphism* of $\mathfrak{G}$ and $\mathfrak{G}'$. We say that $\mathfrak{G}$ and $\mathfrak{G}'$ are *isomorphic* groups if there exists an isomorphism S of $\mathfrak{G}$ and $\mathfrak{G}'$. In this case we shall write $\mathfrak{G} \cong \mathfrak{G}'$ (read $\mathfrak{G}$ is isomorphic to $\mathfrak{G}'$). An isomorphism of $\mathfrak{G}$ and $\mathfrak{G}$ is called an *automorphism* of $\mathfrak{G}$. A homomorphism of $\mathfrak{G}$ into $\mathfrak{G}$ is called an *endomorphism* of $\mathfrak{G}$.

THEOREM 13. *Let $\mathfrak{G}$ be a multiplicative group and* a *be an element of $\mathfrak{G}$. Then the mapping*

$$S_a: \qquad g \to aga^{-1}$$

is an automorphism of $\mathfrak{G}$.

For $(gh)S_a = a(gh)a^{-1} = (aga^{-1})(aha^{-1}) = (gS_a)(hS_a)$, and equation (19) holds. Also S_a is a one-to-one mapping of $\mathfrak{G}$ onto $\mathfrak{G}$, since $aga^{-1} = aha^{-1}$ if and only if $g = h$; every $g = a[a^{-1}ga]a^{-1}$.

The automorphisms S_a are called *inner automorphisms of* $\mathfrak{G}$. Since $S_aS_b = S_{ab}$, the set of all inner automorphisms of $\mathfrak{G}$ forms a group $\mathfrak{J}(\mathfrak{G})$. It is a subgroup of the group $\mathfrak{A}(\mathfrak{G})$ of all automorphisms of $\mathfrak{G}$ (the *auto-*

morphism group of $\mathfrak{G}$). Indeed, the mapping $a \rightarrow S_a$ is a homomorphism of $\mathfrak{G}$ onto the group $\mathfrak{J}(\mathfrak{G})$.

THEOREM 14. *Two elements* a *and* b *define the same inner automorphism of* $\mathfrak{G}$ *if and only if* a = bz *where* z *is in the center of* $\mathfrak{G}$.

If $a = bz$, then $aga^{-1} = b(zgz^{-1})b^{-1} = bgb^{-1}$, and so $S_a = S_b$. Conversely, if $aga^{-1} = bgb^{-1}$, for every g of $\mathfrak{G}$, we put $b^{-1}a = z$ and see that $zg = gz$ for every g of $\mathfrak{G}$, z is in $\mathfrak{Z}$, and $a = bz$, as desired.

A mapping S of a group $\mathfrak{G}$ into (onto) a group $\mathfrak{G}'$ is called an *antihomomorphism* of $\mathfrak{G}$ into (onto) $\mathfrak{G}'$ if $(gOh)S = (hS)O'(gS)$ for every g and h of $\mathfrak{G}$. A one-to-one antihomomorphism of $\mathfrak{G}$ onto $\mathfrak{G}'$ is called an *anti-isomorphism* of $\mathfrak{G}$ and $\mathfrak{G}'$. An anti-isomorphism of a commutative group $\mathfrak{G}$ onto $\mathfrak{G}'$ is, of course, an automorphism of $\mathfrak{G}$. An anti-isomorphism of $\mathfrak{G}$ onto $\mathfrak{G}$ is called an *antiautomorphism* of $\mathfrak{G}$. The *product* ST *of two antiautomorphisms* S *and* T of $\mathfrak{G}$ *is an automorphism of* $\mathfrak{G}$. The mapping

$$g \rightarrow g^{-1}$$

is an antiautomorphism of any group $\mathfrak{G}$. An antihomomorphism of $\mathfrak{G}$ into $\mathfrak{G}$ is called an *antiendomorphism* of $\mathfrak{G}$.

EXERCISES

1. Prove that the mapping $a \rightarrow S_a$ is a homomorphism of $\mathfrak{G}$ onto $\mathfrak{J}(\mathfrak{G})$.

2. Show that the mapping $x \rightarrow 2x$ is an endomorphism of the set $\mathfrak{E}$ of all integers into $\mathfrak{E}$.

3. Determine the group of all automorphisms of the non-cyclic group of order 4.

4. Two elements h and k of a group $\mathfrak{G}$ are said to be *conjugate* if there exists an inner automorphism S_a of $\mathfrak{G}$ such that $hS_a = k$, that is, $k = aha^{-1}$. Two subgroups $\mathfrak{H}$ and $\mathfrak{K}$ of $\mathfrak{G}$ are said to be *conjugate* if $\mathfrak{K} = \mathfrak{H}S_a = a\mathfrak{H}a^{-1}$. Express the concept of normality for subgroups in terms of conjugacy.

5. Let $\mathfrak{H}$ be a proper subgroup of order γ of a group $\mathfrak{G}$ of order $\delta = \gamma\epsilon$, and let $\mathfrak{H}, \mathfrak{H}g_2, \ldots, \mathfrak{H}g_\epsilon$ be the distinct cosets of $\mathfrak{H}$ under $\mathfrak{G}$. Give a complete list of the conjugate subgroups of $\mathfrak{H}$ in $\mathfrak{G}$ and show that the number of elements in $\mathfrak{G}$ conjugate to elements of $\mathfrak{H}$ is, at most, $\gamma\epsilon - (\epsilon - 1) = \delta - (\epsilon - 1) < \delta$.

6. Use Exercise 5 to show that, if $\mathfrak{H}$ is a proper subgroup of $\mathfrak{G}$, at least one element of $\mathfrak{G}$ is not conjugate to any element of $\mathfrak{H}$.

11. Quotient groups. Every homomorphism S of a (multiplicative) group $\mathfrak{G}$ into a (multiplicative) group $\mathfrak{G}'$ maps the identity element e of $\mathfrak{G}$ onto an element eS such that $(eS)(gS) = (eg)S = gS$. By Theorem 1, $eS = e'$ is the identity element of $\mathfrak{G}'$. The kernel of S is defined to be the set of all elements h of $\mathfrak{G}$ such that $hS = e'$ is the identity element of $\mathfrak{G}'$.

THEOREM 15. *The kernel of a homomorphism of* $\mathfrak{G}$ *into* $\mathfrak{G}'$ *is a normal subgroup of* $\mathfrak{G}$.

For if $hh^{-1} = e$, then $(hS)(h^{-1}S) = eS = e'$, and so $(h^{-1})S = (hS)^{-1}$. If $hS = e'$, then $(hS)^{-1} = h^{-1}S = (e')^{-1} = e'$, and so h^{-1} is in $\mathfrak{H}$ for every h of $\mathfrak{H}$. If $hS = e'$ and $kS = e'$, then $(hk)S = (hS)(kS) = e'e' = e'$. Hence $\mathfrak{H}\mathfrak{H} \subseteq \mathfrak{H}$. But then $\mathfrak{H}$ is a non-empty set containing hk^{-1} for every h and k of $\mathfrak{G}$, and $\mathfrak{H}$ is a subgroup of $\mathfrak{G}$. Since $(g^{-1}hg)S = (gS)^{-1}(hS)(gS) = (gS)^{-1}e'(gS) = e'$, we see that $g^{-1}\mathfrak{H}g \subseteq \mathfrak{H}$, and $\mathfrak{H}$ is a normal subgroup of $\mathfrak{G}$.

If $\mathfrak{H}$ is a normal subgroup of a group $\mathfrak{G}$, we may construct a new group called the *quotient group* of $\mathfrak{G}$ by $\mathfrak{H}$. We shall designate this new group by $\mathfrak{G}/\mathfrak{H}$. The elements of the set $\mathfrak{G}/\mathfrak{H}$ will be the cosets of $\mathfrak{G}$ relative to $\mathfrak{H}$. They may be thought of either as right or as left cosets, since every $\mathfrak{H}g = g\mathfrak{H}$. If $\mathfrak{H}g$ is a coset, we have $\mathfrak{H}(hg) = \mathfrak{H}g$ for every element h of $\mathfrak{H}$. Thus we may call g a *representative* of the coset $\mathfrak{H}g$ and see that all representatives have the form hg, where h is any element of $\mathfrak{H}$ and g is any representative.

The operation defining the group $\mathfrak{G}_0 = \mathfrak{G}/\mathfrak{H}$ will be the set product already defined. It is an operation on $(\mathfrak{G}_0, \mathfrak{G}_0)$ to $\mathfrak{G}_0$, since $(\mathfrak{H}g)(\mathfrak{H}k) = \mathfrak{H}(gk)$. The result is a group. To prove this we see, first, that set multiplication has already been seen to be associative. Since $\mathfrak{H}(\mathfrak{H}g) = (\mathfrak{H}g)\mathfrak{H} = \mathfrak{H}g$, the coset $\mathfrak{H}$ is the identity element of $\mathfrak{G}_0$. Also $(\mathfrak{H}g)(\mathfrak{H}g^{-1}) = (\mathfrak{H}g^{-1})(\mathfrak{H}g) = \mathfrak{H}gg^{-1} = \mathfrak{H}$, and so every element $\mathfrak{H}g$ of $\mathfrak{G}/\mathfrak{H}$ has the inverse $\mathfrak{H}g^{-1}$.

THEOREM 16. *The mapping of* $\mathfrak{G}$ *onto* $\mathfrak{G}/\mathfrak{H}$ *defined by* $g \to \mathfrak{H}g$ *is a homomorphism.*

This result is a trivial consequence of the formula $(\mathfrak{H}g)(\mathfrak{H}k) = \mathfrak{H}(gk)$. We also have

THEOREM 17. *Let* S *be a homorphism of* $\mathfrak{G}$ *onto* $\mathfrak{G}'$ *and* $\mathfrak{H}$ *be the kernel of* S. *Then* $\mathfrak{G}'$ *and* $\mathfrak{G}/\mathfrak{H}$ *are isomorphic.*

The ismorphism required is the mapping T defined by $\mathfrak{H}g \to gS$. We first show that every coset determines a unique image element gS. Let g and k be the two representatives of $\mathfrak{H}g$ so that $k = hg$, where h is in $\mathfrak{H}$. Then $kS = (hS)(gS) = e'(gS) = gS$, as desired. Hence the set of pairs $(\mathfrak{H}g, gS)$ is a mapping T of $\mathfrak{G}/\mathfrak{H}$ onto $\mathfrak{G}'$. If $\mathfrak{H}g$ and $\mathfrak{H}k$ have the same image, then $gS = kS$, $(k^{-1}g)S = (kS)^{-1}(gS) = e'$, and so $k^{-1}g$ is in $\mathfrak{H}$, $g = kh$, and $\mathfrak{H}g = \mathfrak{H}k$. This proves that the mapping T is a one-to-one mapping of $\mathfrak{G}/\mathfrak{H}$ onto $\mathfrak{G}'$. But $[(\mathfrak{H}g)(\mathfrak{H}k)]T = [\mathfrak{H}(gk)]T = (gk)S = (gS)(kS) = [(\mathfrak{H}g)T][(\mathfrak{H}k)T]$, as desired.

EXERCISES

1. Let $\mathfrak{S}$ be a normal subgroup of a finite group $\mathfrak{G}$. Prove that $\mathfrak{S}$ contains each subgroup $\mathfrak{T}$ of $\mathfrak{G}$ whose order is relatively prime to the index of $\mathfrak{S}$ under $\mathfrak{G}$.

2. Let $\mathfrak{H}$ be a normal subgroup of $\mathfrak{G}$ and g be an element of finite order ν in $\mathfrak{G}$. Show that the order of the element $\mathfrak{H}g$ of $\mathfrak{G}/\mathfrak{H}$ divides ν.

3. Find all the subgroups $\mathfrak{H}$ of the cyclic group $\mathfrak{G}$ of order 15, and determine all quotient groups $\mathfrak{G}/\mathfrak{H}$.

4. State a theorem on the homomorphs of a cyclic group of prime order.

12. The fundamental theorem. Let S be a homomorphism of a group $\mathfrak{G}$ onto a group $\mathfrak{G}'$, and let $\mathfrak{H}$ be the kernel of S. Then S maps every subset $\mathfrak{K}$ of $\mathfrak{G}$ onto an image set $\mathfrak{K}S$, which consists of the images kS of all elements k of $\mathfrak{K}$. Distinct subsets of $\mathfrak{G}$ may, of course, have the same image set. In particular, the set $\mathfrak{K}\mathfrak{H} = \mathfrak{H}\mathfrak{K} \supseteq \mathfrak{K}$ and has the same image set as $\mathfrak{K}$.

If $\mathfrak{K}$ is any subgroup of $\mathfrak{G}$, its image set is a subgroup $\mathfrak{K}S$ of $\mathfrak{G}'$. Indeed, $(kS)^{-1} = k^{-1}S$ and $(aS)(kS)^{-1} = (ak^{-1})S$ is in $\mathfrak{K}S$ for all elements a and k of $\mathfrak{K}$ and thus for all elements aS and kS of $\mathfrak{K}S$. It is also easy to verify that if $\mathfrak{K}$ is a normal subgroup of $\mathfrak{G}$ (that is, $g\mathfrak{K} = \mathfrak{K}g$ for every g of $\mathfrak{G}$), then $\mathfrak{K}S$ is a normal subgroup of $\mathfrak{G}'$ (that is, $gS\mathfrak{K}S = \mathfrak{K}SgS$ for every gS of $\mathfrak{G}' = \mathfrak{G}S$).

Assume, now, that $\mathfrak{G}' = \mathfrak{G}/\mathfrak{H}$. Then the elements of $\mathfrak{G}'$ are the cosets $g\mathfrak{H}$ for g in $\mathfrak{G}$. Every subset $\mathfrak{K}'$ of $\mathfrak{G}'$ is a set of cosets $k\mathfrak{H}$, and we define the *inverse image* of $\mathfrak{K}'$ under the mapping $g \to \mathfrak{H}g$ to be the set $\mathfrak{K}$, consisting of all the elements of $\mathfrak{G}$ in all the cosets in $\mathfrak{K}'$. The relation between the subgroups of $\mathfrak{G}/\mathfrak{H}$ and the subgroups of $\mathfrak{G}$ may be stated as follows:

THEOREM 18. *Let $\mathfrak{H}$ be a normal subgroup of $\mathfrak{G}$, S be the homomorphism $g \to g\mathfrak{H}$ of $\mathfrak{G}$ onto $\mathfrak{G}/\mathfrak{H} = \mathfrak{G}'$, Σ be the set of all subgroups $\mathfrak{K} \supseteq \mathfrak{H}$ of $\mathfrak{G}$, and Σ' be the set of all subgroups $\mathfrak{K}'$ of $\mathfrak{G}/\mathfrak{H}$. Then the mapping P of Σ into Σ', defined by*

$$\mathfrak{K} \to \mathfrak{K}P = \mathfrak{K}/\mathfrak{H}\,, \tag{20}$$

is a one-to-one mapping of Σ onto Σ' such that $\mathfrak{K}'P^{-1}$ is the inverse image under S of $\mathfrak{K}'$. A subgroup $\mathfrak{K} \supseteq \mathfrak{H}$ of $\mathfrak{G}$ is a normal subgroup of $\mathfrak{G}$ if and only if $\mathfrak{K}/\mathfrak{H} = \mathfrak{K}'$ is a normal subgroup of $\mathfrak{G}'$, and in this case $\mathfrak{G}/\mathfrak{K}$ and $\mathfrak{G}'/\mathfrak{K}'$ are isomorphic.

For if $\mathfrak{K}$ is a subgroup of $\mathfrak{G}$, $\mathfrak{K} \supseteq \mathfrak{H}$, and $\mathfrak{H}$ is a normal subgroup of $\mathfrak{G}$, we have $k\mathfrak{H} = \mathfrak{H}k$ for every k of $\mathfrak{K}$, so that $\mathfrak{H}$ is a normal subgroup of $\mathfrak{K}$. Then $\mathfrak{K}' = \mathfrak{K}/\mathfrak{H}$ is defined and is a subset of $\mathfrak{G}/\mathfrak{H} = \mathfrak{G}'$, and $\mathfrak{K}'$ is a subgroup of $\mathfrak{G}'$. The set $\mathfrak{K}$ is the inverse image of $\mathfrak{K}'$, since $\mathfrak{K}'$ contains a coset $k\mathfrak{H}$ if and only if k is in $\mathfrak{K}$. If $\mathfrak{K}_1 \supseteq \mathfrak{H}$, $\mathfrak{K}_2 \supseteq \mathfrak{H}$, and $\mathfrak{K}_1/\mathfrak{H} = \mathfrak{K}_2/\mathfrak{H}$, then $k_1\mathfrak{H} = k_2\mathfrak{H}$ for every k_1 of $\mathfrak{K}_1$, where k_2 is in $\mathfrak{K}_2$. But then $k_1 = k_2h$, where h is in $\mathfrak{H}$, k_2h is in the group $\mathfrak{K}_2 \supseteq \mathfrak{H}$, and $\mathfrak{K}_1 \subseteq \mathfrak{K}_2$. Similarly, $\mathfrak{K}_2 \subseteq \mathfrak{K}_1$, and so $\mathfrak{K}_1 = \mathfrak{K}_2$. The first part of our theorem will then be completely proved if we can show that P is a mapping of Σ *onto* Σ', that is, every subgroup $\mathfrak{K}'$ of $\mathfrak{G}'$ is the image of a subgroup $\mathfrak{K}$ of $\mathfrak{G}$. This must be the inverse image $\mathfrak{K}$ of $\mathfrak{K}'$, and we merely observe that if k_1 and k_2 are in $\mathfrak{K}$, then $(k_1\mathfrak{H})(k_2\mathfrak{H})^{-1} = (k_1k_2^{-1})\mathfrak{H} = k_3\mathfrak{H}$, where k_3 is in $\mathfrak{K}$. But then $k_1k_2^{-1} = k_3h$ for h in $\mathfrak{H}$, k_3h is in $\mathfrak{K}$, $\mathfrak{K}$ is a subgroup of $\mathfrak{G}$, $\mathfrak{K}'$ contains the identity element $\mathfrak{H}$ of $\mathfrak{G}'$, so $\mathfrak{K} \supseteq \mathfrak{H}$, and $\mathfrak{K}$ is in Σ, as desired.

We have already noticed that if $\mathfrak{K}$ in Σ is a normal subgroup of $\mathfrak{G}$, the group $\mathfrak{K}/\mathfrak{H}$ is a normal subgroup of $\mathfrak{G}'$. Conversely, if $\mathfrak{K}/\mathfrak{H}$ is a normal subgroup of $\mathfrak{G}'$, we know that $(\mathfrak{K}/\mathfrak{H})(g\mathfrak{H}) = g\mathfrak{H}(\mathfrak{K}/\mathfrak{H})$ for every g of $\mathfrak{G}$. Then $k\mathfrak{H}g\mathfrak{H} = kg\mathfrak{H} = g\mathfrak{H}k_1\mathfrak{H} = gk_1\mathfrak{H}$ for every g of $\mathfrak{G}$ and k of $\mathfrak{K}$, where k_1 is in $\mathfrak{K}$, and so $kg = gk_1h$, where h is in $\mathfrak{H}$ and hence in $\mathfrak{K}$, $\mathfrak{K}g \subseteq g\mathfrak{K}$. By symmetry, $g\mathfrak{K} \subseteq \mathfrak{K}g$, and so $\mathfrak{K}g = g\mathfrak{K}$, and $\mathfrak{K}$ is a normal subgroup of $\mathfrak{G}$.

The mapping T, defined by

$$T: \qquad g\mathfrak{K} \to (g\mathfrak{K})T = (g\mathfrak{H})\mathfrak{K}' ,$$

is simply the mapping of the coset $g\mathfrak{K}$ on its image $(gS)(\mathfrak{K}S)$. Thus T maps $\mathfrak{G}/\mathfrak{K}$ onto $\mathfrak{G}'/\mathfrak{K}'$. Since S is a homomorphism, we see that $[(g_1\mathfrak{K})(g_2\mathfrak{K})]T = [(g_1g_2)\mathfrak{K}]T = [(g_1g_2)\mathfrak{H}]\mathfrak{K}' = [(g_1\mathfrak{H})(g_2\mathfrak{H})]\mathfrak{K}' = [(g_1\mathfrak{H})\mathfrak{K}'][(g_2\mathfrak{H})\mathfrak{K}'] = [(g_1\mathfrak{K})T][(g_2\mathfrak{K})T]$. Thus T is a homomorphism of $\mathfrak{G}/\mathfrak{K}$ onto $\mathfrak{G}'/\mathfrak{K}'$. The kernel of T is the set of all $g\mathfrak{K}$ such that $(g\mathfrak{K})T = (g\mathfrak{H})\mathfrak{K}' = \mathfrak{K}'$. But $(g\mathfrak{H})\mathfrak{K}' = \mathfrak{K}'$ if and only if $g\mathfrak{H}$ is an element of $\mathfrak{K}'$, g is an element of $\mathfrak{K}$, and $g\mathfrak{K} = \mathfrak{K}$. Hence T is an isomorphism.

13. Direct products. We begin our discussion of direct products by proving the following result:

LEMMA 4. *Let $\mathfrak{H}$ and $\mathfrak{K}$ be subgroups of $\mathfrak{G}$. Then the elements of $\mathfrak{H}\mathfrak{K}$ are uniquely expressible as products* hk *for* h *in* $\mathfrak{H}$ *and* k *in* $\mathfrak{K}$ *if and only if the intersection of $\mathfrak{H}$ and $\mathfrak{K}$ is the identity group $\mathfrak{I}$.*

For if $\mathfrak{H} \cap \mathfrak{K} = \mathfrak{I}$ and $hk = h_1k_1$ for h and h_1 in $\mathfrak{H}$ and k and k_1 in $\mathfrak{I}$, then $h_1^{-1}h = k_1k^{-1}$ is in $\mathfrak{H} \cap \mathfrak{K}$, $h_1^{-1}h = k_1k^{-1} = e$, $h_1 = h$, and $k_1 = k$. Conversely, let the expression of an element of $\mathfrak{H}\mathfrak{K}$ as a product hk be unique and let d be in $\mathfrak{H} \cap \mathfrak{K}$. Then $(hd)k = h(dk)$, where hd is in $\mathfrak{H}$ and dk is in $\mathfrak{K}$. It follows that $hd = h$, $d = e$, and $\mathfrak{H} \cap \mathfrak{K} = \mathfrak{I}$.

DEFINITION. *A group $\mathfrak{G}$ is called the* direct product *of its subgroups $\mathfrak{H}$ and $\mathfrak{K}$, and we write*

$$\mathfrak{G} = \mathfrak{H} \times \mathfrak{K} , \tag{21}$$

if $\mathfrak{G} = \mathfrak{H}\mathfrak{K}$, $\mathfrak{H} \cap \mathfrak{K} = \mathfrak{I}$, and hk = kh *for every* h *of* $\mathfrak{H}$ *and* k *of* $\mathfrak{K}$.

If $\mathfrak{H}$ and $\mathfrak{K}$ are finite subgroups of $\mathfrak{G}$, the definition of a direct product may be restated as the criterion of the following theorem. The result is an immediate consequence of Lemma 4.

THEOREM 19. *Let $\mathfrak{H}$ and $\mathfrak{K}$ be finite subgroups of a group $\mathfrak{G}$ such that* $hk = kh$ *for every* h *of* $\mathfrak{H}$ *and* k *of* $\mathfrak{K}$. *Then* $\mathfrak{H}\mathfrak{K} = \mathfrak{H} \times \mathfrak{K}$ *if and only if the order of* $\mathfrak{H}\mathfrak{K}$ *is the product of the order of* $\mathfrak{H}$ *and the order of* $\mathfrak{K}$.

If $\mathfrak{G} = \mathfrak{H} \times \mathfrak{H}_1$ and $\mathfrak{H}_1 = \mathfrak{K} \times \mathfrak{M}$ so that $\mathfrak{G} = \mathfrak{H} \times (\mathfrak{K} \times \mathfrak{M})$, it is easy to see that $\mathfrak{G} = (\mathfrak{H} \times \mathfrak{K}) \times \mathfrak{M}$. Then we may write $\mathfrak{G} = \mathfrak{H} \times \mathfrak{K} \times \mathfrak{M}$ without ambiguity. This result may be generalized to direct products of ν factors, and we may write

$$\mathfrak{G} = \mathfrak{G}_1 \times \mathfrak{G}_2 \times \cdots \times \mathfrak{G}_\nu ,$$

where the order in which the factors appear is evidently arbitrary.

We have already seen that if $\mathfrak{H}$ is a normal subgroup of $\mathfrak{G}$, the product $\mathfrak{M} = \mathfrak{H}\mathfrak{K} = \mathfrak{K}\mathfrak{H}$ of $\mathfrak{H}$ and any subgroup $\mathfrak{K}$ of $\mathfrak{G}$ is a subgroup of $\mathfrak{G}$. We then have the following result:

THEOREM 20. *Let $\mathfrak{H}$ and $\mathfrak{K}$ be normal subgroups of $\mathfrak{G}$ and* $\mathfrak{H} \cap \mathfrak{K} = \mathfrak{J}$. *Then* $\mathfrak{H}\mathfrak{K} = \mathfrak{H} \times \mathfrak{K}$.

For $k^{-1}\mathfrak{H}\mathfrak{K} \subseteq \mathfrak{H}$, $h^{-1}\mathfrak{K}h \subseteq \mathfrak{K}$ for every h of $\mathfrak{H}$ and k of $\mathfrak{K}$. Then $(kh)^{-1}(hk) = (h^{-1}k^{-1}h)k = h^{-1}(k^{-1}hk)$ is in $\mathfrak{H} \cap \mathfrak{K}$ and must be equal to the identity element e of $\mathfrak{G}$, $kh = hk$ for every h of $\mathfrak{H}$ and k of $\mathfrak{K}$, and $\mathfrak{H}\mathfrak{K} = \mathfrak{H} \times \mathfrak{K}$.

If $hk = kh$ for every h of $\mathfrak{H}$ and k of $\mathfrak{K}$, then $\mathfrak{H}\mathfrak{K}$ is a group, and $\mathfrak{H}$ and $\mathfrak{K}$ are normal subgroups of $\mathfrak{H}\mathfrak{K}$. Then Theorem 10 yields the following result:

THEOREM 21. *Let $\mathfrak{H}$ and $\mathfrak{K}$ be subgroups of relatively prime orders of a finite group $\mathfrak{G}$ and let* $hk = kh$ *for all elements* h *of* $\mathfrak{H}$ *and* k *of* $\mathfrak{K}$. *Then* $\mathfrak{H}\mathfrak{K} = \mathfrak{H} \times \mathfrak{K}$.

For the order τ of $\mathfrak{H} \cap \mathfrak{K}$ divides the order ρ of $\mathfrak{H}$ as well as the order σ of $\mathfrak{K}$, since $\mathfrak{H} \cap \mathfrak{K}$ is a subgroup both of $\mathfrak{H}$ and of $\mathfrak{K}$. Then $\tau = 1$, $\mathfrak{H} \cap \mathfrak{K} = \mathfrak{J}$, as desired.

The concept of a direct product may be generalized as follows: Let $\mathfrak{H}$ and $\mathfrak{K}$ be arbitrary groups. Consider the set $\mathfrak{G}$ of all pairs (h, k) for h in $\mathfrak{H}$ and k in $\mathfrak{K}$. Define a product by $(h, k)(h_1, k_1) = (hh_1, kk_1)$ and let a be the identity element of $\mathfrak{H}$, b be the identity element of $\mathfrak{K}$. Then (a, b) is an identity element of $\mathfrak{G}$, $(h^{-1}, k^{-1}) = (h, k)^{-1}$, and the product is associative. Hence $\mathfrak{G}$ is a group. The mapping $h \to (h, b)$ is easily seen to be an isomorphism of $\mathfrak{H}$ onto a subgroup $\mathfrak{H}_0$ of $\mathfrak{G}$, and the mapping $k \to (a \cdot k)$ is an isomorphism of $\mathfrak{K}$ onto a subgroup $\mathfrak{K}_0$ of $\mathfrak{G}$. Moreover, $\mathfrak{G} = \mathfrak{H}_0 \times \mathfrak{K}_0$. In this case we say that we have constructed the direct product of $\mathfrak{H}$ and $\mathfrak{K}$ and again write $\mathfrak{G} = \mathfrak{G} \times \mathfrak{K}$. The direct product $\mathfrak{G} = \mathfrak{G}_1 \times \cdots \times \mathfrak{G}_\nu$ of ν arbitrary groups may be constructed by iterating the process just described.

14. Finite cyclic groups. The structure of finite cyclic groups may be obtained quite readily. We first derive

THEOREM 22. *Let* g *have order* ν *and* τ *be prime to* ν. *Then* $\{g^\tau\} = \{g\}$.

For $\{g^\tau\} \subseteq \{g\}$. There exist integers α and β such that $\alpha\tau + \beta\nu = 1$. Then $g = (g^\tau)^\alpha(g^{\nu\beta}) = (g^\tau)^\alpha$ and $\{g\} \subseteq \{g^\tau\}$, $\{g\} = \{g^\tau\}$.

We next prove the following result:

THEOREM 23. *Let* g *be an element of order* ν, δ *be the greatest common divisor of* ν *and* τ, *so that* $\tau = \delta\mu$, $\nu = \delta\lambda$. *Then* λ *is the order of* $\{g^\tau\}$ *and* $\{g^\tau\} = \{g^\delta\}$.

For $g^{\delta\lambda} = e$, and so the order of g^δ cannot exceed λ. If g^δ has order ϵ, then $g^{\delta\epsilon} = e$, $\delta\epsilon$ is divisible by $\delta\lambda$, λ divides ϵ, and $\epsilon \geq \lambda$. Hence $\epsilon = \lambda$, and so the order of g^δ is λ. Now μ and λ are relatively prime, and there exist integers α and β so that $\alpha\mu + \beta\lambda = 1$, $g^\delta = g^{\tau\alpha}g^{\beta\nu} = g^{\tau\alpha}$. Then $\{g^\delta\} \subseteq \{g^\tau\} \subseteq \{g^\delta\}$, and so $\{g^\tau\} = \{g^\delta\}$, as desired.

We now determine all subgroups of a finite cyclic group.

THEOREM 24. *Every subgroup* $\mathfrak{H}$ *of a finite cyclic group* $\{g\}$ *of order* ν *is a cyclic subgroup* $\{g^\delta\}$, *where* δ *divides* ν.

For the elements of $\mathfrak{H}$ are powers g^μ of g. Let δ be the least positive value of μ. Then every element of $\mathfrak{H}$ has the form $g\mu$, where $\mu = \delta\rho + \sigma$ and $0 \leq \sigma < \delta$. Since g^δ is in $\mathfrak{H}$, so is $g^\mu g^{-\delta\rho} = g^\sigma$. Hence our definition of δ implies that $\sigma = 0$, $\mathfrak{H} \subseteq \{g^\delta\} \subseteq \mathfrak{H}$, $\mathfrak{H} = \{g^\delta\}$. By Theorem 23 we see that $\mathfrak{H} = \{g^\epsilon\}$, where ϵ is the g.c.d. of δ and ν. But then $\epsilon \leq \delta$, $\epsilon = \delta$, and δ divides ν.

We now consider the commutative elements of an arbitrary group and derive the following result:

LEMMA 5. *Let* hk = kh *where the order* ρ *of* h *is prime to the order* σ *of* k. *Then* g = hk *has order* $\rho\sigma$ *and* $\{g\} = \{h\} \times \{k\}$. *Conversely, if* g *is a group element of order* $\rho\sigma$ *with* ρ *prime to* σ, *then* g = hk, $\{g\} = \{h\} \times \{k\}$, *where* ρ *is the order of* h *and* σ *is the order of* k.

For if $g = hk$, we have $g^{\rho\sigma} = h^{\rho\sigma}k^{\sigma\rho} = e$. Thus the order ν of g divides $\rho\sigma$. However, $e = g^\nu = h^\nu k^\nu$, and $h^\nu = k^{-\nu}$ is an element of $\{h\}$ and of $\{k\}$. These are groups of relatively prime orders, and Theorem 10 implies that the order of a common subgroup $\{h^\nu\} = \{h^{-\nu}\}$ must divide both ρ and σ and must be the identity group. Then $h^\nu = k^{-\nu} = e$, ρ divides ν, $k^\nu = e$, σ divides ν, $\rho\sigma$ divides ν, $\rho\sigma = \nu$. Evidently, $\{g\} \subseteq \{h\}\{k\}$ of order at most $\rho\sigma$. Thus $\{g\} = \{h\}\{k\} = \{h\} \times \{k\}$. Conversely, if g has order $\rho\sigma$, where ρ is prime σ, there exist integers α and β such that

$$\alpha\rho + \beta\sigma = 1\ . \tag{22}$$

Then $g = g^{\rho\alpha}g^{\sigma\beta} = hk$, where $k = (g^\rho)^\alpha$ and $h = (g^\sigma)^\beta$. By Theorem 23 the order of g^ρ is σ, and the order of g^σ is ρ. The order of k, then, is a divisor

σ_1 of σ, and the order of h is a divisor ρ_1 of ρ. But then σ_1 is prime to ρ_1, and g has order $\rho_1\sigma_1 = \rho\sigma$. This is possible only if $\rho = \rho_1$, $\sigma = \sigma_1$, and $\{g\} = \{h\}\{k\}$, as desired.

Lemma 5 implies that if $\mathfrak{G}$ is a cyclic group of order $\rho\sigma$, where ρ is prime to σ, then $\mathfrak{G} = \mathfrak{H} \times \mathfrak{K}$, where $\mathfrak{H}$ has order ρ and $\mathfrak{K}$ has order σ. This result may be generalized readily, and the generalization is stated as follows:

THEOREM 25. *Let $\mathfrak{G}$ be a cyclic group of order*

$$n = p_1^{e_1} \cdots p_t^{e_t}, \tag{23}$$

where the p_i *are distinct positive prime integers. Then*

$$\mathfrak{G} = \mathfrak{G}_1 \times \cdots \times \mathfrak{G}_t, \tag{24}$$

where $\mathfrak{G}_i$ *is a cyclic group of order* $p_i^{e_i}$.

EXERCISES

1. Determine *all* subgroups of the cyclic group of order 12.
2. Let g have order 24. What is the order of g^{14}?
3. If ϵ, ν, and τ are integers such that ϵ divides ν and ϵ and τ are relatively prime, show that there exists an integer α such that $\alpha\epsilon + \tau$ is relatively prime to ν.
4. If $\mathfrak{G}$ is a cyclic group of order $\nu = \epsilon\delta$ and if h is any element of $\mathfrak{G}$ of order ϵ, show that there is a generator g of $\mathfrak{G}$ with $h = g^\delta$. (*Hint:* Use Exercise 3.)
5. If $\mathfrak{Z}$ is a cyclic group, show that the homomorphisms of $\mathfrak{Z}$ into $\mathfrak{Z}$ form a group isomorphic to $\mathfrak{Z}$.
6. Describe the automorphism group of the cyclic group of order 25.
7. Let $\mathfrak{G}$ be the direct product of two cyclic groups of order 4. Determine all homomorphisms of $\mathfrak{G}$ into the cyclic group of order 8.

15. Finite abelian groups. Let $\mathfrak{G}$ be a finite abelian group. We define the *exponent* e of $\mathfrak{G}$ to be the largest order of an element of $\mathfrak{G}$. Then $\mathfrak{G}$ has exponent e if there is an element g in $\mathfrak{G}$ of order e and the orders of all other elements of $\mathfrak{G}$ are at most e.

THEOREM 26. *The order of any element of a finite abelian group* $\mathfrak{G}$ *divides the exponent of* $\mathfrak{G}$.

For let $\mathfrak{G}$ have exponent e and let g be an element of $\mathfrak{G}$ of order e. If the order f of an element k in $\mathfrak{G}$ does not divide e, there must exist a positive prime p such that $e = p^\alpha e_0$, $f = p^\beta f_0$, where $\beta > \alpha \geq 0$ and p does not divide either f_0 or e_0. By Theorem 23 the element $a = g^{p^\alpha}$ has order e_0, and the element $b = k^{f_0}$ has order p^β. By Lemma 5 the product ab has order $p^\beta e_0 > e$, contrary to hypothesis. Hence the order of every element of $\mathfrak{G}$ divides e.

When the order n of an abelian group $\mathfrak{G}$ is equal to its exponent, our definition implies that there is an element in $\mathfrak{G}$ of order n, and so $\mathfrak{G}$ is cyclic. We combine this result with Theorem 26 as follows:

THEOREM 27. *Let $\mathfrak{G}$ be an abelian group of order* n, 1 *be the identity element of $\mathfrak{G}$, so that* $g^n = 1$. *Suppose that there is no integer a such that* $n > a > 0$, $g^a = 1$ *for every* g *of $\mathfrak{G}$. Then $\mathfrak{G}$ is a cyclic group.*

We are now ready to derive the basic structure theorem for finite abelian groups.

THEOREM 28. *Every abelian group $\mathfrak{G}$ of order* n *is the direct product,*

$$\mathfrak{G} = \mathfrak{G}_1 \times \cdots \times \mathfrak{G}_t\,, \tag{25}$$

of cyclic subgroups $\mathfrak{G}_i$ of orders e_i *where* e_i *is divisible by* e_{i+1} *for* $i = 1, \ldots, t-1$. *The integers* e_i *are unique, and* $n = e_1 \cdots e_t$.

The theorem is true trivially if $n = 1$. Assume it true for all abelian groups of orders $m < n$. Let e_1 be the exponent of $\mathfrak{G}$, so that $\mathfrak{G}$ contains an element g_1 of order e_1. Write 1 for the identity element of $\mathfrak{G}$. We define $\mathfrak{G}_1 = \{g_1\}$ and know that $\mathfrak{G}_1$ is a normal subgroup of $\mathfrak{G}$. The order of $\mathfrak{G}/\mathfrak{G}_1$ is $m = ne_1^{-1} < n$. By the hypothesis of our induction, $\mathfrak{G}/\mathfrak{G}_1 = \mathfrak{H}_2 \times \cdots \times \mathfrak{H}_t$, where $\mathfrak{H}_a = \{\bar{k}_a\}$ has order e_a and e_{a+1} divides e_a for $a = 2, \ldots, t-1$. Moreover,

$$m = e_2 \cdots e_t\,. \tag{26}$$

The coset $\bar{k}_a = k_a\mathfrak{G}_1$ for an element k_a in $\mathfrak{H}_a$ and $(\bar{k}_a)^{e_a} = \mathfrak{G}_1$, $k_a^{e_a} = b_a$ is an element of $\mathfrak{G}_1$. It follows that $b_a = g_1^{\sigma_a\tau_a}$, where σ_a is the g.c.d. of e_1 and $\sigma_a\tau_a$. Then $e_1 = \gamma_a\sigma_a$, where γ_a is prime to τ_a. Hence b_a has order γ_a by Theorem 23.

The order ρ_a of k_a is now $e_a\gamma_a$. For $(\bar{k}_a)^{\rho_a} = \mathfrak{G}_1$ is a consequence of the fact that $\bar{k}_a$ is the homomorphic image of k_a. Hence e_a divides ρ_a, $\rho_a = e_a\delta_a$, $k^{\rho_a} = b_a^{\delta_a} = 1$, γ_a divides δ_a, and so $e_a\gamma_a$ divides ρ_a. But $k_a^{e_a\gamma_a} = b_a^{\gamma_a} = 1$, and so ρ_a divides $e_a\gamma_a$, and $\rho_a = e_a\gamma_a$.

We now apply Theorem 26 to see that $e_a\gamma_a$ divides $e_1 = \sigma_a\gamma_a$, e_a divides σ_a, $\sigma_a = e_a\phi_a$, and $k_a^{e_a} = g_1^{e_a\phi_a\tau_a}$. Put

$$g_a = k_a g_1^{-\phi_a\tau_a} \tag{27}$$

and see that $\bar{g}_a = g_a\mathfrak{G}_1 = \bar{k}_a$, $g_a^{e_a} = 1$. Define $\mathfrak{H}$ to be the product $\{g_2\} \cdots \{g_t\}$ so that $\mathfrak{H}$ is a subgroup of $\mathfrak{G}$, and let S be the homomorphism $g \to \bar{g} = g\mathfrak{G}_1$ of $\mathfrak{G}$ onto $\mathfrak{G}/\mathfrak{G}_1$. The order of $\mathfrak{H}$ is clearly at most m, $\mathfrak{H}S = \mathfrak{G}/\mathfrak{G}_1$ has order m, $\mathfrak{H}$ must have order m, and $\mathfrak{H}$ is the direct product

$$\mathfrak{H} = \{g_2\} \times \cdots \times \{g_t\}\,. \tag{28}$$

Since S maps $\mathfrak{H}$ isomorphically onto $\mathfrak{G}/\mathfrak{G}_1$, the intersection of $\mathfrak{H}$ and $\mathfrak{G}_1$ is $\{1\}$, $\mathfrak{H}\mathfrak{G}_1 = \mathfrak{H} \times \mathfrak{G}_1 = \{g_1\} \times \cdots \times \{g_t\} = \mathfrak{G}$, as desired. It remains only to show that $e_1, \ldots, e_t$ are unique.

Assume that $\mathfrak{G} = \mathfrak{G}_1 \times \cdots \times \mathfrak{G}_t = \mathfrak{H}_1 \times \cdots \times \mathfrak{H}_s$, where $\mathfrak{G}_i = \{g_i\}$ has order e_i and $\mathfrak{H}_j = \{h_j\}$ has order f_j. The assumption that e_{i+1} divides e_i and f_{j+1} divides f_j implies that $g^{e_1} = g^{f_1} = 1$ for every g of $\mathfrak{G}$. Hence $e_1 = f_1$ is the exponent of $\mathfrak{G}$. Suppose, now, that $e_1 = f_1$, $e_2 = f_2, \ldots,$ $e_{a-1} = f_{a-1}$, and $e_a > f_a$. Define $\mathfrak{K}$ to be the subset of $\mathfrak{G}$, consisting of the βth powers of all elements of $\mathfrak{G}$ where $\beta = f_a$. Since $a^a b^a = (ab)^a$, $1^a = 1$, $a^a(a^{-1})^a = (aa^{-1})^a = 1$, we see that $\mathfrak{K}$ is a subgroup of $\mathfrak{G}$. Clearly, $\mathfrak{K} = \{g_1^\beta\} \times \cdots \times \{g_a^\beta\} = \{h_1^\beta\} \times \cdots \times \{h_{a-1}^\beta\}$, where g_i^β has order $e_i\beta^{-1}$, h_i^β has order $e_i\beta^{-1}$ for $i = 1, \ldots, a - 1$. But $g_a^\beta \neq e$, and so the two distinct expressions of $\mathfrak{K}$ yield two distinct orders for $\mathfrak{K}$, which is impossible. This completes our proof.

Theorems 25 and 28 imply the following result:

THEOREM 29. *Every abelian group is expressible as the direct product,*

$$\mathfrak{G} = \mathfrak{C}_1 \times \cdots \times \mathfrak{C}_r , \tag{29}$$

of cyclic groups $\mathfrak{G}_i$ *of prime power orders* $p_i^{n_i}$. *The orders* $p_1^{n_1}, \ldots, p_r^{n_r}$ *uniquely determine* $\mathfrak{G}$ *in the sense of isomorphism.*

16. Permutation groups. Let $\mathfrak{M}$ be a finite set whose n elements are represented by the symbols $x_1, x_2, \ldots, x_n$. Then the set of all one-to-one mappings,

$$P: \qquad x_j \rightarrow x_j P ,$$

of $\mathfrak{M}$ onto $\mathfrak{M}$ forms a finite group Σ_n, with respect to the mapping product, called the *symmetric group of permutations on* n *letters*. Each permutation P carries x_j to $x_jP = x_{i_j}$, where the sequence of integers $i_1, i_2, \ldots, i_n$ is simply a rearrangement of the sequence $1, 2, \ldots, n$. Then we may represent P by the two-rowed notation

$$P = \begin{pmatrix} 1 & 2 & \cdots & n \\ i_1 & i_2 & \cdots & i_n \end{pmatrix} . \tag{30}$$

There are n choices for i_1, $n - 1$ choices for i_2 after i_1 is selected, . . . , one choice for i_n after i_{n-1} is selected. It follows that the order of Σ_n is

$$n(n - 1) \cdots 2 \cdot 1 = n! . \tag{31}$$

In notation (30) the two-rowed symbol for P has the property that the image i_j of j lies below j. This property is independent of the order in which the columns of the symbol are written, and so they may be permuted at will. If Q is any second permutation, we can rearrange the columns of Q so that

$$Q = \begin{pmatrix} i_1 & i_2 & \cdots & i_n \\ j_1 & j_2 & \cdots & j_n \end{pmatrix}. \tag{32}$$

Then our definition of the product of two mappings implies that $x_k(PQ) = (x_kP)Q = (x_{i_k})Q = x_{j_k}$. Hence

$$PQ = \begin{pmatrix} 1 & 2 & \cdots & n \\ j_1 & j_2 & \cdots & j_n \end{pmatrix}. \tag{33}$$

The permutation

$$I = \begin{pmatrix} 1 & 2 & \cdots & n \\ 1 & 2 & \cdots & n \end{pmatrix} \tag{34}$$

is the identity element of Σ_n. If P is given by expression (30), then we may permute the columns of P so that the integers in the second row are in the natural order and so arrive at

$$P = \begin{pmatrix} k_1 & k_2 & \cdots & k_n \\ 1 & 2 & \cdots & n \end{pmatrix}. \tag{35}$$

Then

$$P^{-1} = \begin{pmatrix} 1 & 2 & \cdots & n \\ k_1 & k_2 & \cdots & k_n \end{pmatrix} = \begin{pmatrix} i_1 & i_2 & \cdots & i_n \\ 1 & 2 & \cdots & n \end{pmatrix}. \tag{36}$$

Every subgroup of a Σ_n is called a *permutation group* (on n letters). Every permutation group on m letters may also be regarded as a permutation group on $n > m$ letters, which leaves $n - m$ letters fixed.

A *cycle* C is a permutation of the form

$$C = \begin{pmatrix} 1 & 2 & \cdots & r-1 & r & r+1 & \cdots & n \\ 2 & 3 & \cdots & r & 1 & r+1 & \cdots & n \end{pmatrix}. \tag{37}$$

It carries x_1 to x_2, x_2 to x_3, . . . , x_{r-1} to x_r and x_r back to x_1 and leaves $x_{r+1}, \ldots, x_n$ fixed. It is customary to use the notation

$$C = (1 \;\; 2 \cdots r) \tag{38}$$

for the cycle of permutation (37). We call r the *length* of the cycle. Observe that if $x = x_1$, then $x_2 = xC$, $x_3 = xC^2, \ldots, x_r = xC^{r-1}$, $x_1 = xC^r = x$, and $x_iC^r = xC^{i-1}C^r = xC^rC^{i-1} = xC^{i-1} = x_i$. *Hence the length of a cycle is its group order.*

It will be convenient to use the notation $(x_1 \cdots x_r)$ for the cycle C such that $x_i = x_1C^{i-1}$ and $x_1C^r = x_1$ in the proof of the following result:

THEOREM 30. *Every permutation is expressible as the product* $P = C_1 \cdots C_s$ *of cycles* C_α *of lengths* r_α *where no two of the cycles have a letter* *in common. These cycles commute, and the order of* P *is the least common multiple of* $r_1, \ldots, r_s$.

For we may restrict the set of elements which P permutes to a set $\mathfrak{M}$ of elements $x_1, \ldots, x_n$ such that every $x_iP \neq x_i$. Every element x of $\mathfrak{M}$ determines a corresponding subset $x\{P\}$ of $\mathfrak{M}$ consisting of the images xP^k of x under the cyclic group $\{P\}$. If $x, xP, \ldots, xP^{r-1}$ are distinct and $xP^r = xP^j$, where $0 \leq j < r$, then $x = xP^{r-j}$ and necessarily $j = 0$. Then $xP^r = x$ and the set $x\{P\}$ consists of $x, xP, \ldots, xP^{r-1}$, since if $k = qr + j$, where $0 \leq j < r$, then $xP^k = xP^j$. If $x\{P\}$ and $y\{P\}$ have an element in common, then $xP^i = yP^j$, $x = yP^{j+i}$, and $x\{P\} \subseteq y\{P\}$. By symmetry, $y\{P\} \subseteq x\{P\}$, and so $y\{P\} = x\{P\}$. It follows that $\mathfrak{M}$ may be partitioned into s disjoint subsets $\mathfrak{M}_1, \ldots, \mathfrak{M}_s$, where $\mathfrak{M}_\alpha = z_\alpha\{P\}$ contains r_α elements. Define

$$C_\alpha = (x_\alpha, x_\alpha P, \ldots, x_\alpha P^{n_\alpha - 1}) .$$

Then the product $C_1 \cdots C_s$ has the property that $xC_1 \cdots C_s = xP$ for every x in $\mathfrak{M}$. Indeed, every x of $\mathfrak{M}$ is an element $x = x_\alpha P^j$ for some α and $0 \leq j < r_\alpha$ and $xP = x_\alpha P^{j+1} = xC_\alpha = xC_1 \cdots C_s$, since $(x_\alpha P^j)C_\beta = x_\alpha P^j$ for $\beta \neq \alpha$. It follows that $P = C_1 \cdots C_s$. If y_α is any element of $\mathfrak{M}_\alpha$, then $y_\alpha C_\beta C_\gamma = y_\alpha$ if $\alpha \neq \beta, \gamma \cdot y_\alpha C_\alpha C_\beta = y_\alpha C_\beta C_\alpha = y_\alpha C_\alpha$ for $\alpha \neq \beta$, and so $xC_\alpha C_\beta = xC_\beta C_\alpha$ for all x of $\mathfrak{M}$. It follows that $xP^k = xC_1^k \cdots C_s^k = x$ for every x of $\mathfrak{M}$ if and only if $y_\alpha C_\alpha^k = y_\alpha$ for every y_α of $\mathfrak{M}_\alpha$, $C_\alpha^k = I$. Then k is divisible by r_α for $\alpha = 1, \ldots, s$, and the order of P is the least common multiple of $r_1, \ldots, r_s$.

17. Computation of transforms. The mapping

$$P \rightarrow Q^{-1}PQ$$

is an inner automorphism of a permutation group G for every element Q of G. The image element $Q^{-1}PQ$ is called the *transform* of P by Q. Transforms of P may be computed easily when the representation of P as a product of cycles is given. Indeed, let $P = C_1 \cdots C_s$, so that

$$Q^{-1}PQ = (Q^{-1}C_1Q) \cdots (Q^{-1}C_sQ) . \tag{39}$$

This will yield the representation of $Q^{-1}PQ$ as a product of cycles $Q^{-1}C_iQ$ as soon as the following result is obtained.

THEOREM 31. *Let* $\mathrm{C} = (\mathrm{a}_1, \ldots, \mathrm{a}_r)$ *and*

$$\mathrm{Q} = \begin{pmatrix} \mathrm{a}_1 & \mathrm{a}_2 & \cdots & \mathrm{a}_r & \mathrm{a}_{r+1} & \cdots & \mathrm{a}_n \\ \mathrm{b}_1 & \mathrm{b}_2 & \cdots & \mathrm{b}_r & \mathrm{b}_{r+1} & \cdots & \mathrm{b}_n \end{pmatrix} . \tag{40}$$

Then $\mathrm{Q}^{-1}\mathrm{CQ} = (\mathrm{b}_1, \ldots, \mathrm{b}_r)$.

This result states that $Q^{-1}PQ$ is obtained from P by applying Q to the cycles of P. For example, if $P = (1234)(567)$ and $Q = (174)(256)$, then $Q^{-1}PQ = (7531)(624)$. The result is proved by observing that

$$(41)\qquad Q^{-1} = \begin{pmatrix} b_1 & b_2 & \cdots & b_r & b_{r+1} & \cdots & b_n \\ a_1 & a_2 & \cdots & a_r & a_{r+1} & \cdots & a_n \end{pmatrix}$$

and

$$(42)\qquad C = \begin{pmatrix} a_1 & a_2 & \cdots & a_{r-1} & a_r & a_{r+1} & \cdots & a_n \\ a_2 & a_3 & \cdots & a_r & a_1 & a_{r+1} & \cdots & a_n \end{pmatrix},$$

so that

$$(43)\qquad Q^{-1}C = \begin{pmatrix} b_1 & b_2 & \cdots & b_{r-1} & b_r & b_{r+1} & \cdots & b_n \\ a_2 & a_3 & \cdots & a_r & a_1 & a_{r+1} & \cdots & a_n \end{pmatrix}.$$

18. The regular representation of a group. Every group $\mathfrak{G}$ is isomorphic to a group $\mathfrak{R}(\mathfrak{G})$ which consists of one-to-one transformations of $\mathfrak{G}$ itself. The transformations are called *right multiplications* and are the mappings

$$R_g: \qquad x \to xg \qquad (x \text{ in } \mathfrak{G}),$$

where xg is the product in the group $\mathfrak{G}$. Each R_g is a one-to-one mapping of $\mathfrak{G}$ onto $\mathfrak{G}$. For if y is any element of $\mathfrak{G}$, we have $y = xg$ if and only if $x = yg^{-1}$. Thus every element of $\mathfrak{G}$ is the image xR_g of a unique element x of $\mathfrak{G}$, as desired.

We have now shown that the transformations R_g are one-to-one mappings of $\mathfrak{G}$ onto $\mathfrak{G}$, and we now consider the set $\mathfrak{R}(\mathfrak{G})$ of all R_g. Since $(xg)h = x(gh)$, we have

$$R_{gh} = R_g R_h .$$

Thus the mapping

$$S: \qquad g \to R_g$$

of $\mathfrak{G}$ onto $\mathfrak{R}(\mathfrak{G})$ must be a homomorphic mapping of $\mathfrak{G}$ onto what is necessarily a group $\mathfrak{R}(\mathfrak{G})$. However, R_g is the identity transformation only when $x = xg$ for an x of $\mathfrak{G}$, and Theorem 1 implies that g is then the identity element of $\mathfrak{G}$. Hence S is an isomorphism of $\mathfrak{G}$ onto $\mathfrak{R}(\mathfrak{G})$.

In the finite case $\mathfrak{R}(\mathfrak{G})$ is a permutation group, and we have the following result:

THEOREM 32. *Every finite group $\mathfrak{G}$ is isomorphic to a permutation group.*

EXERCISES

1. Let $\mathfrak{H}$ be any subgroup of a finite group $\mathfrak{G}$ so that $\mathfrak{G} = \mathfrak{H} \cup \mathfrak{H}g_2 \cup \cdots \cup \mathfrak{H}g_m$. Show that the mapping $g \to T_g$ is a homomorphism of $\mathfrak{G}$ onto the group of the permutations T_g defined by $\mathfrak{H}k \to (\mathfrak{H}k)Tg = \mathfrak{H}kg$.

2. Let $\mathfrak{G}$ be the group $\mathfrak{G}_6$ of Exercise 4 of Section 9. Find the regular representation of $\mathfrak{G}$.

3. Determine the representations of $\mathfrak{G}_6$ as permutation groups on cosets for all subgroups $\mathfrak{H}$ of $\mathfrak{G}_6$.

19. Composition series. A normal subgroup $\mathfrak{H}$ of a group $\mathfrak{G}$ is called a *maximal* normal subgroup of $\mathfrak{G}$ if there exists no normal subgroup $\mathfrak{K}$ of $\mathfrak{G}$ such that $\mathfrak{G} \supset \mathfrak{K} \supset \mathfrak{H}$. We call $\mathfrak{G}$ a *simple group* if the identity group $\mathfrak{I}$ is a maximal normal subgroup of $\mathfrak{G}$. The following theorem is an immediate consequence of Theorem 18.

THEOREM 33. *A normal subgroup $\mathfrak{H}$ of $\mathfrak{G}$ is maximal if and only if $\mathfrak{G}/\mathfrak{H}$ is simple.*

A sequence of subgroups,

$$\mathfrak{G} = \mathfrak{G}_0 \supseteq \mathfrak{G}_1 \supseteq \cdots \supseteq \mathfrak{G}_\lambda = \mathfrak{I}, \tag{44}$$

is called a *normal series* for $\mathfrak{G}$ if $\mathfrak{G}_\alpha$ is a normal subgroup of $\mathfrak{G}_{\alpha-1}$ for $\alpha = 1, \cdots, \lambda$. A normal series is said to be *redundant* if $\mathfrak{G}_\alpha = \mathfrak{G}_{\alpha-1}$ for some $\alpha \geq 1$. Thus equation (44) is a *non-redundant* normal series if $\mathfrak{G}_0 \supset \mathfrak{G}_1 \supset \cdots \supset \mathfrak{G}_\lambda = \mathfrak{I}$. Every redundant normal series may be converted into a non-redundant normal series by deleting those $\mathfrak{G}_\alpha$ in which $\mathfrak{G}_\alpha = \mathfrak{G}_{\alpha-1}$.

Let series (44) and

$$\mathfrak{G} = \mathfrak{H}_0 \supseteq \mathfrak{H}_1 \supseteq \cdots \supseteq \mathfrak{H}_\mu = \mathfrak{I} \tag{45}$$

be two normal series for the same group $\mathfrak{G}$. We say that the two series are *isomorphic* (*have isomorphic factor groups*) if $\lambda = \mu$ and the λ factor groups $\mathfrak{G}_{\alpha-1}/\mathfrak{G}_\alpha$ are isomorphic in some order to the groups $\mathfrak{H}_{\beta-1}/\mathfrak{H}_\beta$. If $\mathfrak{G}_{\alpha-1} = \mathfrak{G}_\alpha$, then $\mathfrak{G}_{\alpha-1}/\mathfrak{G}_\alpha$ is isomorphic to $\mathfrak{H}_{\beta-1}/\mathfrak{H}_\beta$ if and only if $\mathfrak{H}_{\beta-1} = \mathfrak{H}_\beta$ Hence the deletion of $\mathfrak{G}_\alpha$ from series (44) and $\mathfrak{H}_\beta$ from series (45) converts the two isomorphic series into two new series which are also isomorphic. It follows that two isomorphic redundant normal series may be converted by deletions into two isomorphic non-redundant normal series.

Theorem 7 has a generalization which we state as follows:

THEOREM 34. *Let $\mathfrak{H}$ and $\mathfrak{K}$ be subgroups of $\mathfrak{G}$, $\mathfrak{D} = \mathfrak{H} \cap \mathfrak{K}$, $\mathrm{k}\mathfrak{H} = \mathfrak{H}\mathrm{k}$ for every k of $\mathfrak{K}$. Then $\mathfrak{H}\mathfrak{K}$ is a subgroup of $\mathfrak{G}$, $\mathfrak{D}$ is a normal subgroup of $\mathfrak{K}$, $\mathfrak{H}$ is a normal subgroup of $\mathfrak{H}\mathfrak{K}$, and*

$$\mathfrak{H}\mathfrak{K}/\mathfrak{H} \cong \mathfrak{K}/\mathfrak{D}. \tag{46}$$

Here $\mathfrak{H}\mathfrak{K}$ is trivially a subgroup of $\mathfrak{G}$, $\mathfrak{K}$ is a subgroup of $\mathfrak{H}\mathfrak{K}$, and $\mathfrak{H}$ is a normal subgroup of $\mathfrak{H}\mathfrak{K}$. The intersection of any subgroup $\mathfrak{G}_1$ of a group $\mathfrak{G}$, with a normal subgroup is a normal subgroup of $\mathfrak{G}_1$. Hence $\mathfrak{D}$ is a normal subgroup of $\mathfrak{K}$. The cosets of $\mathfrak{H}\mathfrak{K}$ all have the form $\mathfrak{H}k$ for k in $\mathfrak{K}$ and

$\mathfrak{H}k = \mathfrak{H}k_1$ if and only if $k_1 = dk$, where d is in $\mathfrak{H}$, $d = k_1k^{-1}$ is in $\mathfrak{D}$, $\mathfrak{D}k = \mathfrak{D}k_1$. It follows that the mapping $\mathfrak{H}k \to \mathfrak{D}k$ is a one-to-one mapping S of $\mathfrak{H}\mathfrak{K}/\mathfrak{H}$ onto $\mathfrak{K}/\mathfrak{D}$. Then S is an isomorphism of $\mathfrak{H}\mathfrak{K}/\mathfrak{H}$ onto $\mathfrak{K}/\mathfrak{D}$, since $[(\mathfrak{H}k)(\mathfrak{H}k_1)]S = (\mathfrak{H}kk_1)S = \mathfrak{D}kk_1 = (\mathfrak{D}k)(\mathfrak{D}k_1) = [(\mathfrak{H}k)S][(\mathfrak{H}k_1)S]$.

We use this result to prove

THEOREM 35. *Let $\mathfrak{B}$ and $\mathfrak{C}$ be subgroups of $\mathfrak{G}$, $\mathfrak{B}_0$ be a normal subgroup of $\mathfrak{B}$, and $\mathfrak{C}_0$ be a normal subgroup of $\mathfrak{C}$. Then*

$$\text{(47)} \qquad \mathfrak{B}_0(\mathfrak{B} \cap \mathfrak{C})/\mathfrak{B}_0(\mathfrak{B} \cap \mathfrak{C}_0) \cong \mathfrak{C}_0(\mathfrak{C} \cap \mathfrak{B})/\mathfrak{C}_0(\mathfrak{C} \cap \mathfrak{B}_0)\,.$$

For we take $\mathfrak{K} = \mathfrak{B} \cap \mathfrak{C}$ and $\mathfrak{H} = \mathfrak{B}_0(\mathfrak{B} \cap \mathfrak{C}_0)$. Since $\mathfrak{B}_0$ is a normal subgroup of $\mathfrak{B}$, we see that $\mathfrak{B}_0 b = b\mathfrak{B}_0$ for every element b of $\mathfrak{B}$ and hence for every element b of $\mathfrak{K}$. Then $\mathfrak{H}$ and $\mathfrak{K}$ satisfy the conditions of Theorem 34. Now $\mathfrak{H}\mathfrak{K} = \mathfrak{B}_0(\mathfrak{B} \cap \mathfrak{C}_0)(\mathfrak{B} \cap \mathfrak{C}) = \mathfrak{B}_0(\mathfrak{B} \cap \mathfrak{C})$, since the product of a group by a subgroup is the whole group. Also the elements of $\mathfrak{D} = \mathfrak{H} \cap \mathfrak{K}$ have the form b_0c_0, where b_0 is in $\mathfrak{B}_0$ and c_0 is in $\mathfrak{B} \cap \mathfrak{C}_0$. Since $\mathfrak{K} \subseteq \mathfrak{C}$, we have $\mathfrak{D} \subseteq \mathfrak{C}$, b_0c_0 is in $\mathfrak{C}$, c_0 is in $\mathfrak{C}$, b_0 must be in $\mathfrak{C}$, b_0 is in $\mathfrak{C} \cap \mathfrak{B}_0$. Then $\mathfrak{D} \subseteq (\mathfrak{C} \cap \mathfrak{B}_0)(\mathfrak{B} \cap \mathfrak{C}_0)$. Conversely, if b_0 is in $\mathfrak{C} \cap \mathfrak{B}_0$ and c_0 is in $\mathfrak{B} \cap \mathfrak{C}_0$, then b_0c_0 is in $\mathfrak{H} = \mathfrak{B}_0(\mathfrak{B} \cap \mathfrak{C}_0)$ and in $\mathfrak{K} = \mathfrak{B} \cap \mathfrak{C}$. Hence $\mathfrak{D} = (\mathfrak{C} \cap \mathfrak{B}_0)(\mathfrak{B} \cap \mathfrak{C}_0)$. It follows from Theorem 34 that

$$\text{(48)} \qquad \mathfrak{B}_0(\mathfrak{B} \cap \mathfrak{C})/\mathfrak{B}_0(\mathfrak{B} \cap \mathfrak{C}_0) \cong \mathfrak{B} \cap \mathfrak{C}/(\mathfrak{C} \cap \mathfrak{B}_0)(\mathfrak{B} \cap \mathfrak{C}_0)\,.$$

Interchanging the roles of $\mathfrak{B}$ and $\mathfrak{C}$ in relation (48), we see that

$$\text{(49)} \qquad \mathfrak{C}_0(\mathfrak{C} \cap \mathfrak{B})/\mathfrak{C}_0(\mathfrak{C} \cap \mathfrak{B}_0) \cong \mathfrak{C} \cap \mathfrak{B}/(\mathfrak{B} \cap \mathfrak{C}_0)(\mathfrak{C} \cap \mathfrak{B}_0)\,.$$

This yields relation (47).

A normal series $\mathfrak{G} = \mathfrak{K}_0 \supseteq \mathfrak{K}_1 \supseteq \cdots \supseteq \mathfrak{K}_\nu$ of a group $\mathfrak{G}$ is called a *refinement* of a normal series (23) of $\mathfrak{G}$ if every $\mathfrak{G}_\alpha$ is one of the $\mathfrak{K}_\beta$, that is, the series of $\mathfrak{K}_\beta$ is obtained from the series of $\mathfrak{G}_\alpha$ by inserting a sequence of groups $\mathfrak{K}_\gamma$ between each $\mathfrak{G}_{\alpha-1}$ and $\mathfrak{G}_\alpha$. We are now ready to derive the following result:

THEOREM 36. *Any two normal series of a group $\mathfrak{G}$ have isomorphic refinements.*

Consider the groups $\mathfrak{G}_{\alpha\beta} = \mathfrak{G}_\alpha(\mathfrak{G}_{\alpha-1} \cap \mathfrak{H}_\beta)$ for $\alpha = 1, \ldots, \lambda$ and $\beta = 0, \ldots, \mu$. Then $\mathfrak{G}_{\alpha 0} = \mathfrak{G}_\alpha(\mathfrak{G}_{\alpha-1} \cap \mathfrak{G}) = \mathfrak{G}_\alpha\mathfrak{G}_{\alpha-1} = \mathfrak{G}_{\alpha-1}$, $\mathfrak{G}_{\alpha_\mu} = \mathfrak{G}_\alpha(\mathfrak{G}_{\alpha-1} \cap \mathfrak{J}) = \mathfrak{G}_\alpha$. Also $\mathfrak{G}_{\alpha,\, \beta-1} = \mathfrak{G}_\alpha(\mathfrak{G}_{\alpha-1} \cap \mathfrak{H}_{\beta-1})$, and $\mathfrak{H}_\beta$ is a normal subgroup of $\mathfrak{H}_{\beta-1}$. By Theorem 35 we see that $\mathfrak{G}_{\alpha,\, \beta}$ is a normal subgroup of $\mathfrak{G}_{\alpha,\, \beta-1}$. We may insert the groups $\mathfrak{G}_{\alpha 1}, \ldots, \mathfrak{G}_{\alpha,\, \mu-1}$ between $\mathfrak{G}_{\alpha,\, 0} = \mathfrak{G}_{\alpha-1}$ and $\mathfrak{G}_{\alpha,\, \mu} = \mathfrak{G}_\alpha$ and obtain a refinement of sequence (44) in which we have adjoined $\lambda(\mu - 1)$ new groups. The refinement is then a sequence of $\lambda + \lambda(\mu - 1) = \lambda\mu$ groups $\mathfrak{G}_{\alpha\beta}$. Similarly, the sequence of groups obtained by inserting the groups $\mathfrak{H}_{\beta\alpha} = \mathfrak{H}_\beta(\mathfrak{H}_{\beta-1} \cap \mathfrak{G}_\alpha)$ for $\beta = 1, \ldots, \mu$ and $\alpha = 1, \ldots, \lambda - 1$ in sequence (45) is a refinement of equation (24), with $\mu + \mu(\lambda - 1) = \lambda\mu$ members $\mathfrak{H}_{\beta\alpha}$. Put $\mathfrak{B} = \mathfrak{G}_{\alpha-1}$, $\mathfrak{B}_0 = \mathfrak{G}_\alpha$, $\mathfrak{C} = \mathfrak{H}_{\beta-1}$, and $\mathfrak{C}_0 = \mathfrak{H}_\beta$ in Theorem 36 and see that

$$\mathfrak{H}_{\beta,\,\alpha-1}/\mathfrak{H}_{\beta,\,\alpha} \cong \mathfrak{G}_{\alpha,\,\beta-1}/\mathfrak{G}_{\alpha,\,\beta} \qquad (\alpha = 1, \ldots, \lambda;\ \beta = 1, \ldots, \mu).$$

Thus the two refinements are isomorphic, as desired.

A non-redundant normal series of a group $\mathfrak{G}$ is called a *composition series* of $\mathfrak{G}$ if the factor groups are all simple groups. Every non-redundant refinement of a composition series must then coincide with the composition series itself. Theorem 36 then has the following consequence (called the "Jordan-Hölder Theorem"):

THEOREM 37. *Any two composition series of a group $\mathfrak{G}$ are isomorphic.*

EXERCISES

1. Determine all composition series of a cyclic group of order 12.
2. Determine all composition series of the symmetric group Σ_3.
3. Find the representations of the permutations of Σ_4 as products of cycles.
4. Find all subgroups of Σ_4.
5. Show that Σ_4 has three subgroups of order 8 and that these are conjugate subgroups, that is, each is obtainable from any other by an inner automorphism of Σ_4.
6. Determine all composition series of Σ_4.
7. Find all subgroups of order 4 of Σ_4.
8. Which of the subgroups in Exercise 7 are normal subgroups of Σ_4?

20. References. The presentation of this chapter is an improved revision of that given in chapters i and vi of the author's *Modern Higher Algebra.* Some use has been made of the material in Hans Zassenhaus, *Lehrbuch der Gruppentheorie* (Leipzig and Berlin, 1937). Attention is also called to the following classical texts on the subject of groups:

1. Speiser, A. *Die Theorie der Gruppen von endlicher Ordnung,* 3d edition. Berlin, 1937. 262 pp.

2. Miller, G. A., Blichfeldt, H., and Dickson, L. E. *Theory and Applications of Finite Groups.* New York, 1916. 388 pp.

3. Netto, E. *The Theory of Substitutions.* Translated by F. N. Cole in 1892. 301 pp.

4. Burnside, W. *Theory of Groups of Finite Order.* Cambridge, 1897. 388 pp.

CHAPTER II

Rings and Fields

1. Rings. An additive abelian group is usually called a *module*, and its subgroups are called *submodules*. The identity element of a module $\mathfrak{A}$ is called the *zero* element of $\mathfrak{A}$ and is represented by the symbol 0. Then $a + x = a$ for (even one element) a of $\mathfrak{A}$ if and only if $x = 0$. The equation $b + x = 0$ has the unique solution $x = -b$ (the inverse of b relative to the addition operation) and $-(-b) = b$. The equation $x + a = b$ has the unique solution $x = b + (-a)$, and we write $x = b - a$. Each element a of $\mathfrak{A}$ generates a cyclic submodule $\{a\}$, consisting of all elements $\nu \cdot a$, where ν ranges over all integers. If ν is positive, $\nu \cdot a$ is the sum $a + a + \cdots + a$ with ν summands, $0 \cdot a = 0$, and $(-\nu) \cdot a = -(\nu \cdot a)$. This defines $\nu \cdot a$ for all integers ν.

We now define the ring concept. Since we shall not consider non-associative rings here, we shall include the associative law as one of our defining postulates.

DEFINITION. *A* ring *is a module* $\mathfrak{A}$ *with a product operation* ab *on* $(\mathfrak{A}, \mathfrak{A})$ *to* $\mathfrak{A}$ *such that*

I. *The module* $\mathfrak{A}$ *contains at least two elements.*

II. *The distributive laws*

$$\mathrm{a}(\mathrm{b} + \mathrm{c}) = \mathrm{ab} + \mathrm{ac}, \quad (\mathrm{b} + \mathrm{c})\mathrm{a} = \mathrm{ba} + \mathrm{ca}$$

hold for every a, b, c *of* $\mathfrak{A}$.

III. *Products satisfy the associative law, that is,*

$$\mathrm{a}(\mathrm{bc}) = (\mathrm{ab})\mathrm{c}$$

for every a, b, c *of* $\mathfrak{A}$.

A ring $\mathfrak{A}$ is called a *commutative* ring if $ab = ba$ for every a and b of $\mathfrak{A}$. We call a ring $\mathfrak{A}$ a *division ring* if the set $\mathfrak{A}^*$ of all non-zero elements of $\mathfrak{A}$ forms a group with respect to the product operation of $\mathfrak{A}$. A *field* is a commutative division ring.

A subset $\mathfrak{B}$ of a ring $\mathfrak{A}$ is called a *subring* of $\mathfrak{A}$ if $\mathfrak{B}$ is a ring with respect to the addition and multiplication operations of $\mathfrak{A}$. But $\mathfrak{B}$ is a submodule of $\mathfrak{A}$ if and only if $a - b$ is in $\mathfrak{B}$ for every a and b of $\mathfrak{B}$. Since II and III hold throughout $\mathfrak{A}$, we can make the following conclusion:

THEOREM 1. *Let $\mathfrak{B}$ be a subset of a ring $\mathfrak{A}$ and let $\mathfrak{B}$ consist of at least two elements. Then $\mathfrak{B}$ is a subring of $\mathfrak{A}$ if and only if* $a - b$ *and* ab *are in* $\mathfrak{B}$ *for every* a *and* b *of* $\mathfrak{B}$.

If a is in a ring $\mathfrak{A}$, we have $0 + 0 = 0$, and the distributive laws imply that $a(0 + 0) = a0 + a0 = a0$, $(0 + 0)a = 0a + 0a = 0a$. Then $a0 = 0a = 0$. Also $[a + (-a)]b = 0 = ab + (-a)b$, so that $(-a)b = -(ab)$. Similarly, $a(-b) = -(ab)$. Then $(-a)(-b) = -[a(-b)] = -[-(ab)] = ab$.

THEOREM 2. *The equations*

$$a0 = 0a = 0, \quad (-a)b = a(-b) = -(ab), \quad (-a)(-b) = ab$$

are valid in every ring.

An element a of a ring $\mathfrak{A}$ is called a *left divisor of zero* if a is not zero and there exists an element $b \neq 0$ in $\mathfrak{A}$ such that $ab = 0$. Then b is a *right divisor of zero*. An element $a \neq 0$ is called an *absolute* left divisor of zero if $ab = 0$ for every b of $\mathfrak{A}$.

A ring $\mathfrak{A}$ is said to have a *unity* element e if there exists an element e in $\mathfrak{A}$ such that

$$ae = ea = a \tag{1}$$

for every a of $\mathfrak{A}$. The element e is unique; for, if $ae = ea = a$ and $af = fa = a$, then $ef = e = f$. We usually designate the unity element of a ring by the symbol 1.

If $\mathfrak{A}$ is a ring with a unity element 1, we call an element u of $\mathfrak{A}$ a *unit* of $\mathfrak{A}$ if there exists an element v of $\mathfrak{A}$ such that

$$uv = vu = 1\,. \tag{2}$$

The units of $\mathfrak{A}$ form a group $\mathfrak{U}$ with respect to the product operation of $\mathfrak{A}$, called the *unit group* of $\mathfrak{A}$. Indeed, 1 is in $\mathfrak{U}$, and u^{-1} is in $\mathfrak{U}$ for every u of $\mathfrak{U}$. If u_1 and u_2 are in $\mathfrak{U}$, then $(u_1u_2)(u_2^{-1}u_1^{-1}) = 1$, and so u_1u_2 is in $\mathfrak{U}$, and $\mathfrak{U}$ is a group.

EXERCISES

1. What is the unit group of the ring $\mathfrak{E}$ of all ordinary integers?
2. Let $\mathfrak{J}$ be the set of all complex numbers $a + bi$ such that a and b are integers, $i^2 = -1$. Find the unit group of $\mathfrak{J}$.

2. Ring homomorphism. If $\mathfrak{A}$ and $\mathfrak{A}'$ are two rings, they are also modules. Let S be a *module homomorphism* of $\mathfrak{A}$ onto (into) $\mathfrak{A}'$. Then S is called a (ring) *homomorphism* of $\mathfrak{A}$ *onto* (*into*) $\mathfrak{A}'$ if

$$(ab)S - (aS)(bS)$$

for every a and b of $\mathfrak{A}$. If $(ab)S = (bS)(aS)$ for every a and b of $\mathfrak{A}$, we call S an *antihomomorphism* of $\mathfrak{A}$ into (onto) $\mathfrak{A}'$.

A homomorphism S of $\mathfrak{A}$ onto $\mathfrak{A}'$ is called an *isomorphism* of $\mathfrak{A}$ and $\mathfrak{A}'$ if S is a one-to-one mapping. If such a mapping exists, we say that $\mathfrak{A}$ and $\mathfrak{A}'$ are *isomorphic rings*. The relation of isomorphism of rings is an equivalence relation. A homomorphism of $\mathfrak{A}$ into $\mathfrak{A}$ is called an *endomorphism*, and an isomorphism of $\mathfrak{A}$ onto $\mathfrak{A}$ is called an *automorphism*. The analogous concepts of *anti-isomorphism*, *antiendomorphism*, and *antiautomorphism* are defined similarly.

If $\mathfrak{B}$ is a subring of $\mathfrak{A}$, we sometimes call $\mathfrak{A}$ an *extension* of $\mathfrak{B}$. The following result on a *process* of extension is quite important.

THEOREM 3. *Let $\mathfrak{B}$ and $\mathfrak{A}'$ be disjoint rings such that there exists an isomorphism* S *of $\mathfrak{B}$ onto a subring $\mathfrak{B}'$ of $\mathfrak{A}'$. Then there exists an extension $\mathfrak{A}$ of $\mathfrak{B}$ and an isomorphism* T *of $\mathfrak{A}$ onto $\mathfrak{A}'$ such that* bS = bT *for every* b *of $\mathfrak{B}$.*

For let $\mathfrak{C}$ be the set which consists of all the elements of $\mathfrak{A}'$ which are not in $\mathfrak{B}'$ and let

$$\mathfrak{A} = (\mathfrak{C} \cup \mathfrak{B}) .$$

Define $aT = a$ for every a of $\mathfrak{C}$ and $aT = aS$ for every a of $\mathfrak{B}$. Then T is clearly a one-to-one mapping of $\mathfrak{A}$ onto $\mathfrak{A}'$, which maps $\mathfrak{B}$ onto $\mathfrak{B}'$. For every a and b of $\mathfrak{A}$ the sum $aT + bT = sT$ and the product $(aT)(bT) = pT$ are unique elements sT and pT. They are the images of unique elements s and p of $\mathfrak{A}$, and we define $a + b = s$ and $ab = p$. It should then be clear that $\mathfrak{A}$ is a ring and that T is the isomorphism of $\mathfrak{A}$ onto $\mathfrak{A}'$ of our theorem.

EXERCISES

1. Let S be a homomorphism of a ring $\mathfrak{A}$ into $\mathfrak{A}'$. Show that $0S$ is the zero element of $\mathfrak{A}'$ and that eS is the unity element of $\mathfrak{A}S$ if e is the unity element of $\mathfrak{A}$ and 0 is the zero element of $\mathfrak{A}$.
2. Determine all automorphisms of the ring of integers.
3. Let $\mathfrak{C}$ be the ring of all complex numbers. What are all automorphisms of $\mathfrak{C}$ which leave each real number fixed?

3. The characteristic of a ring. The elements of a ring generate cyclic submodules. When every one of these modules has order not exceeding a fixed positive integer, the abelian group $\mathfrak{A}$ has a finite exponent γ which is called the *characteristic* of $\mathfrak{A}$, and we write

$$\gamma = \gamma(\mathfrak{A}) .$$

There will then be an element g in $\mathfrak{A}$ whose additive order is γ and $\gamma \cdot a = 0$ for every a of $\mathfrak{A}$.

If *every* element $\neq 0$ of $\mathfrak{A}$ has infinite additive order, we shall say that $\mathfrak{A}$ has *characteristic zero* and write $\gamma(\mathfrak{A}) = 0$. In all other cases $\mathfrak{A}$ must have at least one element of finite order, and it must also be true that for every integer $\lambda > 0$ there exists an element a_λ in $\mathfrak{A}$ such that the order of a_λ is greater than λ. The *characteristic* $\gamma(\mathfrak{A})$ of such a ring is said to be *infinite*, and we write $\gamma(\mathfrak{A}) = \infty$.

If $\mathfrak{B}$ is a subring of $\mathfrak{A}$ and $\gamma(\mathfrak{A}) = 0$, it should be obvious that $\gamma(\mathfrak{B}) = 0$. If $\gamma(\mathfrak{A})$ is finite, the ring $\mathfrak{B}$ cannot have an element of order greater than $\gamma(\mathfrak{A})$, $\gamma(\mathfrak{B}) \leq \gamma(\mathfrak{A})$. If $\gamma(\mathfrak{A}) = \infty$, then clearly $\gamma(\mathfrak{B}) \leq \gamma(\mathfrak{A})$, and we have proved the following result:

THEOREM 4. *Let $\mathfrak{B}$ be a subring of $\mathfrak{A}$. Then the characteristic of $\mathfrak{B}$ does not exceed the characteristic of $\mathfrak{A}$.*

If α and β are positive integers, the product formula,

$$(\alpha \cdot a)(\beta \cdot b) = (\alpha\beta) \cdot (ab) , \tag{3}$$

holds for all elements a and b in any ring $\mathfrak{A}$. When $\mathfrak{A}$ has a unity element e, we use equation (3) to obtain

$$(a \cdot e)b = a \cdot b . \tag{4}$$

It follows that if e has finite additive order γ, then $\gamma \cdot b = (\gamma \cdot e)b = 0b = 0$ for every b of $\mathfrak{A}$. Thus the *additive order of the unity element* of a ring $\mathfrak{A}$ *is the characteristic* of $\mathfrak{A}$ in the case where $\mathfrak{A}$ has a unity element whose additive order is finite.

If $\mathfrak{D}$ is a division ring, it has a unity element e. If the order of e under addition is a finite integer γ and $\gamma = \alpha\beta$, where $\alpha > 1$ and $\beta > 1$, then $\alpha \cdot e \neq 0$, $\beta \cdot e \neq 0$, $(\alpha \cdot e) \cdot (\beta \cdot e) = \gamma \cdot e = 0$, contrary to the hypothesis that $\mathfrak{D}$ is a division ring. Hence γ is a prime. If e has infinite additive order, $\mathfrak{D}$ must have characteristic zero. For if g is a non-zero element of $\mathfrak{D}$ of finite additive order λ, we have $\lambda \cdot g = 0$, g^{-1} exists, and we use equation (3) to see that $(\lambda \cdot g)(1 \cdot g^{-1}) = \lambda \cdot e = 0(g^{-1}) = 0$, contrary to hypothesis. We state this result as follows:

THEOREM 5. *The characteristic of a division ring either is zero or is a prime.*

In the study of rings it is sometimes desirable to adjoin a unity element to a given ring. We shall show how to perform this construction and shall derive the following result:

THEOREM 6. *Let $\mathfrak{B}$ be a ring. Then $\mathfrak{B}$ is a subring of a ring $\mathfrak{A}$ with a unity quantity* e, *where $\mathfrak{A}$ and $\mathfrak{B}$ have the same characteristic.*

We suppose, first, that $\mathfrak{C}$ is a cyclic additive group $\{e\}$ which has no elements in common with $\mathfrak{B}$ and whose order $\gamma(\mathfrak{C})$ is infinite if $\gamma(\mathfrak{B}) = 0$, is equal to $\gamma(\mathfrak{B})$ in all other cases. Consider the set $\mathfrak{A}'$ of all pairs $(\beta \cdot e, b)$ for $\beta \cdot e$ in $\mathfrak{C}$ and b in $\mathfrak{B}$. Define

$$\begin{aligned} (5) \qquad (\beta \cdot e, b) + (\alpha \cdot e, a) &= (\beta \cdot e + \alpha \cdot e, b + a)\,, \\ (\beta \cdot e, b)(\alpha \cdot e, a) &= (\alpha\beta \cdot e, \beta \cdot a + \alpha \cdot b + ab)\,. \end{aligned}$$

We leave to the reader the verification of the fact that $\mathfrak{A}'$ is a ring, that $(0 \cdot e, 0)$ is the zero element of $\mathfrak{A}'$, and that $(e, 0)$ is the unity element of $\mathfrak{A}'$. Clearly,

$$\alpha \cdot (\beta \cdot e, b) = (\alpha\beta \cdot e, \alpha \cdot b) = 0$$

if and only if $\alpha\beta \cdot e = 0$ and $\alpha \cdot b = 0$. If $\gamma(\mathfrak{B}) = 0$, then $\alpha \cdot b = 0$ if and only if $\alpha = 0$ or $b = 0$. In this case $\alpha\beta \cdot e = 0$ for $\beta \neq 0$ if and only if $\alpha = 0$ and thus $\gamma(\mathfrak{A}') = \gamma(\mathfrak{B}) = 0$. If $\gamma(\mathfrak{B}) = \infty$, then $\gamma(\mathfrak{A}') = \infty$ by Theorem 4. There remains the case where $\gamma(\mathfrak{B}) = \gamma$ is a finite integer, and in this case we have assumed that $\gamma \cdot e = 0$, $\gamma \cdot (\beta \cdot e, b) = (\gamma\beta \cdot e, \gamma \cdot b) = 0$, $\mathfrak{A}'$ has characteristic at most $\gamma(\mathfrak{B})$, $\gamma(\mathfrak{B}) \leq \gamma(\mathfrak{A}')$, and $\gamma(\mathfrak{B}) = \gamma(\mathfrak{A}')$. We observe that the mapping $bS = (0, b)$ maps $\mathfrak{B}$ isomorphically onto a subring $\mathfrak{B}'$ of $\mathfrak{A}'$. Apply Theorem 3 to construct a ring $\mathfrak{A} \supseteq \mathfrak{B}$ and isomorphic to $\mathfrak{A}'$. It is the ring desired.

EXERCISES

1. Let $\mathfrak{E}$ be the ring of all ordinary integers. Find two new operations $x \dotplus y$ and $x \cdot y$ such that the mapping $x \dotplus x + 1$ is an isomorphism of $\mathfrak{E}$ onto $\mathfrak{E}'$, where $\mathfrak{E}'$ is the same set as $\mathfrak{E}$ but $x \rightarrow y$ and $x \cdot y$ are the operations of $\mathfrak{E}'$.
2. What are the zero element and unity element of the ring $\mathfrak{E}'$ of Exercise 1?
3. Show that if $\mathfrak{F}$ is a field, the unity element of $\mathfrak{F}$ generates a field called the *prime subfield* of $\mathfrak{F}$.

4. Ideals. The *product* $\mathfrak{B}\mathfrak{C}$ of two submodules $\mathfrak{B}$ and $\mathfrak{C}$ of a ring $\mathfrak{A}$ is the set of all finite sums $b_1c_1 + \cdots + b_\lambda c_\lambda$ with b_i in $\mathfrak{B}$ and c_i in $\mathfrak{C}$. Then $\mathfrak{B}\mathfrak{C}$ is a submodule of $\mathfrak{A}$. The product $\mathfrak{B}c$ of a submodule $\mathfrak{B}$ of $\mathfrak{A}$ and an element c of $\mathfrak{A}$ is defined to be the set of all products bc for b in $\mathfrak{B}$. Evidently, $\mathfrak{B}c$ is a submodule of $\mathfrak{A}$. The product $c\mathfrak{B}$ is a submodule of $\mathfrak{A}$, defined similarly. Note that a submodule $\mathfrak{B}$ of $\mathfrak{A}$ is a subring of $\mathfrak{A}$ if and only if $\mathfrak{B} \neq 0$, $\mathfrak{B}\mathfrak{B} \subseteq \mathfrak{B}$.

A submodule $\mathfrak{R}$ of $\mathfrak{A}$ is called a *right ideal* of $\mathfrak{A}$ if $\mathfrak{R}\mathfrak{A} \subseteq \mathfrak{R}$. If c is any element of $\mathfrak{A}$, the submodule $c\mathfrak{A}$ is a right ideal. For $\mathfrak{A}\mathfrak{A} \subseteq \mathfrak{A}$, $(c\mathfrak{A})\mathfrak{A} = c(\mathfrak{A}\mathfrak{A}) \subseteq c\mathfrak{A}$. A submodule $\mathfrak{L}$ of $\mathfrak{A}$ is called a *left ideal* of $\mathfrak{A}$ if $\mathfrak{A}\mathfrak{L} \subseteq \mathfrak{L}$. We call a submodule $\mathfrak{M}$ an *ideal* (a *two-sided ideal*) of $\mathfrak{A}$ if $\mathfrak{M}$ is both a left ideal and a right ideal of $\mathfrak{A}$. It should be clear that a subset $\mathfrak{M}$ of $\mathfrak{A}$ is an ideal of $\mathfrak{A}$ if and only if $m - n$, ma, and am are all in $\mathfrak{M}$ for every m and n of $\mathfrak{M}$ and a of $\mathfrak{A}$.

The set consisting of zero alone is called the *zero ideal*. All other (right, left, or two-sided) ideals $\mathfrak{M}$ of $\mathfrak{A}$ are subrings of $\mathfrak{A}$, since $\mathfrak{M}\mathfrak{M} \subseteq \mathfrak{M}$ in all cases. The ring $\mathfrak{A}$ is an ideal of $\mathfrak{A}$ called the *unit ideal*. The zero ideal and the unit ideal are called the *trivial* ideals of $\mathfrak{A}$. When the only (two-sided) ideals of $\mathfrak{A}$ are its trivial ideals, we call the ring a *simple* ring. The reader should show that a division ring is a simple ring.

The *sum* of two submodules $\mathfrak{B}$ and $\mathfrak{C}$ of a ring $\mathfrak{A}$ is the set $(\mathfrak{B}, \mathfrak{C})$ of all sums $b + c$ with b in $\mathfrak{B}$ and c in $\mathfrak{C}$. It is easy to see that if $\mathfrak{B}$ and $\mathfrak{C}$ are right (left, or two-sided) ideals of $\mathfrak{A}$, their sum is also a right (left, or two-sided) ideal of $\mathfrak{A}$. The intersection $\mathfrak{B} \cap \mathfrak{C}$ of two right (left, or two-sided) ideals of $\mathfrak{A}$ should also be shown by the reader to be a right (left, or two-sided) ideal of $\mathfrak{A}$.

The product $\mathfrak{L}\mathfrak{R}$ of a left ideal $\mathfrak{L}$ and a right ideal $\mathfrak{R}$ of $\mathfrak{A}$ is an ideal of $\mathfrak{A}$. The *product* $\mathfrak{B}\mathfrak{C}$ of two ideals of $\mathfrak{A}$ is an ideal of $\mathfrak{A}$ contained in $\mathfrak{B} \cap \mathfrak{C}$.

Every element a of a ring $\mathfrak{A}$ generates an ideal of $\mathfrak{A}$ called a *principal* ideal, which we designate by (a). It consists of all finite sums of terms of the form $\nu \cdot a$, ab, ca, gah, where ν is an integer and b, c, g, h are in $\mathfrak{A}$. When $\mathfrak{A}$ is a commutative ring with a unity element, we see that

$$(a) = a\mathfrak{A}$$

consists of all products ab for b in $\mathfrak{A}$.

If $a_1, \ldots, a_r$ are in $\mathfrak{A}$, they *span* an ideal usually designated by $(a_1, \ldots, a_r)$. When $\mathfrak{A}$ is a commutative ring with a unity element, this ideal is the sum $(a_1\mathfrak{A}, \ldots, a_r\mathfrak{A})$ of the principal ideals $a_i\mathfrak{A}$.

The term "direct product" was defined for multiplicative groups. For modules this term is replaced by *direct sum*, and we see that $(\mathfrak{B}, \mathfrak{C})$ is the direct sum $\mathfrak{B} + \mathfrak{C}$ of $\mathfrak{B}$ and $\mathfrak{C}$ if and only if $\mathfrak{B} \cap \mathfrak{C} = 0$. Then $(\mathfrak{B}, \mathfrak{C}) = \mathfrak{B} + \mathfrak{C}$ if and only if a sum $b + c = 0$ with b in $\mathfrak{B}$ and c in $\mathfrak{C}$ only when $b = c = 0$.

If $\mathfrak{A} = \mathfrak{B} + \mathfrak{C}$ where $\mathfrak{B}$ and $\mathfrak{C}$ are non-zero ideals of $\mathfrak{A}$, then $\mathfrak{B}$ and $\mathfrak{C}$ are subrings of $\mathfrak{A}$ such that $\mathfrak{B}\mathfrak{C} \subseteq \mathfrak{B} \cap \mathfrak{C} = 0$, $\mathfrak{C}\mathfrak{B} \subseteq \mathfrak{B} \cap \mathfrak{C}$. In this case we write

$$\mathfrak{A} = \mathfrak{B} \oplus \mathfrak{C}\,,$$

and call $\mathfrak{A}$ the *direct sum* of its *component* subrings $\mathfrak{B}$ and $\mathfrak{C}$. Conversely, if $\mathfrak{A} = \mathfrak{B} + \mathfrak{C}$ for subrings $\mathfrak{B}$ and $\mathfrak{C}$ of $\mathfrak{A}$ such that $\mathfrak{B}\mathfrak{C} = \mathfrak{C}\mathfrak{B} = 0$, then $\mathfrak{B}$ and $\mathfrak{C}$ are ideals of $\mathfrak{A}$ and $\mathfrak{A} = \mathfrak{B} \oplus \mathfrak{C}$.

The concept of an ideal arises from the study of homomorphisms. The *kernel* of a homomorphism S of a ring $\mathfrak{A}$ into a ring $\mathfrak{A}'$ is the set $\mathfrak{B}$ of all elements b of $\mathfrak{A}$ such that $bS = 0'$ is the zero element of $\mathfrak{A}'$. Then we have the following result:

THEOREM 7. *The kernel of a ring homomorphism is an ideal.*

For if $bS = 0'$ and $cS = 0'$, we have $(b - c)S = bS - cS = 0' - 0' = 0'$. Also $(ab)S = (aS)(bS) = (aS)0' = 0'$, $(ba)S = (bS)(aS) = 0'$.

EXERCISES

1. Let $\mathfrak{B}$ be an ideal of a ring $\mathfrak{A}$. Call $a \cong c$ for a and c in $\mathfrak{A}$ if $a - c$ is in $\mathfrak{B}$. Prove that this relation is an equivalence relation. The corresponding classes of elements $\{a\}$ are called *residue classes* of $\mathfrak{A}$ modulo $\mathfrak{B}$.

2. Let $\mathfrak{E}$ be the ring of ordinary integers. Use the fact that $1 = 3 - 2$ to show that $\mathfrak{E} = (\mathfrak{B}, \mathfrak{C})$ where $\mathfrak{B} = (2)$ and $\mathfrak{C} = (3)$.

5. Difference rings. Every submodule $\mathfrak{B}$ of a module $\mathfrak{A}$ is a normal subgroup. The cosets of $\mathfrak{A}$ relative to $\mathfrak{B}$ are then the sets $a + \mathfrak{B}$, and the term *quotient group* is replaced by *difference group*. The difference group $\mathfrak{A} - \mathfrak{B}$ (read $\mathfrak{A}$ modulo $\mathfrak{B}$) consists of the cosets $a + \mathfrak{B}$, with addition defined by

$$(a + \mathfrak{B}) + (c + \mathfrak{B}) = (a + c) + \mathfrak{B}\,. \tag{6}$$

The mapping

$$S: \qquad a \to a + \mathfrak{B}$$

is a homomorphism of the group $\mathfrak{A}$ onto the group $\mathfrak{A} - \mathfrak{B}$.

Let $\mathfrak{A}$ be a ring and $\mathfrak{B}$ be an ideal of $\mathfrak{A}$. Define the product of two elements of $\mathfrak{A} - \mathfrak{B}$ by

$$(a + \mathfrak{B})(c + \mathfrak{B}) = ac + \mathfrak{B}\,. \tag{7}$$

This definition is valid if and only if the product coset is unique. It need not be unique, since we have defined it in terms of the representatives a and c of the cosets $a + \mathfrak{B}$ and $c + \mathfrak{B}$ rather than in terms of the cosets themselves. If $a_1 + \mathfrak{B} = a + \mathfrak{B}$ and $c_1 + \mathfrak{B} = c + \mathfrak{B}$, then $a_1 = a + b$ and $c_1 = c + b_0$, where b and b_0 are in $\mathfrak{B}$. Then $a_1c_1 = ac + (bc + ab_0 + bb_0) = ac + b_1$, where b_1 is in the ideal $\mathfrak{B}$. Hence $ac + \mathfrak{B} = a_1c_1 + \mathfrak{B}$, and the product is unique. Evidently, S is a homomorphism of the ring $\mathfrak{A}$ onto the mathematical system consisting of the difference module $\mathfrak{A} - \mathfrak{B}$ and the product operation just defined. It follows that $\mathfrak{A} - \mathfrak{B}$ is a ring and that S is a ring homomorphism. We leave the verification of the details as an exercise for the reader.

THEOREM 8. *Let* S *be a homomorphism of a ring* $\mathfrak{A}$ *onto a ring* $\mathfrak{A}'$ *and* $\mathfrak{B}$ *be the kernel of* S. *Then the mapping*

$$\text{T:} \qquad \text{aS} \to \text{a} + \mathfrak{B}$$

is an isomorphism of $\mathfrak{A}'$ *and* $\mathfrak{A} - \mathfrak{B}$.

In our study of groups we saw that T is an isomorphism of the module $\mathfrak{A}'$ onto $\mathfrak{A} - \mathfrak{B}$. But $[(aS)(cS)]T = [(ac)S]T = ac + \mathfrak{B} = (a + \mathfrak{B})(c + \mathfrak{B}) = [(aS)T][(cS)T]$, as desired.

If S is the homomorphism $a \to a + \mathfrak{B}$ of $\mathfrak{A}$ onto $\mathfrak{A} - \mathfrak{B}$, every subring $\mathfrak{C}$ of $\mathfrak{A}$ is mapped onto zero or a subring $\mathfrak{C}S$ of $\mathfrak{A} - \mathfrak{B}$. The set $(\mathfrak{C}, \mathfrak{B})$, consisting of all sums $c + b$ where c is in $\mathfrak{C}$ and b is in $\mathfrak{B}$, is mapped onto the same subring of $\mathfrak{A} - \mathfrak{B}$ as $\mathfrak{C}$. Also $(\mathfrak{C}, \mathfrak{B}) \supseteq \mathfrak{B}$ and is a subring of $\mathfrak{A}$. We now state the ring case of Theorem 1.1 (i.e., Theorem 1 of chapter i).

THEOREM 9. *Let $\mathfrak{A}$ be a ring, $\mathfrak{B}$ be an ideal of $\mathfrak{A}$, $\mathfrak{M}$ be the set of all subrings of $\mathfrak{A}$ which contain $\mathfrak{B}$, and $\mathfrak{M}_0$ be the set consisting of zero and of all subrings of $\mathfrak{A} - \mathfrak{B}$. Then $\mathfrak{M}$ consists of the inverse images of the elements of $\mathfrak{M}_0$, and the mapping*

$$T: \qquad \mathfrak{C} \to \mathfrak{C}\mathrm{T} = \mathfrak{C} - \mathfrak{B}$$

is a one-to-one mapping of $\mathfrak{M}$ onto $\mathfrak{M}_0$ such that $\mathfrak{C}_0\mathrm{T}^{-1}$ is the inverse image of $\mathfrak{C}_0$ for every $\mathfrak{C}_0$ of $\mathfrak{M}_0$. An element $\mathfrak{C}$ of $\mathfrak{M}$ is an ideal of $\mathfrak{A}$ if and only if $\mathfrak{C}\mathrm{T}$ is an ideal of $\mathfrak{A} - \mathfrak{B}$, and then

$$\mathfrak{A} - \mathfrak{C} \cong (\mathfrak{A} - \mathfrak{B}) - (\mathfrak{C} - \mathfrak{B}) \, . \tag{8}$$

We have already proved this property for groups, and so it is only necessary to extend it to rings. If $\mathfrak{C}$ is a ring, its image $\mathfrak{C} - \mathfrak{B}$ is clearly a ring. Conversely, if $\mathfrak{C}_0$ is a subring of $\mathfrak{A} - \mathfrak{B}$, the product $(c_1 + \mathfrak{B})(c_2 + \mathfrak{B}) = c_3 + \mathfrak{B}$ is in $\mathfrak{C}_0$; c_3 is in the inverse image $\mathfrak{C}_0T^{-1} = \mathfrak{C}$; and $\mathfrak{C}$ is a ring. The final statement of the theorem is all that remains. If $\mathfrak{C}$ is an ideal, we know that $c_1 = ca$ and $c_2 = ac$ are in $\mathfrak{C}$ for every c of $\mathfrak{C}$ and a of $\mathfrak{A}$, so that $(c + \mathfrak{B})(a + \mathfrak{B}) = ca + \mathfrak{B} = c_1 + \mathfrak{B}$ is in $\mathfrak{C} - \mathfrak{B}$. Conversely, if $(c + \mathfrak{B})(a + \mathfrak{B}) = c_1 + \mathfrak{B}$, where $c_1 + \mathfrak{B}$ is in $\mathfrak{C}_0$ for every a of $\mathfrak{A}$ and $c + \mathfrak{B}$ of $\mathfrak{C}_0$, then ca is in $\mathfrak{C}$ for every c of $\mathfrak{C}$ and a of $\mathfrak{A}$. Similarly, ac is in $\mathfrak{C}$, and so the inverse image of an ideal of $\mathfrak{A} - \mathfrak{B}$ is an ideal of $\mathfrak{A}$. The group $\mathfrak{A} - \mathfrak{C}$ is isomorphic to $(\mathfrak{A} - \mathfrak{B}) - (\mathfrak{C} - \mathfrak{B})$ by Theorem 1.1. It is trivial to see that this isomorphism is preserved under multiplication, and the theorem is proved.

EXERCISES

1. Let $\mathfrak{E}$ be the ring of all integers, $\mathfrak{B} = (2)$, $\mathfrak{C} = (3)$, $\mathfrak{M} = (6)$. Show that $\mathfrak{E}_6 = \mathfrak{E} - \mathfrak{M} = \mathfrak{B}_0 \oplus \mathfrak{C}_0$, where $\mathfrak{B}_0 \cong \mathfrak{E} - \mathfrak{B}$ and $\mathfrak{C}_6 \cong \mathfrak{E} - \mathfrak{C}$.

2. Let $m = 24$. Determine all ideals of $\mathfrak{E}_{24} = \mathfrak{E} - (24)$ and find their inverse images in $\mathfrak{E}$.

3. Show that the prime subfield of a field is either the field of all rational numbers or the field $\mathfrak{E}_p$.

6. Polynomials over a ring. If $\mathfrak{B}$ is a subring of a ring $\mathfrak{A}$ and a is any element of $\mathfrak{A}$, we designate by $\mathfrak{B}[a]$ the set of all polynomials in a with coefficients in $\mathfrak{B}$. Each such polynomial is a finite sum of terms, every one of which is a finite product with factors which are either in $\mathfrak{B}$ or are equal to a. Since multiplication in $\mathfrak{A}$ need not be commutative, such polynomials as aba, ba^2, and a^2b may all be distinct. The set $\mathfrak{B}[a]$ is a subring of $\mathfrak{A}$.

An element x of a ring $\mathfrak{A}$ is said to be a *scalar with respect to a subset* $\mathfrak{B}$ of $\mathfrak{A}$ if $bx = xb$ for every b of $\mathfrak{B}$. The set $\mathfrak{B}^{\mathfrak{A}}$ of all scalars of $\mathfrak{A}$ with respect to $\mathfrak{B}$ is a subring of $\mathfrak{A}$; for if $xb = bx$ and $yb = by$, then $(x - y)b = xb - yb = bx - by = b(x - y)$ and $(xy)b = x(yb) = x(by) = (xb)y = b(xy)$. The set $\mathfrak{A}^{\mathfrak{A}}$ consists of all elements z of $\mathfrak{A}$ such that $za = az$ for every a of $\mathfrak{A}$. It is a subring of $\mathfrak{A}$ called the *center* of $\mathfrak{A}$.

A scalar x of a ring $\mathfrak{A}$ relative to a subring $\mathfrak{B}$ is said to be *algebraic* over $\mathfrak{B}$ if there exist elements $b_0, \ldots, b_\nu$ not all zero and in $\mathfrak{B}$ such that

$$b_0 + b_1x + \cdots + b_\nu x^\nu = 0 . \tag{9}$$

A scalar x is called an *indeterminate* over $\mathfrak{B}$ if x is not algebraic over $\mathfrak{B}$. Observe that, if x is a scalar over $\mathfrak{B}$, there is only a single expression bx^λ with λ factors equal to x and all other factors in $\mathfrak{B}$. When x is algebraic over $\mathfrak{B}$, two distinct polynomials in x may be equal. When x is an indeterminate, two polynomials are equal if and only if their coefficients are equal.

If x and y are indeterminates over $\mathfrak{B}$, the subrings $\mathfrak{B}[x]$ and $\mathfrak{B}[y]$ are isomorphic. Indeed, the expression of an element of $\mathfrak{B}[x]$ in the form

$$f(x) = b_0 + b_1x + \cdots + b_\nu x^\nu \tag{10}$$

is unique. The mapping

$$f(x) \rightarrow f(y) = b_0 + b_1y + \cdots + b_\nu y^\nu$$

may then be readily shown to be an isomorphism of $\mathfrak{B}[x]$ onto $\mathfrak{B}[y]$.

The foregoing result may be generalized as follows:

THEOREM 10. *Let* $\mathfrak{B}$ *be a ring,* S *be an isomorphism of* $\mathfrak{B}$ *onto a ring* $\mathfrak{B}'$, x *be an indeterminate over* $\mathfrak{B}$, x′ *be an indeterminate over* $\mathfrak{B}'$. *Then*

$$\mathrm{b}_0 + b_1\mathrm{x} + \cdots + \mathrm{b}_\nu \mathrm{x}^\nu \rightarrow \mathrm{b}_0\mathrm{S} + (\mathrm{b}_1\mathrm{S})\mathrm{x}' + \cdots + (\mathrm{b}_\nu\mathrm{S})(\mathrm{x}')^\nu \tag{11}$$

is an isomorphism of $\mathfrak{B}[\mathrm{x}]$ *onto* $\mathfrak{B}'[\mathrm{x}']$.

The proof of this result is trivial, and we leave the details to the reader.

7. Construction of $\mathfrak{A}[x]$. If $\mathfrak{A}$ is any ring, it will be desirable to construct a ring $\mathfrak{A}[x]$ consisting of all polynomials in an indeterminate x

over $\mathfrak{A}$. This ring need not contain x, but we simply observe that there will exist a ring $\mathfrak{C}$ such that $\mathfrak{A}$ is a subring of $\mathfrak{C}$, x is in $\mathfrak{C}$ and is a scalar relative to $\mathfrak{A}$.

We first extend $\mathfrak{A}$ to a ring $\mathfrak{A}'$ with a unity element. If $\mathfrak{A}$ has a unity element, we take $\mathfrak{A}' = \mathfrak{A}$. Otherwise we use Theorem 6 to construct $\mathfrak{A}'$.

Consider the set C of all infinite sequences

$$f = (a_0, a_1, \ldots) , \tag{12}$$

where the a_i are in $\mathfrak{A}'$ and only a finite number of the a_i are not zero. Define the sum $f + g$ of f and

$$g = (b_0, b_1, \ldots) , \tag{13}$$

by

$$f + g = (a_0 + b_0, a_1 + b_1, \ldots) , \tag{14}$$

and the product fg by

$$fg = h = (c_0, c_1, \ldots) , \tag{15}$$

where

$$c_\gamma = \sum_{\alpha+\beta=\gamma} a_\alpha b_\beta . \tag{16}$$

Then $f + g$ and fg are unique elements of $\mathfrak{C}$.

It is easy to see that equation (14) implies that $\mathfrak{C}$ is a module. Every element a of $\mathfrak{A}'$ determines a unique element $aS = (a, 0, \ldots)$ of $\mathfrak{C}$, and the mapping $a \to aS$ is an isomorphism of $\mathfrak{A}'$ onto the set $\mathfrak{A}'S$ of all the image elements. Then $\mathfrak{A}'S$ is a ring. If we identify a and aS, we see that every element f of $\mathfrak{C}$ is expressible uniquely in the form

$$f = f(x) = a_0 + a_1 x + \cdots + a_\nu x^\nu , \tag{17}$$

where $x = (0, 1, 0, \ldots)$. It is now easy to see that $\mathfrak{C}$ is a ring, x is in $\mathfrak{C}$, $\mathfrak{C} \supseteq \mathfrak{A}$ in the sense of Theorem 3, x is an indeterminate over $\mathfrak{A}$, and $\mathfrak{C} = \mathfrak{A}'[x] \supseteq \mathfrak{A}[x]$. We leave the details of this verification to the reader.

8. The division algorithm. Consider a ring $\mathfrak{A}$ with a unity element 1 and let x be an indeterminate over $\mathfrak{A}$. The elements of $\mathfrak{A}[x]$ then have the form

$$f(x) = a_0 + a_1 x + \cdots + a_\nu x^\nu \qquad (a_\alpha \text{ in } \mathfrak{A}). \tag{18}$$

If $a_\nu \neq 0$, we call a_ν the *leading coefficient* of $f(x)$ and $a_\nu x^\nu$ the *leading term* of $f(x)$. We also say that $f(x)$ has *degree* ν. A non-zero constant polynomial has degree 0. When we express an element $f(x)$ of $\mathfrak{A}[x]$ in the form (18), where we do not know whether or not a_ν is zero, we call a_ν the *virtual leading coefficient* of $f(x)$, $a_\nu x^\nu$ the *virtual leading term* of $f(x)$, and say that $f(x)$ has *virtual degree* ν. The following properties are immediate consequences of our definition:

LEMMA 1. *Let* f(x) *have the form* (18) *and* g(x) *have the form*

$$g(x) = b_0 + b_1 x + \cdots + b_\mu x^\mu \qquad (b_\beta \text{ in } \mathfrak{A}). \tag{19}$$

Then the virtual leading term of f(x)g(x) *is* $a_\nu b_\mu x^{\mu+\nu}$, *the virtual leading coefficient of* f(x)g(x) *is* $a_\nu b_\mu$, *and* f(x)g(x) *has virtual degree* $\mu + \nu$. *If* $a_\nu b_\mu \neq 0$, *the product* f(x)g(x) *has degree* $\mu + \nu$.

LEMMA 2. *The degree of a sum does not exceed the degrees of its summands. If* f(x) *and* g(x) *have distinct degrees, the degree of* f(x) + g(x) *is the maximum of the degrees of* f(x) *and* g(x).

We are now ready to derive the *division algorithm* for polynomials.

THEOREM 11. *Let* f(x) *and* g(x) *be given by equations* (18) *and* (19), *where* b_μ *is a unit of* $\mathfrak{A}$. *Then there exist unique polynomials* q(x), $q_1(x)$, r(x), *and* $r_1(x)$ *in* $\mathfrak{A}[x]$ *such that* r(x) *and* $r_1(x)$ *have degrees less than* μ, q(x) *and* $q_1(x)$ *have virtual degrees* $\nu - \mu$, and

$$f(x) = q(x)g(x) + r(x) = g(x)q_1(x) + r_1(x)\,.$$

The existence of the polynomials $q(x)$, $q_1(x)$, $r(x)$, $r_1(x)$ is trivial if $\nu < \mu$, since we then take $q(x) = q_1(x) = 0$, $r(x) = r_1(x) = f(x)$. When $\nu \geq \mu$, we prove the existence theorem by an induction on the virtual degree of $f(x)$. The existence theorem is true for polynomials $f_0(x)$ of virtual degree less than μ, and we assume it true for polynomials of virtual degree $\nu_0 < \nu$, where $\nu_0 \geq \mu$. Since b_μ is a unit of $\mathfrak{A}$, it has an inverse c_μ in $\mathfrak{A}$, and the polynomial $a_\nu c_\mu x^{\nu-\mu} g(x)$ has the same virtual leading term as $f(x)$. Then $f_0(x) = f(x) - (a_\nu c_\mu x^{\nu-\mu})$; $g(x)$ has virtual degree $\nu - 1$; and the hypothesis of our induction implies that $f_0(x) = q_0(x)g(x) + r(x)$, where the degree of $r(x)$ is less than μ and $q_0(x)$ has virtual degree $\nu - \mu - 1$. Then $f(x) = q(x)g(x) + r(x)$, where $q(x) = a_\nu c_\mu x^{\nu-\mu} + q_0(x)$ has virtual degree $\nu - \mu$. This completes our proof of the existence of $q(x)$ and $r(x)$. The existence of $q_1(x)$ and $r_1(x)$ follows by symmetry.

If $f(x) = q(x)g(x) + r(x) = p(x)g(x) + s(x)$, where $p(x)$ has virtual degree $\nu - \mu$ and $s(x)$ has degree less than μ, then $[q(x) - p(x)]g(x) = s(x) - r(x)$ has degree less than μ. Since the leading coefficient of $g(x)$ is a unit of $\mathfrak{A}$, its product by the leading coefficient d of $q(x) - p(x)$ can be zero only if $q(x) - p(x) = 0$. But when $db_\mu \neq 0$, the degree of $[q(x) - p(x)]g(x)$ equals or exceeds μ. It follows that $q(x) = p(x)$ and $s(x) = r(x)$. The uniqueness of $q_1(x)$ and $r_1(x)$ follows by symmetry.

The polynomial $q(x)$ is called the ***right quotient*** [quotient on division of $f(x)$ by $g(x)$ on the right], and the polynomial $r(x)$ the ***right remainder*** on the division of $f(x)$ by $g(x)$. Similarly, we call $q_1(x)$ the ***left quotient*** and $r_1(x)$ the ***left remainder***.

If $g(x)$ has degree 1, the polynomials $r(x)$ and $r_1(x)$ have degree zero and are elements of $\mathfrak{A}$. Define polynomials $f_R(c)$ (read f right of c) and $f_L(c)$ by

(20) $$f_R(c) = a_0 + a_1c + \cdots + a_\nu c^\nu ,$$

(21) $$f_L(c) = a_0 + ca_1 + \cdots + c^\nu a_\nu .$$

Then we have the following REMAINDER THEOREM:

THEOREM 12. *The left remainder* $r_1(x)$ *and the right remainder* $r(x)$ *in the division of* $f(x)$ *by* $x - c$ *are* $f_L(c)$ *and* $f_R(c)$, *respectively.*

For $f(x) - f_R(c) = a_1(x - c) + a_2(x^2 - c^2) + \cdots + a_\nu(x^\nu - c^\nu)$. However, $x^\alpha - c^\alpha = (x - c)Q_\alpha(x, c) = Q_\alpha(x, c)(x - c)$, where

$$Q_\alpha(x, c) = Q_\alpha(c, x) = x^{\alpha-1} + cx^{\alpha-2} + \cdots + c^{\alpha-2}x + c^{\alpha-1}.$$

Hence $f(x) - f_R(c) = q(x)(x - c)$, where

$$q(x) = \sum_{\alpha=1}^{\nu} a_\alpha Q_\alpha(x, c) .$$

By the uniqueness property of Theorem 11 we see that $r(x) = f_R(c)$. Similarly, $r_1(x) = f_L(c)$.

As an immediate consequence of Theorem 12 we have the FACTOR THEOREM:

THEOREM 13. *A polynomial* $f(x)$ *of* $\mathfrak{A}[x]$ *has* $x - c$ *as a right (left) factor if and only if* $f_R(c) = 0[f_L(c) = 0]$.

Observe that Theorem 11 states that $x - c$ is a right factor of $f(x)$ if and only if $r(x) = 0$. Thus Theorem 13 is merely a translation of Theorem 12 in the case $r(x) = 0$.

9. Polynomials in *n* independent indeterminates. If $\mathfrak{A}$ is a ring and x_1 is an indeterminate over $\mathfrak{A}$, the set $\mathfrak{A}_1 = \mathfrak{A}[x_1]$ of all polynomials in x_1 with coefficients in $\mathfrak{A}$ is a ring. If x_2 is an indeterminate over $\mathfrak{A}_1$, we can form the ring $\mathfrak{A}_2 = \mathfrak{A}_1[x_2] = \mathfrak{A}[x_1, x_2]$. After n such steps we arrive at a ring $\mathfrak{A}[x_1, \ldots, x_n]$. The elements of $\mathfrak{A}[x_1, \ldots, x_n]$ are expressible as polynomials:

(22) $$f(x_1, \ldots, x_n) = \sum_{i_k=0}^{\nu_k} a_{i_1 \cdots i_n} x_1^{i_1} \cdots x_n^{i_n} .$$

This expression is unique. This statement is true for $n = 1$, and we assume it true for $\mathfrak{A}_{n-1} = \mathfrak{A}[x_1, \ldots, x_{n-1}]$. Then

$$(23) \qquad f(x_1, \ldots, x_n) = \sum_{i=0}^{\nu_n} b_i x_n^i,$$

where

$$(24) \qquad b_i = \sum_{i_k=0}^{\nu_k} a_{i_1 \cdots i_{n-1}} x_1^{i_1} \cdots x_{n-1}^{i_{n-1}}.$$

The expression of the b_i in form (24) is unique, and the expression of $f(x_1, \ldots, x_n)$ in form (23) is unique by cases $n = 1$ and $n - 1$. This yields the uniqueness in equation (22).

If $\mathfrak{B}$ is a ring containing the subring $\mathfrak{A}$ and if $x_1, \ldots, x_n$ are indeterminates over $\mathfrak{A}$, we say that $x_1, \ldots, x_n$ are *independent* if the expression of an element $f(x_1, \ldots, x_n)$ of $\mathfrak{A}[x_1, \ldots, x_n]$ is unique. We have given an inductive construction of $\mathfrak{A}[x_1, \ldots, x_n]$ and now observe that any two determinations of $\mathfrak{A}[x_1, \ldots, x_n]$ are isomorphic. Indeed, let $y_1, \ldots, y_n$ be independent indeterminates over a ring $\mathfrak{A}'$ and let S be an isomorphism of $\mathfrak{A}$ onto $\mathfrak{A}'$. Then the mapping

$$(25) \qquad f(x_1, \ldots, x_n) \to \sum_{i_k=0}^{\nu_k} a_{i_1 \cdots i_n}) S y_1^{i_1} \cdots y_n^{i_n}$$

is an isomorphism of $\mathfrak{A}[x_1, \ldots, x_n]$ onto $\mathfrak{A}'[y_1, \ldots, y_n]$.

The *degree* of $x_1^{i_1} \cdots x_n^{i_n}$ is defined to be $i_1 + \cdots + i_n$. The degree of $f(x_1, \cdots, x_n)$ of equation (22) is defined to be the maximum degree of any term with non-zero coefficient $a_{i_1 \cdots i_n}$.

A polynomial $f(x_1, \ldots, x_n)$ is called a *homogeneous polynomial* (or a *form*) if the degrees of all its terms are equal. If the degree of $f(x_1, \ldots, x_n)$ is q and $f(x_1, \ldots, x_n)$ is a form, we call $f(x_1, \ldots, x_n)$ an *n-ary q-ic* form.

10. Integral domains and fields. A ring $\mathfrak{A}$ is called an *integral domain* if $\mathfrak{A}$ is a commutative ring with a unity element and contains no divisors of zero. A *field* is a commutative division ring. Every field is an integral domain. Every integral domain can be imbedded in a unique field called its *quotient field.* We shall prove the following slight generalization of the result we just stated:

THEOREM 14. *Let $\mathfrak{A}$ be a commutative ring without divisors of zero. Then $\mathfrak{A}$ is contained in a field $\mathfrak{K}$ called the* quotient field *of $\mathfrak{A}$. Every field $\mathfrak{W}$ which contains $\mathfrak{A}$ contains a subfield $\mathfrak{K}_0 \supseteq \mathfrak{A}$ such that $\mathfrak{K}_0$ is isomorphic to $\mathfrak{K}$.*

Let $\mathfrak{G}$ be the set of all ordered pairs

$$\frac{a}{b}, \tag{26}$$

where $b \neq 0$ and a are in $\mathfrak{A}$. A pair c/d is said to be equivalent to a/b, and we write

$$\frac{a}{b} \cong \frac{c}{d} \tag{27}$$

if

$$ad = bc\,. \tag{28}$$

This relation is trivially symmetric and reflexive. If $ad = bc$ and $cf = de$, where $bdf \neq 0$, then $adf = bcf = bde$, $(af - be)d = 0$, $d \neq 0$, and $af = be$. Hence if $a/b \cong c/d$ and $c/d \cong e/f$, then $a/b \cong e/f$, and so the relation is an equivalence relation.

The pairs a/b may now be put into *equivalence classes*,

$$\alpha = \left\{\frac{a}{b}\right\}, \tag{29}$$

where α consists of all pairs equivalent to a/b. Let $\mathfrak{H}$ be the set consisting of all equivalence classes. Define

$$\alpha + \beta = \left\{\frac{ad + bc}{bd}\right\}, \qquad \alpha\beta = \left\{\frac{ac}{bd}\right\}. \tag{30}$$

Since $bd \neq 0$ when $b \neq 0$ and $d \neq 0$, the pairs in definition (30) of $\alpha + \beta$ and $\alpha\beta$ are in $\mathfrak{G}$, and the corresponding classes are in $\mathfrak{H}$. We shall leave for the reader the verification of the fact that if $a/b \cong a'/b'$ and $c/d \cong c'/d'$, then

$$\frac{ad + bc}{bd} \cong \frac{a'd' + b'c'}{b'd'}, \qquad \frac{ac}{bc} \cong \frac{a'c'}{b'b'}. \tag{31}$$

To see that $\mathfrak{H}$ is a module, we observe that $\alpha + \beta = \beta + \alpha$, $\alpha + 0 = \alpha$ if $0 = \{0/b\}$, and $\alpha + \beta = 0$ if $\beta = -\alpha = \{-a/b\}$. Also $\alpha\beta = \beta\alpha$, $\alpha e = \alpha$ if $e = \{b/b\}$, and $\alpha\beta = e$ if $\alpha = \{a/b\}$ with $ab \neq 0$ and $\beta = \{b/a\}$. Addition and multiplication may readily be seen to satisfy the associative law.

We have proved that $\mathfrak{H}$ is a field. The mapping $a \to \{ab/b\}$, where b is any non-zero element of $\mathfrak{A}$, is an isomorphism of $\mathfrak{A}$ onto the subring $\mathfrak{A}_0$ of all classes $\{ab/b\}$, since $\{ab/b\} + \{cb/b\} = \{(a + c)b^2/b^2)\} = \{(a + c)b/b\}$ and $\{ab/b\}\{cb/b\} = \{acb^2/b^2\} = \{(ac)b/b\}$. We use the construction of Theorem 3 to replace $\mathfrak{H}$ by a field $\mathfrak{K} \supseteq \mathfrak{A}$, actually consisting of the elements of the ring and those classes a defined by those pairs a/b not equivalent to ac/c. This field is the *quotient field* of $\mathfrak{A}$.

If $\mathfrak{W} \supseteq \mathfrak{A}$ and $\mathfrak{W}$ is a field, then $\mathfrak{W}$ contains b^{-1} for every non-zero b of $\mathfrak{A}$. The mapping defined by

$$(32) \qquad a \rightarrow a, \qquad \{a/b\} \rightarrow ab^{-1},$$

is a one-to-one mapping of $\mathfrak{K}$ onto the subfield $\mathfrak{K}_0$ consisting of all quotients ab^{-1} for a and $b \neq 0$ in $\mathfrak{A}$. It is evidently an isomorphism of $\mathfrak{K}$ and $\mathfrak{K}_0 \supseteq \mathfrak{A}$, and our proof is complete.

11. Divisibility in a commutative ring. An element a of a commutative ring $\mathfrak{A}$ is said to be *divisible by* b if $a = bc$, where c is also in $\mathfrak{A}$. Two non-zero elements a and b are called *associates* if b divides a and a divides b. Then $a = bc$, $b = ad$, and so $a = a(cd)$. If $\mathfrak{A}$ is an integral domain, we have $cd = 1$. Thus *two elements of an integral domain* $\mathfrak{A}$ *are associates if and only if each is the product of the other by a unit of* $\mathfrak{A}$.

If c divides both a and b, we call c a *common divisor* of a and b. If d is a common divisor of a and b such that every common divisor of a and b divides d, we call d a *greatest common divisor* of a and b. *Any two greatest common divisors of* a *and* b *are associates*; for, if d and d_1 are both greatest common divisors, we see that d divides d_1 and d_1 divides d.

Let d divide a and b and let $d = ag + bh$, where g and h are in the ring $\mathfrak{A}$. Then d is a greatest common divisor of a and b. For if c divides $a = ca_0$ and c divides $b = cb_0$, then $d = ca_0g + cb_0h = c(a_0g + b_0h)$, and c divides d.

A commutative ring is called a *principal ideal ring* if every ideal of $\mathfrak{A}$ is a principal ideal. If a and b are in $\mathfrak{A}$, the ideal $(a, b) = a\mathfrak{A} + b\mathfrak{A}$ is a principal ideal (d); then d divides a and b, and the element d of $a\mathfrak{A} + b\mathfrak{A}$ has the form $d = ag + bh$. Thus every two non-zero elements a and b of a principal ideal ring $\mathfrak{A}$ have a greatest common divisor d of the form $ag + bh$.

Two elements a and b of an integral domain $\mathfrak{J}$ are said to be relatively prime if the only common divisors of a and b are units. In a principal ideal ring $\mathfrak{J}$, the ideal determined by relatively prime elements must be the unit ideal $\mathfrak{J}$, and so we write $(a, b) = 1$ in this case.

If g is a non-zero element of an integral domain $\mathfrak{J}$ and has a factorization $g = bc$, where neither b nor c is a unit of $\mathfrak{J}$, we call g a *composite* element of $\mathfrak{J}$. If $g \neq 0$ and 1 is not a composite element of $\mathfrak{J}$, we call g a *prime* element of $\mathfrak{J}$.

The concepts just defined are basic in ring theory as well as in the theory of integers. We pass on now to some properties of ideals.

EXERCISES

1. Let $\mathfrak{E}$ be the ring of all ordinary integers and m be an integer without square factors. Show that the set $\mathfrak{J} = \mathfrak{E}[\sqrt{m}]$ of all numbers of the form $a + b\sqrt{m}$ with a and b in $\mathfrak{E}$ is an integral domain.

2. Find the units of the ring $\mathfrak{J}$ of Exercise 1 for all $m < 0$. *Hint:* If $u = a + b\sqrt{m}$ is a unit, so is $u' = a - b\sqrt{m}$. Let $uv = 1$, where $v = c + d\sqrt{m}$ and $v' = c - d\sqrt{m}$, so that $u'v' = 1$. Then $uv \cdot u'v' = 1$, and so $a^2 - b^2m$ divides 1.

3. If a and b are positive integers, we can always find integers q and r such that $0 \leq r < b$ and $a = bq + r$. Show that the greatest common divisor of a and b is also the g.c.d. of b and r.

4. Let a and b be integers where $a > 0$ divides b. What is the g.c.d. of a and b?

5. Use Exercises 3 and 4 to derive a process called the Euclidean g.c.d. process for finding the g.c.d. of any two integers.

6. Use the Euclidean process to find the g.c.d. of the following pairs of integers:

(*a*) (720, 63), (*b*) (21924, 2144), (*c*) (8381, 1015),

(*d*) (4078, 814), (*e*) (4233, 884), (*f*) (982, 363).

Hint: The work may be arranged as in the following solution of (*a*)

$$\begin{array}{rrr}
3 & 2 & 11 \\
9\,\overline{|\,27} & \overline{|\,63\,|} & \overline{720} \\
 & & 63 \\
 & 54 & \overline{90} \\
 & \overline{9} & 63 \\
 & & \overline{27}
\end{array}$$

The g.c.d. (720, 63) = 9.

12. Prime and maximal ideals. If $\mathfrak{A}$ is any ring, an ideal $\mathfrak{M}$ of $\mathfrak{A}$ is called a *maximal* ideal of $\mathfrak{A}$ if $\mathfrak{A} \supset \mathfrak{M} \supset (0)$ and there exists no ideal $\mathfrak{N}$ of $\mathfrak{A}$ such that $\mathfrak{A} \supset \mathfrak{N} \supset \mathfrak{M}$.

THEOREM 15. *An ideal $\mathfrak{M}$ of a ring $\mathfrak{A}$ is maximal if and only if $\mathfrak{A} - \mathfrak{M}$ is a simple ring.*

The result just stated is an immediate consequence of Theorem 9. We apply it to the case where $\mathfrak{A}$ is commutative, as follows:

THEOREM 16. *Let $\mathfrak{A}$ be a commutative ring with a unity element. Then $\mathfrak{M}$ is a maximal ideal of $\mathfrak{A}$ if and only if $\mathfrak{A} - \mathfrak{M}$ is a field.*

For a field $\mathfrak{K}$ is a simple ring, since, if $\mathfrak{N} \neq 0$ is an ideal of $\mathfrak{A}$ and $n \neq 0$ is in $\mathfrak{N}$, the element n^{-1} is in $\mathfrak{K}$, nn^{-1} is in $\mathfrak{N}$, $1k = k$ is in $\mathfrak{N}$ for every k of $\mathfrak{K}$, $\mathfrak{N} = \mathfrak{K}$, and $\mathfrak{K}$ is simple. Thus if $\mathfrak{K} = \mathfrak{A} - \mathfrak{M}$ is a field, it is a simple ring, and $\mathfrak{M}$ is maximal by Theorem 15. Conversely, let $\mathfrak{M}$

be a maximal ideal of the ring $\mathfrak{A}$ and let $\mathfrak{B}$ be the sum of the principal ideal (a) and $\mathfrak{M}$ for any a of $\mathfrak{A}$ not in $\mathfrak{M}$. Then $\mathfrak{B}$ is an ideal of $\mathfrak{A}$, $\mathfrak{B} \supset \mathfrak{M}$, $\mathfrak{B} = \mathfrak{A}$, and $\mathfrak{B}$ contains 1. But then $1 = ca + m$, where c is in $\mathfrak{A}$ and m is in $\mathfrak{M}$. The homomorphic image of 1 is the unity element $1 + \mathfrak{M}$ of $\mathfrak{A} - \mathfrak{M}$ and $1 + \mathfrak{M} = (c + \mathfrak{M})(a + \mathfrak{M})$, every non-zero element $a + \mathfrak{M}$ of $\mathfrak{A} - \mathfrak{M}$ has an inverse $c + \mathfrak{M}$ in $\mathfrak{A} - \mathfrak{M}$, and $\mathfrak{A} - \mathfrak{M}$ is a field.

An ideal $\mathfrak{N}$ is said to be *divisible by* $\mathfrak{M}$ if $\mathfrak{N} \subseteq \mathfrak{M}$. An element a is said to be divisible by an ideal $\mathfrak{M}$ if $(a) \subseteq \mathfrak{M}$, and so a is in $\mathfrak{M}$. We call an ideal $\mathfrak{P}$ a *prime* ideal of $\mathfrak{A}$ if a product ab of elements a and b of $\mathfrak{A}$ is divisible by $\mathfrak{P}$ if and only if one of the elements a and b is in $\mathfrak{P}$.

We next characterize prime ideals as follows:

THEOREM 17. *An ideal $\mathfrak{P}$ of a commutative ring $\mathfrak{A}$ is a prime ideal if and only if a product $\mathfrak{B}\mathfrak{C}$ of two ideals is divisible by $\mathfrak{P}$ if and only if $\mathfrak{B}$ or $\mathfrak{C}$ is divisible by $\mathfrak{P}$.*

For let $\mathfrak{P}$ divide a product $\mathfrak{B}\mathfrak{C}$ only if $\mathfrak{P}$ divides $\mathfrak{B}$ or $\mathfrak{C}$. Then $\mathfrak{P}$ divides bc if and only if $\mathfrak{P}$ contains bc and $\mathfrak{P}$ contains $(b)(c)$. But then $\mathfrak{P}$ divides (b) or (c), $\mathfrak{P}$ contains b or c, and $\mathfrak{P}$ is a prime ideal. Conversely, let $\mathfrak{P}$ be a prime ideal which divides $\mathfrak{B}\mathfrak{C}$. If $\mathfrak{P}$ does not divide $\mathfrak{B}$, there is an element b of $\mathfrak{B}$ which is not in $\mathfrak{P}$. But $(b)\mathfrak{C}$ is in $\mathfrak{P}$, and, if $\mathfrak{P}$ did not divide $\mathfrak{C}$, there would be an element c of $\mathfrak{C}$ not in $\mathfrak{P}$; bc is in $\mathfrak{P}$, contrary to the hypothesis that $\mathfrak{P}$ is a prime ideal. This completes our proof.

We are now ready to complete the characterization of prime ideals.

THEOREM 18. *Let $\mathfrak{A}$ be a commutative ring with a unity element. Then $\mathfrak{P}$ is a prime ideal if and only if $\mathfrak{A} - \mathfrak{P}$ is an integral domain.*

For $\mathfrak{P}$ is a prime ideal if and only if ab is in $\mathfrak{P}$ only when a or b is in $\mathfrak{P}$. This is equivalent to the statement that $(a + \mathfrak{P})(b + \mathfrak{P}) \subseteq \mathfrak{P}$ if and only if $a + \mathfrak{P} \subseteq \mathfrak{P}$ or $b + \mathfrak{P} \subseteq \mathfrak{P}$. Since $\mathfrak{P}$ is the zero element of $\mathfrak{A} - \mathfrak{P}$ and since the homomorphic image $\mathfrak{A} - \mathfrak{P}$ of a commutative ring $\mathfrak{A}$ with a unity element is a commutative ring with a unity element, we have shown that $\mathfrak{P}$ is a prime ideal if and only if $\mathfrak{A} - \mathfrak{P}$ has no divisors of zero and is an integral domain.

It should now be clear that every maximal ideal of a commutative ring with a unity element is a prime ideal. The converse need not be true. We shall continue our discussion of rings by a study of two integral domains which are principal ideal rings such that all prime ideals are maximal ideals.

13. The ring of integers. Let $\mathfrak{E}$ be the ring consisting of all ordinary integers. We shall prove the following result:

THEOREM 19. *Every non-zero ideal of $\mathfrak{E}$ is a principal ideal* (m), *where* $\mathrm{m} > 0$. *Every prime ideal of $\mathfrak{E}$ is a maximal ideal $\mathfrak{P} = (\mathrm{p})$, where* p *is a positive prime integer.*

If $\mathfrak{M}$ is an ideal of $\mathfrak{E}$ and a is in $\mathfrak{M}$, so is $(-1)a = -a$. Hence every non-zero ideal contains positive integers. Let m be the least positive integer in $\mathfrak{M}$. Then if a is in $\mathfrak{M}$, we may write $a = qm + r$, where $0 \leq r < m$. But qm is in $\mathfrak{M}$, and so $a - qm = r$ is in $\mathfrak{M}$. It follows that $r = 0$, $a = qm$, $\mathfrak{M} \subseteq (m) \subseteq \mathfrak{M}$, $\mathfrak{M} = (m)$. If $m = ab$, where $a > 1$ and $b > 1$, then it is easy to see that $(m) = (a)(b)$. But (m) does not contain either (a) or (b), since otherwise either $a = cm$, $m = ab = (bc)m$, $bc = 1$, $b = \pm 1$, or we can show that $a = \pm 1$. Hence $\mathfrak{P}$ is a prime ideal only if $\mathfrak{P} = (p)$, where p is a positive prime. Conversely, if $\mathfrak{P} = (p)$ and $\mathfrak{P}$ contains ab, then $ab = cp$, where c is in $\mathfrak{E}$. Then p divides ab and divides a or b. Hence $\mathfrak{P}$ is a prime ideal.

It remains to show that

$$\mathfrak{E}_p = \mathfrak{E} - (p)$$

is a field whenever p is a prime. We observe that the elements of $\mathfrak{E}_p$ are the cosets $(p), 1 + (p), \ldots, p - 1 + (p)$. If a is any integer $1, 2, \ldots, p - 1$, it cannot be divisible by p and so must be prime to p. Then

$$ab + cp = 1$$

for integers b and c. But then $[a + (p)][b + (p)] \subseteq [1 - cp + (p)] = [1 + (p)]$. Since $1 + (p)$ is the unity element of $\mathfrak{E}_p$, we have shown that $\mathfrak{E}_p$ is a field.

The non-zero elements of $\mathfrak{E}_p$ form a group of order $p - 1$. By Theorem 1.10 we have the so-called FERMAT THEOREM, which we shall state in terms of the concept of congruence. Write

$$a \equiv b \pmod{m}$$

(read a is congruent to b modulo m), if $a - b$ is divisible by m. Then $a \equiv b \pmod{m}$ if and only if $a - b$ is in (m) and a and b determine the same coset in

$$\mathfrak{E}_m = \mathfrak{E} - (m)\,.$$

We then have the following consequence:

THEOREM 20. *Let* p *be a prime and* a *be any integer not divisible by* p. *Then* $a^{p-1} \equiv 1$ (*mod* p).

The Euler *ϕ-function* is the number of *residue classes* (that is, cosets) $a + (m)$ in the difference ring $\mathfrak{E}_m$ which are defined by integers a which are prime to m. When a and b are prime to m, their product is prime to m by the FUNDAMENTAL THEOREM OF ARITHMETIC. Then $\phi(m)$ is the number of elements in the set $\mathfrak{G}$ of all classes $g + (m)$ with g prime to m. This set has a product operation on $(\mathfrak{G}, \mathfrak{G})$ to $\mathfrak{G}$, and $1 + (m)$ is the identity element for multiplication in $\mathfrak{G}$. But if a is prime to m, the Division Algorithm for $\mathfrak{E}$ has been seen to imply that there exist integers b and c such that $ab + cm = 1$, $[b + (m)][a + (m)] = [1 + (m)]$. It follows that $\mathfrak{G}$ is a group of order (m). We apply Theorem 1.10 to obtain the Euler theorem.

THEOREM 21. *Let* $\phi(\mathrm{m})$ *be the number of integers* g *such that* $0 < \mathrm{g} \leq \mathrm{m}$ *and* g *is prime to* m. *Then*

$$\mathrm{a}^{\phi(\mathrm{m})} \equiv 1 \; (mod\ \mathrm{m})$$

for every a *prime to* m.

The number $\phi(m)$ may be computed by the use of the following result:

THEOREM 22. *If* a *and* b *are relatively prime, we have* $\phi(\mathrm{ab}) = \phi(\mathrm{a})\phi(\mathrm{b})$. *If* p *is a prime and* ν *is a positive integer,* we have $\phi(\mathrm{p}^\nu) = \mathrm{p}^\nu - \mathrm{p}^{\nu-1}$.

The first part of this result will be proved by considering the structure of $\mathfrak{E}_m$.

LEMMA 3. *Let* $\mathrm{m} = \mathrm{bc}$ *for relatively prime integers* b *and* c. *Then* $\mathfrak{E}_{\mathrm{m}} = \mathfrak{B} \oplus \mathfrak{C}$, *where* $\mathfrak{B} \cong \mathfrak{E}_{\mathrm{b}}$ *and* $\mathfrak{C} \cong \mathfrak{E}_{\mathrm{c}}$.

Since b and c are relatively prime, there exist integers b_1 and c_1 such that $bb_1 + cc_1 = 1$. Then every integer a has the form $a = (ab_1)b + (ac_1)c$. It follows that $\mathfrak{E}$ is the sum $\mathfrak{E} = (\mathfrak{H}, \mathfrak{K})$ of $\mathfrak{H} = (c)$ and $\mathfrak{K} = (b)$. The intersection of $\mathfrak{H}$ and $\mathfrak{K}$ consists of those integers divisible by both b and c and so in (m). Then $\mathfrak{E}_m = (\mathfrak{B}, \mathfrak{C})$, where $\mathfrak{B} = \mathfrak{H} - (m)$ and $\mathfrak{C} = \mathfrak{K} - (m)$. The intersection of $\mathfrak{B}$ and $\mathfrak{C}$ is now the zero ideal, $\mathfrak{B}$ and $\mathfrak{C}$ are ideals of $\mathfrak{E}_m$, and $\mathfrak{E}_m = \mathfrak{B} \oplus \mathfrak{C}$. Evidently, $\mathfrak{E}_m - \mathfrak{B} \cong \mathfrak{C} \cong \mathfrak{E} - \mathfrak{H}$ by Theorem 8 and 9, so that $\mathfrak{C} \cong \mathfrak{E}_c$. Similarly, $\mathfrak{B} \cong \mathfrak{E} - \mathfrak{K} = \mathfrak{E}_b$.

An integer a is prime to m if and only if the class $a_0 = a + (m)$ is a unit of $\mathfrak{E}_m$. Write $a_0 = a_{01} + a_{02}$, where $a_{01} = a_1 + (m)$ is in $\mathfrak{B}$ and $a_{02} = a_2 + (m)$ is in $\mathfrak{C}$, as in Lemma 3. Then $a + (m)$ has an inverse $d_0 = d + (m)$ in $\mathfrak{B} \oplus \mathfrak{C} = \mathfrak{E}_m$ if and only if $d_0 = d_{01} + d_{02}$, where $a_{01}d_{01}$ is the unit e_1 of $\mathfrak{B}$ and $a_{02}d_{02}$ is the unit e_2 of $\mathfrak{C}$. But then a_1 is one of $\phi(b)$ elements of $\mathfrak{B} \cong \mathfrak{E}_b$, a_2 is one of $\phi(c)$ elements of $\mathfrak{C} \cong \mathfrak{E}_c$, and so $\phi(bc) = \phi(b)\phi(c)$.

An integer a is prime to p^ν if and only if it is prime to p. Every integer is congruent modulo p^ν to one and only one of the p^ν distinct integers

$$r_1 + r_2p + \cdots + r_\nu p^{\nu-1},$$

where $r_a = 0, 1, \ldots, p - 1$. The only integers in this set having p as a factor are those where $r_1 = 0$, and there are $p^{\nu-1}$ such integers. Hence $\phi(p^\nu) = p^\nu - p^{\nu-1}$.

EXERCISES

1. Compute $\phi(m)$ for the following values of m:

$$(a)\ 189, \qquad (b)\ 180, \qquad (c)\ 700, \qquad (d)\ 5500.$$

2. Compute the inverse of the residue class $[b]$ modulo m for the following values of m and b:

$$(a)\ b = 7,\ m = 11; \qquad (c)\ b = 21,\ m = 23;$$
$$(b)\ b = 9,\ m = 13; \qquad (d)\ b = 7,\ m = 20.$$

14. Factorization theory in $\mathfrak{F}[x]$. Consider a field $\mathfrak{F}$, and let x be an indeterminate over $\mathfrak{F}$. By Section 8, if $f(x)$ and $g(x)$ are non-zero polynomials of $\mathfrak{F}[x]$, the degree of $f(x)g(x)$ is the sum of the degrees of $f(x)$ and $g(x)$. Then $f(x)g(x) \neq 0$ if $f(x) \neq 0$, $g(x) \neq 0$. Hence $\mathfrak{F}[x]$ is an integral domain. Moreover, the units of $\mathfrak{F}[x]$ are the non-zero elements of $\mathfrak{F}$.

Two polynomials are associates if and only if they differ by a constant factor, that is, by a non-zero factor in $\mathfrak{F}$. Thus every non-zero polynomial is associated with a monic polynomial, that is, a polynomial

$$f(x) = x^{\nu} + a_1x^{\nu-1} + \cdots + a_{\nu},$$

with coefficients a_i in $\mathfrak{F}$ and leading coefficient 1.

Therem 11 may be restated as follows in the present case:

THEOREM 23. *Let* f(x) *and* g(x) *be non-zero polynomials of respective degrees* ν *and* μ. *Then there exist unique polynomials* q(x) *and* r(x) *where* q(x) = 0 *or has degree* $\nu - \mu$, r(x) *has degree less than* g(x), *and* f(x) = q(x)g(x) + r(x).

We now derive the existence of a unique g.c.d. (greatest common divisor) for any two non-zero elements of $\mathfrak{F}[x]$. A polynomial $d(x)$ is called a g.c.d. of $f(x) \neq 0$ and $g(x) \neq 0$ if $d(x)$ divides $f(x)$ and $g(x)$, $d(x)$ is monic, and every common divisor of $f(x)$ and $g(x)$ divides $d(x)$.

THEOREM 24. *If* f(x) $\neq$ 0 *and* g(x) $\neq$ 0 *there exist polynomials* a(x) *and* b(x) *such that*

$$a(x)f(x) + b(x)g(x) = d(x)$$

is the unique g.c.d. of f(x) *and* g(x).

We shall give a ring-theoretic proof of this result, beginning with the following property:

LEMMA 4. *The ring* $\mathfrak{J} = \mathfrak{F}[x]$ *is a principal ideal ring.*

For let $\mathfrak{B}$ be a non-zero ideal of $\mathfrak{J}$. Then $\mathfrak{B}$ contains the associates of all elements of $\mathfrak{B}$ and hence contains monic polynomials. There must exist a monic polynomial $d = d(x)$ in $\mathfrak{B}$ of minimum degree. We use

Theorem 23 to write $f(x) = q(x)d(x) + r(x)$ for any $f(x)$ in $\mathfrak{B}$ where the degree of $r(x)$ is less than the degree of $d(x)$. If $r(x) \neq 0$, it has a monic associate $ar(x) = af(x) - aq(x)d(x)$ which must be in $\mathfrak{B}$. This contradicts our assumption about the degree of $d(x)$, and so $r(x) = 0$, $f(x) = q(x)d(x)$, $\mathfrak{B} \subseteq (d) \subseteq \mathfrak{B}$, and $\mathfrak{B} = (d)$.

To prove Theorem 24, we let f and g be non-zero polynomials of $\mathfrak{J} = \mathfrak{F}[x]$ and let $\mathfrak{B}$ be the ideal $(f\mathfrak{J}, g\mathfrak{J})$. Then $\mathfrak{B} = (d)$, and $d = af + bg$, d may be taken to be monic, f and g are in (d), and d divides f and g, as desired.

If $f(x)$ and $g(x)$ have no common factors except unit factors, we say that $f(x)$ and $g(x)$ are *relatively prime* or that $f(x)$ *is prime to* $g(x)$. By Theorem 24 there exist polynomials $a(x)$ and $b(x)$ such that $a(x)f(x) + b(x)g(x) = 1$. Then we have

LEMMA 5. *Let* f(x) *divide the product* g(x)h(x) *where* f(x) *is prime to* g(x). *Then* f(x) *divides* h(x).

For $a(x)f(x)h(x) + b(x)g(x)h(x) = h(x)$, $g(x)h(x) = f(x)q(x)$, and $h(x) = f(x)[a(x)h(x) + b(x)q(x)]$.

A polynomial $f(x)$ is called an *irreducible* polynomial of $\mathfrak{F}[x]$, and we say that $f(x)$ is irreducible in $\mathfrak{F}$ if $f(x)$ is a prime element of the ring $\mathfrak{F}[x]$. When $f(x)$ is irreducible, its only divisors are associates of $f(x)$, and so $f(x)$ is prime to any given non-zero polynomial $g(x)$, or $f(x)$ divides $g(x)$. Applying Lemma 5, we have

LEMMA 6. *Let* f(x) *be an irreducible polynomial divisor of a product of polynomials. Then* f(x) *divides one of the factors.*

If $f(x)$ is any non-constant polynomial, the process of factoring $f(x)$ as a product of non-constant factors must terminate. Indeed, if $f(x)$ has degree ν, a factorization of $f(x)$ as a product $f(x) = f_1(x) \cdots f_{\nu+1}(x)$ of non-constant factors $f_i(x)$ is impossible, since the degree of $f_1(x) \cdots f_{\nu+1}(x)$ is at least $\nu + 1$. It follows that the first part of the following theorem must be true.

THEOREM 25. *Every non-constant polynomial* f(x) *can be factored as the product.*

$$f(x) = a_\nu f_1(x) \cdots f_r(x) ,$$

where a_ν *is the leading coefficient of* f(x) *and the factors* $f_i(x)$ *are monic irreducible polynomials of* $\mathfrak{F}$[x]. *The factors* $f_i(x)$ *are unique apart from the order in which they appear in the product.*

To prove the factorization unique, we note that the theorem is true trivially when $f(x)$ has degree $\nu = 1$. Let it be true for polynomials of degree less than ν, and let $f(x) = a_\nu f_1(x) \cdots f_r(x) = a_\nu g_1(x) \cdots g_s(x)$. Then $f_1(x)$ divides $g_1(x) \cdots g_s(x)$ and must divide one of the $g_i(x)$. Since

$g_i(x)$ is irreducible and monic, its only monic non-constant divisor is $g_i(x)$, $f_1(x) = g_i(x)$. Relabel the $g_i(x)$ so that $g_1(x) = f_1(x)$. By Theorem 23 we have $f_2(x) \cdots f_r(x) = g_2(x) \cdots g_s(x) = \varphi(x)$, where the degree of $\phi(x)$ is less than ν. By the hypothesis of our induction, $r = s$, and the polynomials $f_2(x), \ldots, f_r(x)$ are a reordering of $g_2(x), \ldots, g_r(x)$. This completes our proof.

We close this section with the following remark:

THEOREM 26. *Let* $f(x) = a_0x^n + \cdots + a_n$ *where* $a_0, \ldots, a_n$ *are in a field* $\mathfrak{F}$ *and let* $f(\beta_i) = 0$ *for* $n + 1$ *distinct elements* $\beta_1, \ldots, \beta_{n+1}$ *in* $\mathfrak{F}$. Then $a_0 = a_1 = \cdots = a_n = 0$.

For otherwise there is a non-zero coefficient a_j and $a_j^{-1}f(x) = g(x) = x^m + \gamma_1 x^{m-1} + \cdots + \gamma_m$ with the γ_i in $\mathfrak{F}$. Since $g(\beta_1) = 0$, we use the factor Theorem 13 to write $g(x) = (x - \beta_1)g_1(x)$, where $g(\beta_i) = (\beta_i - \beta_1)g_1(\beta_i) = 0$. But $\beta_i \neq \beta_1$ for $i = 2, \ldots, n + 1$, and so $g_1(\beta_i) = 0$. After, at most, m such steps, we obtain $g(x) = (x - \beta_1) \cdots (x - \beta_m)$, $g(\beta_{m+1}) = (\beta_{m+1} - \beta_1) \cdots (\beta_{m+1} - \beta_1) = 0$. But $\mathfrak{F}$ is a field, no factor $\beta_{m+1} - \beta_i = 0$, which is impossible.

EXERCISES

1. State the polynomial analogues of the results of Exercises 3, 4, and 5 of Section 11.

2. Use the g.c.d. process of Exercise 1 to find the g.c.d. of $f = f(x)$ and $g = g(x)$ in the following cases:

(*a*) $f = x^3 + x^2 + x + 2,\ g = x^2 + 2x + 2$;

(*b*) $f = x^4 + 15x^3 - 2x^2 - 34x - 60;\ g = f'(x)$;

(*c*) $f = x^4 - 2x^3 - 2x - 1,\ g = x^5 - 2x^3 - 2x^2 - 3x - 2$;

(*d*) $f = x^8 - 2x^6 + x^5 + 2x^2 - x - 1, g = x^8 + x^5 + x^4 - x - 2$;

(*e*) $f = x^3 - 2x + 4,\ g = x^6 - 2x^4 + 4X^3 + x^2 - 2x + 2$;

(*f*) $f = x^4 - 2x^3 + x^2 - 1,\ g = x^5 - 3x^3 + 2x^2 - 1$;

(*g*) $f = x^4 + x^3 - x^2 + x - 2,\ g = x^4 + x^3 - 3x^2 - x + 2$.

15. Ideal theory in $\mathfrak{F}[x]$. As in Section 13, we derive the following result:

THEOREM 27. *Every prime ideal of* $\mathfrak{F}[x]$ *is a maximal ideal* $\mathfrak{P} = (f)$, *where* $f = f(x)$ *is a monic irreducible polynomial.*

For we have already seen that if $f(x) = f$ is irreducible, then $f(x)$ divides $g(x)h(x)$ if and only if f divides $g(x)$ or $h(x)$. Hence (f) is a prime ideal if f is irreducible. Conversely, if (f) is a prime ideal, then f must be irreducible, since otherwise $f = gh$, where $g(x)$ and $h(x)$ are not constant polynomials, and f does not divide $g(x)$ or $h(x)$. The polynomials $a(x)$ of $\mathfrak{F}[x]$ define residue classes

$$a + (f)$$

in the ring

$$\mathfrak{F}[x] - (f),$$

and $a + (f) \neq 0$ if and only if a is not divisible by f, a is prime to f. The polynomial 1 defines the unity quantity $1 + (f)$ of $\mathfrak{F}[x] - (f)$. But if $a + (f) \neq 0$, there exist polynomials b and c such that $ab + cf = 1$, $[a + (f)][b + (f)] = 1 - cf + (f) = 1 + (f)$, and $\mathfrak{F}[x] - (f)$ is a field. Hence every prime ideal of $\mathfrak{F}[x]$ is a maximal ideal.

16. References. The material of chapter ii is basic material such as is given in chapters i and ii of the author's *Modern Higher Algebra*. See also G. Birkhoff and S. MacLane, *A Survey of Modern Algebra*, and N. H. McCoy, *Rings and Ideals*.

CHAPTER III

Vector Spaces and Matrices

1. Vector spaces. Let $\mathfrak{L}$ be a module and $\mathfrak{J}$ be an integral domain. Consider a mapping

$$S: \qquad (a, \alpha) \rightarrow (a, \alpha)S = \alpha a = a\alpha = aS_\alpha$$

on $(\mathfrak{L}, \mathfrak{J})$ to $\mathfrak{L}$, where the image element αa is then a unique element of $\mathfrak{L}$ for every a of $\mathfrak{L}$ and α of $\mathfrak{J}$. We call S an operation of *scalar multiplication* and refer to αa as the *scalar product* of the *vector* a in $\mathfrak{L}$ by the *scalar* α in $\mathfrak{J}$. The mapping S_α, defined by a particular element α of $\mathfrak{J}$, maps $\mathfrak{L}$ onto an image set $\alpha\mathfrak{L}$ consisting of all αa for a in $\mathfrak{L}$.

A mathematical system (designated by $\mathfrak{L}$) consisting of $\mathfrak{L}$, $\mathfrak{J}$, and S is called a *vector space* over $\mathfrak{J}$ if the following properties hold:

I. *Every* S_α *is an endomorphism of* $\mathfrak{L}$ *onto its submodule* $\alpha\mathfrak{L}$, *that is,*

$$\alpha(a + b) = \alpha a + \alpha b \tag{1}$$

for every a *and* b *of* $\mathfrak{L}$ *and* α *of* $\mathfrak{J}$.

II. *The mappings* S_α *are one-to-one endomorphisms for every* $\alpha \neq 0$ *of* $\mathfrak{J}$, *that is,*

$$\alpha a = 0 \tag{2}$$

for a non-zero a *of* $\mathfrak{L}$ *only if* $\alpha = 0$. *The mapping* S_1 *defined by the unity element* 1 *of* $\mathfrak{J}$ *is the identity automorphism of* $\mathfrak{L}$, *that is,*

$$1a = a \tag{3}$$

for every a *of* $\mathfrak{L}$.

III. *The mapping* S_α *is an additive function of* α, *that is,*

$$(\alpha + \beta)a = \alpha a + \beta a \tag{4}$$

for every α *and* β *of* $\mathfrak{J}$ *and* a *of* $\mathfrak{L}$.

IV. *The mapping* $S_{\alpha\beta} = S_\alpha S_\beta = S_\beta S_\alpha$, *that is,*

$$\alpha(\beta a) = (\alpha\beta)a \tag{5}$$

for every α *and* β *of* $\mathfrak{J}$ *and* a *of* $\mathfrak{L}$.

If ζ is the zero element of $\mathfrak{J}$, then $(\zeta + \zeta)a = \zeta a + \zeta a = \zeta a$, and so ζa must be the zero element of the module $\mathfrak{L}$. Then equation (2) holds for $\alpha = \zeta$, and we simply write $0a = 0$. Also $\alpha(0 + 0) = \alpha 0 + \alpha 0 = \alpha 0$, and so $\alpha 0 = 0$ for every α of $\mathfrak{J}$. Since $\alpha + (-\alpha) = 0$, we see that $[\alpha + (-\alpha)]a = \alpha a + (-\alpha)a = 0a = 0$. Hence

(6) $$(-\alpha)a = -(\alpha a)\,.$$

If $\mathfrak{J}$ is a field, the first condition of II is superfluous. For α has an inverse α^{-1} in $\mathfrak{J}$, and we apply equation (5) to see that $\alpha^{-1}(\alpha a) = (\alpha^{-1}\alpha)a = 1a = a$. Then $\alpha a = 0$ if and only if $\alpha^{-1}(\alpha a) = \alpha^{-1}0 = 0 = a$.

A subset $\mathfrak{M}$ of a vector space $\mathfrak{L}$ over $\mathfrak{J}$ is called a *subspace over* $\mathfrak{J}$ of $\mathfrak{L}$ if $\mathfrak{M}$ forms a vector space with respect to the defining operation S on $\mathfrak{L}$. Then $\mathfrak{M}$ is a subspace of $\mathfrak{L}$ if and only if $\mathfrak{M}$ contains

(7) $$\alpha a + \beta b$$

for every a and b of $\mathfrak{M}$ and α and β of $\mathfrak{J}$. We call $\alpha a + \beta b$ a *linear combination* of a and b with *coefficients* α and β in $\mathfrak{J}$. More generally, an expression

(8) $$\alpha_1 a_1 + \cdots + \alpha_t a_t$$

is called a *(finite) linear combination* of $a_1, \ldots, a_t$ with coefficients $\alpha_1, \ldots, \alpha_t$. Thus *$\mathfrak{M}$ is a subspace of $\mathfrak{L}$ if and only if $\mathfrak{M}$ contains all finite linear combinations of its elements.* But we actually see that $\mathfrak{M}$ is a subspace of $\mathfrak{L}$ if and only if $\mathfrak{M}$ contains

(9) $$a + b, \quad \alpha a$$

for every a and b of $\mathfrak{M}$ and α of $\mathfrak{J}$.

The set consisting of zero alone is a subspace of any vector space $\mathfrak{L}$ over $\mathfrak{J}$, called the *zero subspace.* The set $a\mathfrak{J}$, consisting of all αa for α in $\mathfrak{J}$, is a subspace of $\mathfrak{L}$ for every a of $\mathfrak{L}$.

The polynomial ring $\mathfrak{J}[x]$ is a simple example of a vector space over $\mathfrak{J}$. If $\mathfrak{F}$ is a subfield of a field $\mathfrak{K}$, then $\mathfrak{K}$ is a vector space over $\mathfrak{F}$, where $\mathfrak{S}$ is the operation of multiplication in $\mathfrak{K}$. More generally, every division ring is a vector space over its center.

2. Sums of subspaces. The *sum*

(10) $$\mathfrak{Q} = (\mathfrak{M}, \mathfrak{N})$$

of subspaces $\mathfrak{M}$ and $\mathfrak{N}$ of a vector space $\mathfrak{L}$ over $\mathfrak{J}$ is the set of all sums

(11) $$q = m + n$$

for m in $\mathfrak{M}$ and n in $\mathfrak{N}$. Similarly, $(\mathfrak{L}_1, \ldots, \mathfrak{L}_t)$ is the sum of the subspaces $\mathfrak{L}_1, \ldots, \mathfrak{L}_t$ of $\mathfrak{L}$ over $\mathfrak{J}$ and consists of all elements $x = x_1 + \cdots + x_t$ for x_i in $\mathfrak{L}_i$.

If $\mathfrak{Q} = (\mathfrak{M}, \mathfrak{N})$ is the module direct sum of the subspaces $\mathfrak{M}$ and $\mathfrak{N}$, we write

$$\mathfrak{Q} = \mathfrak{M} + \mathfrak{N} \tag{12}$$

and call $\mathfrak{Q}$ the *supplementary* sum of $\mathfrak{M}$ and $\mathfrak{N}$. Then $\mathfrak{Q} = (\mathfrak{M}, \mathfrak{N}) = \mathfrak{M} + \mathfrak{N}$ if and only if every element q of $\mathfrak{Q}$ is uniquely expressible in the form $q = m + n$ for m in $\mathfrak{M}$ and n in $\mathfrak{N}$. If $q = m + n = m_1 + n_1$, then $(m - m_1) + (n - n_1) = 0$, where $m - m_1$ is in $\mathfrak{M}$ and $n - n_1$ is in $\mathfrak{N}$. Thus $\mathfrak{Q}$ is a supplementary sum if and only if 0 is uniquely expressible as the sum of an element in $\mathfrak{M}$ and an element in $\mathfrak{N}$. But this is true if and only if

$$\mathfrak{M} \cap \mathfrak{N} = 0\,. \tag{13}$$

The sum $(\mathfrak{L}_1, \ldots, \mathfrak{L}_t)$ of subspaces $\mathfrak{L}_i$ of $\mathfrak{L}$ consists of all sums $x = x_1 + \cdots + x_t$ for x_i in $\mathfrak{L}_i$. It is the supplementary sum

$$\mathfrak{L} = \mathfrak{L}_1 + \cdots + \mathfrak{L}_t \tag{14}$$

if and only if the expression of x of $\mathfrak{L}$ in the form $x = x_1 + \cdots + x_t$ is unique. Then $\mathfrak{L} = \mathfrak{L}_1 + \cdots + \mathfrak{L}_t$ only when a sum

$$x_1 + \cdots + x_t = 0\,, \tag{15}$$

for x_i in $\mathfrak{L}_i$, if and only if $x_1 = \cdots = x_t = 0$.

The subspace $a\mathfrak{J}$ has already been defined for every a of $\mathfrak{L}$. Then if $a_1, \ldots, a_t$ are any elements of $\mathfrak{L}$, the sum

$$\mathfrak{M} = (a_1\mathfrak{J}, \ldots, a_t\mathfrak{J}) \tag{16}$$

consists of all linear combinations,

$$\alpha_1 a_1 + \cdots + \alpha_t a_t \tag{17}$$

with coefficients α_i in $\mathfrak{J}$. We shall say that $\mathfrak{M}$ is *spanned* by $a_1, \ldots, a_t$. If

$$\mathfrak{M} = a_1\mathfrak{J} + \cdots + a_t\mathfrak{J}\,, \tag{18}$$

we know that $\alpha_1 a_1 + \cdots + \alpha_t a_t = 0$ for $\alpha_1, \ldots, \alpha_t$ in $\mathfrak{J}$ if and only if $\alpha_1 = \cdots = \alpha_t = 0$. In this case we shall say that $a_1, \ldots, a_t$ are *linearly independent* in $\mathfrak{J}$ and that $a_1, \ldots, a_t$ *form a basis* of $\mathfrak{M}$. If $(a_1\mathfrak{J}, \ldots, a_t\mathfrak{J}) \neq a_1\mathfrak{J} + \cdots + a_t\mathfrak{J}$, there must exist element $\alpha_1, \ldots, \alpha_t$ in $\mathfrak{J}$ and not all zero such that $\alpha_1 a_1 + \cdots + \alpha_t a_t = 0$. In this case we say that $a_1, \ldots, a_t$ are *linearly dependent* in $\mathfrak{J}$.

We shall pass on to the special case where $\mathfrak{J}$ is a field.

3. Vector spaces over a field. Let $\mathfrak{L}$ be a vector space over a field $\mathfrak{F}$. Then we have the following useful elementary property:

LEMMA 1. *Let $\mathfrak{M}$ be a subspace of $\mathfrak{L}$ and* u *be an element of $\mathfrak{L}$ which is not in $\mathfrak{M}$. Then* $(\mathfrak{M}, u\mathfrak{F}) = \mathfrak{M} + u\mathfrak{F}$.

For if $(\mathfrak{M}, u\mathfrak{F}) \neq \mathfrak{M} + u\mathfrak{F}$, there must exist an element m in $\mathfrak{M}$ and an element $\alpha \neq 0$ in $\mathfrak{F}$ such that $m + \alpha u = 0$. But $u = -\alpha^{-1}m$ is then in $\mathfrak{M}$, contrary to hypothesis.

We use this result to prove the following theorem:

THEOREM 1. *Let* $a_1, \ldots, a_t$ *span a subspace $\mathfrak{M}$ of a vector space $\mathfrak{L}$ over $\mathfrak{F}$. Then $\mathfrak{M}$ has a basis consisting of* r *of the elements* $a_1, \ldots, a_t$.

There is clearly no loss of generality if we assume that every a_i is not zero. The theorem is true trivially if $t = 1$, since then $\mathfrak{M} = a_1\mathfrak{F}$. Assume it true for subspaces $\mathfrak{N}$ spanned by $t - 1$ elements. Then $\mathfrak{N} = (a_1\mathfrak{F}, \ldots a_{t-1}\mathfrak{F}) = u_1\mathfrak{F} + \cdots + u_s\mathfrak{F}$, where each u_j is one of the elements $a_1, \ldots, a_{t-1}$. If a_t is in $\mathfrak{N}$, then $\mathfrak{M} = (\mathfrak{N}, a_t\mathfrak{F}) \subseteq \mathfrak{N} \subseteq \mathfrak{M}$ and $\mathfrak{M} = u_1\mathfrak{F} + \cdots + u_s\mathfrak{F}$, as desired. Otherwise $\mathfrak{M} = \mathfrak{N} + a_t\mathfrak{F} = u_1\mathfrak{F} + \cdots + u\mathfrak{F} + a_t\mathfrak{F}$, and the theorem is proved.

We are now ready to prove the uniqueness of the number of elements in a basis of a finitely spanned vector space. We state the result from which this property is derived as follows:

THEOREM 2. *Let* $\mathfrak{L} = u_1\mathfrak{F} + \cdots + u_n\mathfrak{F}$. *Then every set of* $n + 1$ *elements of $\mathfrak{L}$ are linearly dependent.*

Consider $n + 1$ elements a_i of $\mathfrak{L}$. Then

$$(19) \qquad a_i = \alpha_{i1}u_1 + \cdots + \alpha_{in}u_n \qquad (i = 1, \ldots, n + 1),$$

where the α_{ij} are in $\mathfrak{F}$. If $n = 1$ and $a_1 = a_2 = 0$, then $a_1 + a_2 = 0$, as desired. Otherwise, $a_1 = \alpha_{11}u_1$, a_2 and $\alpha_{21}u_1$, and $\alpha_{21}a_1 + (-\alpha_{11})a_2 = \alpha_{11}\alpha_{21}u_1 - \alpha_{11}\alpha_{21}u_1 = 0$, where α_{11} and α_{21} are not both zero. This proves the theorem for $n = 1$, and we assume it true for spaces with a basis of $n - 1$ elements. When $a_1, \ldots, a_{n+1}$ are all in $\mathfrak{L}_0 = u_1\mathfrak{F} + \cdots + u_{n-1}\mathfrak{F}$, our hypothesis implies that $\gamma_1a_1 + \cdots + \gamma_na_n + 0a_{n+1} = 0$, where $\gamma_1, \ldots, \gamma_n$ are not all zero and are in $\mathfrak{F}$, and our result is true again. Hence let at least one a_i be not in $\mathfrak{L}_0$. Relabel the a_i so that a_{n+1} is not in $\mathfrak{L}_0$, that is, $\alpha_{n+1,\, n} \neq 0$. Then the n elements $b_i = a_i - \alpha_{in}(\alpha_{n+1,\, n})^{-1}a_{n+1}$ are in $\mathfrak{L}_0$ for $i = 1, \ldots, n$, and there then exists elements $\gamma_1, \ldots, \gamma_n$ not all zero and in $\mathfrak{F}$ such that $\gamma_1b_1 + \cdots + \gamma_nb_n = \gamma_1a_1 + \cdots + \gamma_na_n + (-\alpha_{n+1,\bullet}^{-1})(\gamma_1\alpha_{1n} + \cdots + \gamma_n\alpha_{nn})a_{n-1} = 0$. This completes our proof.

If $\mathfrak{L} = u_1\mathfrak{F} + \cdots + u_n\mathfrak{F} = v_1\mathfrak{F} + \cdots + v_m\mathfrak{F}$, then Theorem 2 and the fact that $v_1, \ldots, v_m$ are linearly independent in $\mathfrak{F}$ imply that $m \leqq n$. Similarly, $n \neq m$, so $m = n$. It follows that *the number of elements in a basis of a finitely spanned vector space* $\mathfrak{L}$ *over a field is a unique integer called the* dimension *of* $\mathfrak{L}$ *over* $\mathfrak{F}$. Thus every finitely spanned vector space over a field is a finite-dimensional vector space.

THEOREM 3. *Every subspace* $\mathfrak{M}$ *of a finite-dimensional space* $\mathfrak{L}$ *over a field* $\mathfrak{F}$ *is finite-dimensional. Then* $\mathfrak{M} = \mathfrak{L}$ *if and only if* $\mathfrak{M}$ *and* $\mathfrak{L}$ *have the same dimension.*

We may assume that $\mathfrak{M} \neq 0$ and take n to be the dimension of $\mathfrak{L}$ over $\mathfrak{F}$. Theorem 1 says that if we select any set consisting of a finite number of elements of $\mathfrak{M}$, we can select a subset of linearly independent elements. Theorem 2 says that the number of elements in this linearly independent subset cannot exceed n. Thus there is a subset of $\mathfrak{M}$ containing a maximum number $m \leq n$ of linearly independent elements $v_1, \ldots, v_m$. Then $\mathfrak{M} \supseteq \mathfrak{M}_m = v_1\mathfrak{F} + \cdots + v_m\mathfrak{F}$, $(\mathfrak{M}_m, y\mathfrak{F}) = \mathfrak{M}_m$ by Lemma 1 for every y of $\mathfrak{M}$, $\mathfrak{M} \subseteq \mathfrak{M}_m$, and $\mathfrak{M} = v_1\mathfrak{F} + \cdots + v_m\mathfrak{F}$. If $m = n$, then $(\mathfrak{M}, x\mathfrak{F}) = \mathfrak{M}$ for every x of $\mathfrak{L}$ by Lemma 1, and so $\mathfrak{M} \supseteq \mathfrak{L}$, $\mathfrak{M} = \mathfrak{L}$.

If $\mathfrak{M}$ is a subspace of $\mathfrak{L}$ and $\mathfrak{M} \neq \mathfrak{L}$, 0, we call $\mathfrak{M}$ a *proper* subspace of $\mathfrak{L}$. We then have the following result:

THEOREM 4. *Let* $\mathfrak{M}$ *be a proper subspace of a vector space* $\mathfrak{L}$ *of dimension* n *over* $\mathfrak{F}$. *Then there exists a subspace* $\mathfrak{N}$ *of* $\mathfrak{L}$ *called a* complement *of* $\mathfrak{M}$ *in* $\mathfrak{L}$ *such that* $\mathfrak{L} = \mathfrak{M} + \mathfrak{N}$.

For if $\mathfrak{L} \neq \mathfrak{M}$, there exists an element u_1 in $\mathfrak{L}$ and not in $\mathfrak{M}$. Then $(\mathfrak{M}, u_1\mathfrak{F}) = \mathfrak{M} + u_1\mathfrak{F}$ by Lemma 1. If $\mathfrak{L} \neq \mathfrak{M} + u_1\mathfrak{F}$, there exists an element u_2 in $\mathfrak{L}$ and not in $\mathfrak{M} + u_1\mathfrak{F}$, and $(\mathfrak{M} + u_1\mathfrak{F}, u_2\mathfrak{F}) = \mathfrak{M} + u_1\mathfrak{F} + u_2\mathfrak{F}$. After a finite number of steps this process must terminate, since $\mathfrak{L}$ is finite-dimensional. Then $\mathfrak{L} = \mathfrak{M} + u_1\mathfrak{F} + \cdots + u_r\mathfrak{F}$ and $\mathfrak{L} = \mathfrak{M} + \mathfrak{N}$, where $\mathfrak{N} = u_1\mathfrak{F} + \cdots + u_r\mathfrak{F}$, as desired.

Theorem 4 is equivalent to the statement that if $\mathfrak{L}$ has dimension n over $\mathfrak{F}$ and if $u_1, \ldots, u_m$ are $m < n$ linearly independent elements of $\mathfrak{L}$, then there exist elements $u_{m+1}, \ldots, u_n$ in $\mathfrak{L}$ such that $u_1, \ldots, u_n$ form a basis of $\mathfrak{L}$ over $\mathfrak{F}$.

4. Linear mappings. A homomorphism of a vector space $\mathfrak{L}$ over an integral domain $\mathfrak{J}$ into (onto) a vector space $\mathfrak{M}$ over the same ring $\mathfrak{J}$ is a module homomorphism S of $\mathfrak{L}$ into (onto) $\mathfrak{M}$ such that

$$(\alpha a)S = \alpha(aS) \tag{20}$$

for every a of $\mathfrak{L}$ and every α of $\mathfrak{J}$. A vector-space homomorphism is usually called a *linear mapping*. A vector-space isomorphism of $\mathfrak{L}$ onto $\mathfrak{M}$ is called a *non-singular* linear mapping. A homomorphism of $\mathfrak{L}$ into $\mathfrak{L}$ is called a *linear transformation* of $\mathfrak{L}$. A one-to-one linear transformation of $\mathfrak{L}$ onto $\mathfrak{L}$ is called a *non-singular linear transformation* of $\mathfrak{L}$.

The *kernel* $\mathfrak{N}$ of a linear mapping S of $\mathfrak{L}$ into $\mathfrak{M}$ is the module homomorphism kernel, that is, the set of all vectors x of $\mathfrak{L}$ such that $xS = 0$. Since

$$(\alpha x + \beta y)S = \alpha(xS) + \beta(yS) ,$$

we see that if $xS = yS = 0$, then $(\alpha x + \beta y)S = 0$. Hence $\mathfrak{N}$ is a subspace of $\mathfrak{L}$. We call $\mathfrak{N}$ the *null space* of $\mathfrak{L}$ *relative to the mapping* S.

Every linear mapping S of $\mathfrak{L}$ *into* $\mathfrak{M}$ maps $\mathfrak{L}$ *onto* an *image space* $\mathfrak{L}S \subseteq \mathfrak{M}$. The space $\mathfrak{L}S$ is called the *range* of S.

If $\mathfrak{L}$ is a finite-dimensional vector space over a field $\mathfrak{F}$, both $\mathfrak{N}$ and $\mathfrak{L}S$ have finite dimension. Indeed, if $\mathfrak{L}$ is spanned by $u_1, \ldots, u_n$, the range is spanned by $u_1S, \ldots, u_nS$. The dimension of $\mathfrak{L}S$ is called the *rank* of S, and the dimension of $\mathfrak{N}$ is called the *nullity* of S.

THEOREM 5. *Let* S *be a linear mapping of a finite-dimensional vector space* $\mathfrak{L}$ *over a field* $\mathfrak{F}$ *into a vector space* $\mathfrak{M}$ *over* $\mathfrak{F}$. *Then the dimension of* $\mathfrak{L}$ *over* $\mathfrak{F}$ *is the sum of the rank of* S *and the nullity of* S.

Indeed, Theorem 4 implies that $\mathfrak{L} = \mathfrak{N} + \mathfrak{L}_0$, where $\mathfrak{N}$ is the null space of S. It is then only necessary to show that $\mathfrak{L}_0$ and $\mathfrak{L}S$ have the same dimension. Every element x of $\mathfrak{L}$ is uniquely expressible in the form $x = y + z$, where y is in $\mathfrak{N}$ and z is in $\mathfrak{L}_0$. Then $xS = yS + zS = 0 + zS$, and so S maps $\mathfrak{L}_0$ onto $\mathfrak{L}S$. If $z_1S = z_2S$, then $(z_1 - z_2)S = 0$, $z_1 - z_2$ is in $\mathfrak{N}$ and in $\mathfrak{L}_0$, and $z_1 - z_2 = 0$. Hence S induces an isomorphism of $\mathfrak{L}_0$ and $\mathfrak{L}S$, and they have the same dimension, as desired.

EXERCISE

Prove that isomorphic spaces of finite dimension have the same dimension.

5. The space of *n*-tuples. A sequence

$$a = (\alpha_1, \ldots, \alpha_n) \tag{21}$$

of n elements α_i in a field $\mathfrak{F}$ is called an *n-tuple*. The elements α_i are called the *coordinates* of a. If $b = (\beta_1, \ldots, \beta_n)$, we define

$$a + b = (\alpha_1 + \beta_1, \ldots, \alpha_n + \beta_n) . \tag{22}$$

We also define

$$\alpha a = a\alpha = (\alpha\alpha_1, \ldots, \alpha\alpha_n) , \tag{23}$$

for every α of $\mathfrak{F}$. The set $\mathfrak{V}_n$ of all n-tuples over a field $\mathfrak{F}$ may now be shown to be a vector space of dimension n over $\mathfrak{F}$. Moreover, if e_i is the n-tuple with $\alpha_i = 1$ and $\alpha_j = 0$ for $j \neq i$, we see that

$$a = \alpha_1 e_1 + \cdots + \alpha_n e_n , \tag{24}$$

where the coefficient α_i is the unique ith coordinate of a. Hence $\mathfrak{V}_n = e_1\mathfrak{F} + \cdots + e_n\mathfrak{F}$.

THEOREM 6. *Every* n*-dimensional vector space over* $\mathfrak{F}$ *is* isomorphic to $\mathfrak{V}_n$.

For let $\mathfrak{L}$ be an n-dimensional vector space over $\mathfrak{F}$ and $\mathfrak{L} = u_1\mathfrak{F} + \cdots + u_n\mathfrak{F}$. Then every element a of $\mathfrak{L}$ may be expressed as the sum $a = \alpha_1 u_1 + \cdots + \alpha_n u_n$, where the n-tuple $(\alpha_1, \ldots, \alpha_n)$ of coefficients is unique. Then

$$a \to aS = (\alpha_1, \ldots, \alpha_n) \tag{25}$$

is a one-to-one mapping of $\mathfrak{L}$ onto $\mathfrak{V}_n$. By equations (22) and (23) we see that $(a + b)S = aS + bS$, $(\alpha a)S = \alpha(aS)$, and S is an isomorphism of $\mathfrak{L}$ and $\mathfrak{V}_n$.

EXERCISES

1. Determine the dimension of the vector space spanned by the three triples u_1, u_2, u_3 in the following cases:

(*a*) $u_1 = (1\ 1\ 1)$, $u_2 = (1\ 1\ 0)$, $u_3 = (1\ 0\ 0)$;

(*b*) $u_1 = (4\ -1\ 5)$, $u_2 = (4\ -1\ 0)$, $u_3 = (-4\ 1\ -5)$;

(*c*) $u_1 = (4\ -1\ 5)$, $u_2 = (8\ -2\ 10)$, $u_3 = (-4\ 1\ -5)$;

(*d*) $u_1 = (4\ -1\ 5)$, $u_2 = (-1\ 1\ -2)$, $u_3 = (7\ -1\ 8)$.

2. Let $\mathfrak{L}$ be the space of all vectors $(\alpha_1\ \alpha_2\ \alpha_3\ \alpha_4)$ with rational α_i. Determine the dimension of the subspace $\mathfrak{M}$ of $\mathfrak{L}$ spanned by $(1\ 1\ -1\ 0)$, $(0\ 0\ 1\ 1)$, and $(1\ 1\ 0\ 1)$ and give a basis of a complement of $\mathfrak{M}$ in $\mathfrak{L}$.

6. Matrices.

A rectangular array,

$$A = \begin{pmatrix} a_{11} & a_{12} & \cdots & a_{1n} \\ a_{21} & a_{22} & \cdots & a_{2n} \\ \cdot & \cdot & \cdots & \cdot \\ a_{m1} & a_{m2} & \cdots & a_{mn} \end{pmatrix}, \tag{26}$$

with elements a_{ij} in a field $\mathfrak{F}$, is called an $m \times n$ (read m-by-n) *rectangular matrix.* If $m = n$, we call A a *square* matrix. Notation (26) may be abbreviated by writing

$$A = (a_{ij}) \qquad (i = 1, \ldots, m;\ j = 1, \ldots, n). \tag{27}$$

The horizontal lines

$$a_i = (a_{i1}, a_{i2}, \ldots, a_{in}) \tag{28}$$

of elements of A are n-tuples, called the *rows* of A. The vertical lines

$$a^{(j)} = \begin{pmatrix} a_{ij} \\ a_{2j} \\ \cdot \\ \cdot \\ \cdot \\ a_{mj} \end{pmatrix} \tag{29}$$

are called the columns of A and are m-tuples *written vertically*. Then a_{ij} is a symbol which represents the element of A which appears in its ith row and jth column. Each a_i is a one-by-n matrix, and each $a^{(j)}$ is an m-by-one matrix.

The elements a_{ii} are called the *diagonal* elements of A, and the line $a_{11}, a_{22} \cdots$ of these elements (which ends with a_{mm} or a_{nn} according as $m \leq n$ or $m > n$) is called the *main diagonal* of A. The elements a_{ij} with $j > i$ are said to lie *above* the main diagonal, and those with $j < i$ *below* the main diagonal.

The matrix

$$A' = (\beta_{ji}), \quad \beta_{ji} = a_{ij} \qquad (j = 1, \ldots, n; i = 1, \ldots, m) \tag{30}$$

is an $n \times m$ matrix called the *transpose* of A. Each row of A' is the transpose of the corresponding column of A, and each column of A' is the transpose of the corresponding row of A. We may then say that A' is obtained from A by the operation of interchanging rows with columns. Clearly,

$$(A')' = A \,. \tag{31}$$

If A is a *square* matrix whose elements above the main diagonal are all zero, we call A an *upper triangular matrix*. When the elements below the main diagonal of A are all zero, we call A a *lower triangular matrix*. We refer to matrices of either type simply as *triangular* matrices. A triangular matrix which is both upper and lower triangular is called a *diagonal* matrix.

A diagonal matrix whose diagonal elements are all equal to an element a of $\mathfrak{F}$ is called a *scalar* matrix and is represented by the symbol aI. If $a = 1$, we call $aI = I$ the *identity* matrix. When it is desirable to indicate that the number of rows in I is n, we shall write

$$I = I_n \,. \tag{32}$$

A matrix whose elements are all zero is called a *zero* matrix. We usually use the symbol 0 to represent an arbitrary zero matrix. However, if it is desirable to indicate that 0 is an $m \times n$ zero matrix, we use the symbol

$$0_{m,\,n}\,. \tag{33}$$

A matrix A has what are called *submatrices*. If we delete $m - r$ rows and $n - s$ columns of an $m \times n$ matrix A, what remains is an $r \times s$ submatrix $M_{r,\,s}$ of A. The elements on the intersections of the $m - r$ and $n - s$ deleted rows and columns also form a submatrix $N_{m-r,\,n-s}$ of A. These two submatrices are called *complementary submatrices* of A. Of course, if $m = r$ or $n = s$, the matrix $N_{m-r,\,n-s}$ will not exist.

Each element a_{ij} of A defines a 1×1 submatrix of A. When $m > 1$ and $n > 1$, the complementary submatrix of a_{ij} is an $(m - 1) \times (n - 1)$ matrix.

Let C be an $r \times s$ submatrix of A defined by

$$C = (\gamma_{ij}), \quad \gamma_{ij} = a_{p+i,\,q+j} \qquad (i = 1, \ldots, r; j = 1, \ldots, s), \tag{34}$$

so that the row subscripts of the elements a_{ij} of C are *consecutive* integers and the column subscripts *also have this property*. Then C is called a *subblock* of A. Any matrix may be partitioned into subblocks, and we may write A as a $\rho \times \sigma$ matrix,

$$A = (A_{\lambda\mu}) \qquad (\lambda = 1, \ldots, \rho; \mu = 1, \ldots, \sigma), \tag{35}$$

whose elements $A_{\lambda\mu}$ are subblocks of A. All the subblocks $A_{\lambda 1}, A_{\lambda 2}, \ldots, A_{\lambda\sigma}$ must have the same number of rows, and all the subblocks $A_{1\mu}, A_{2\mu}, \ldots, A_{\rho\mu}$ must have the same number of columns.

We shall use the notation

$$A = \begin{pmatrix} I_r & 0 \\ 0 & 0 \end{pmatrix} \tag{36}$$

later. This is a partitioning of A into a subblock I_r which is an identity matrix of r rows, a subblock $0_{r,\,n-r}$ to the right of I_r, a subblock $0_{m-r,\,r}$ below I_r, and $0_{m-r,\,n-r}$ for the remaining subblock. When $m = r$, this matrix must be interpreted as being the matrix

$$(I_r \quad 0_{r,\,n-r})\,;$$

and when $n = r$, it becomes

$$\begin{pmatrix} I_r \\ 0_{m-r,\,r} \end{pmatrix}.$$

If $m = n = r$, the matrix of (36) becomes

$$A = I_r .$$

If a matrix A has the form

$$(37)\qquad A = \begin{pmatrix} A_1 & 0 & \cdots & 0 \\ 0 & A_2 & \cdots & 0 \\ \cdot & \cdot & \cdots & 0 \\ 0 & 0 & \cdots & A_t \end{pmatrix},$$

we shall write

$$(38)\qquad A = \text{diag}\,\{A_1, \ldots, A_t\} .$$

The dimensions of the matrices A_i will then clearly determine the dimension of the matrix A of equation (37). Note that a diagonal matrix then has the form

$$(39)\qquad D = \text{diag}\,\{\alpha_1, \ldots, \alpha_n\} ,$$

where $\alpha_1, \ldots, \alpha_n$ are the diagonal elements of D.

7. The vector space $\mathfrak{M}_{m,n}$. The *sum* of two $m \times n$ matrices,

$$(40)\qquad A = (\alpha_{ij}), \quad B = (\beta_{ij}) \qquad (i = 1, \ldots, m; j = 1, \ldots, n),$$

is defined to be the matrix

$$(41)\qquad A + B = (\gamma_{ij}), \; \gamma_{ij} = \alpha_{ij} + \beta_{ij} \quad (i = 1, \ldots, m; j = 1, \ldots, n)$$

obtained by adding corresponding elements of A and B. The *scalar product* of a matrix A by an element α of F is defined by

$$(42)\qquad \alpha A = (\delta_{ij}), \quad \delta_{ij} = \alpha\alpha_{ij} \qquad (i = 1, \ldots, m; j = 1, \ldots, n).$$

It is now easy to see that the set

$$(43)\qquad \mathfrak{M}_{m,n}$$

of all $m \times n$ matrices is an mn-dimensional vector space over $\mathfrak{F}$. Indeed, if E_{ij} is the $m \times n$ matrix with unity in the ith row and jth column and zeros everywhere else, we see that every $m \times n$ matrix A of array (26) is uniquely expressible in the form

$$(44)\qquad A = \sum_{i=1,\ldots,m}^{j=1,\ldots,n} \alpha_{ij}E_{ij} .$$

Hence the mn matrices E_{ij} form a basis of $\mathfrak{M}_{m,n}$ over $\mathfrak{F}$.

The *zero* element of $\mathfrak{M}_{mn}$ is the $m \times n$ zero matrix. If $A = (\alpha_{ij})$, then

$-A = (\beta_{ij})$, where $\beta_{ij} = -\alpha_{ij}$. A scalar matrix αI is actually the scalar product of I by α.

A matrix A is called a *symmetric* matrix if $A = A'$. The set of all symmetric n-rowed square matrices forms a subspace $\mathfrak{S}_n$ of $\mathfrak{M}_n = \mathfrak{M}_{n,n}$. A matrix A is called a *skew matrix* if $A' = -A$. The set of all skew n-rowed square matrices also forms a subspace $\mathfrak{T}_n$ of $\mathfrak{M}_n$. Every matrix A in $\mathfrak{M}_n$ over a field $\mathfrak{F}$ of characteristic not 2 is uniquely expressible in the form

$$A = S + T, \tag{45}$$

where S is in $\mathfrak{S}_n$ and T is in $\mathfrak{T}_n$. Indeed, $2S = A + A'$ and $2T = A - A'$.

8. The matrix of a linear mapping. Let $\mathfrak{L}$ be an m-dimensional vector space over a field $\mathfrak{F}$, $\mathfrak{L}'$ be an n-dimensional vector space over $\mathfrak{F}$, and S be a linear mapping of $\mathfrak{L}$ into $\mathfrak{L}'$. Assume that

$$\mathfrak{L} = u_1\mathfrak{F} + \cdots + u_m\mathfrak{F}, \qquad \mathfrak{L}' = v_1\mathfrak{F} + \cdots + v_n\mathfrak{F}. \tag{46}$$

Then

$$u_iS = \alpha_{i1}v_1 + \cdots + \alpha_{in}v_n \qquad (i = 1, \ldots, m). \tag{47}$$

If $x = \xi_1u_1 + \cdots + \xi_mu_m$ is any element of $\mathfrak{L}$, we have $xS = \xi_1(u_1S) + \cdots + \xi_m(u_mS)$, and we use equation (47) to obtain

$$xS = \eta_1v_1 + \cdots + \eta_nv_n, \tag{48}$$

where

$$\eta_j = \sum_{i=1}^{m} \xi_i\alpha_{ij}. \tag{49}$$

The matrix $A = (\alpha_{ij})$ is an $m \times n$ matrix, called the *matrix of* S *relative to the basis* $u_1, \ldots, u_m$ *of* $\mathfrak{L}$ *and the basis* $v_1, \ldots, v_n$ *of* $\mathfrak{L}'$. We shall study the effect on A of a change of basis later.

We now define the *product* of matrices. Let $\mathfrak{L} = u_1\mathfrak{F} + \cdots + u_m\mathfrak{F}$, $\mathfrak{L}' = v_1\mathfrak{F} + \cdots + v_n\mathfrak{F}$, and $\mathfrak{L}'' = w_1\mathfrak{F} + \cdots + w_q\mathfrak{F}$ and suppose that S is a linear mapping of $\mathfrak{L}$ into $\mathfrak{L}'$ and T is a linear mapping of $\mathfrak{L}'$ into $\mathfrak{L}''$. Then we have already seen that

$$x \to x(ST) = (xS)T \tag{50}$$

is a mapping ST of $\mathfrak{L}$ into $\mathfrak{L}''$, called the *product* of S and T. But $(\alpha x + \beta y)(ST) = [(\alpha x + \beta y)S]T = [\alpha(xS) + \beta(yS)]T = \alpha x(ST) + \beta y(ST)$, and so ST is a *linear* mapping of $\mathfrak{L}$ into $\mathfrak{L}''$.

Let $A = (\alpha_{ij})$ be the $m \times n$ matrix of S, as in equation (49), and $B = (\beta_{jk})$ be the $n \times q$ matrix of T, defined by

$$(51) \qquad y = \eta_1 v_1 + \cdots + \eta_m v_m \rightarrow yT = \zeta_1 w_1 + \cdots + \zeta_q w_q ,$$

where

$$(52) \qquad \zeta_k = \sum_{j=1}^{m} \eta_j \beta_{jk} \qquad (k = 1, \ldots , q) .$$

Then

$$x\,(ST) = \sum_{i,\, j,\, k} (\xi_i \alpha_{ij} \beta_{jk})\, w_k .$$

Hence the matrix C of ST with respect to the basis $u_1, \ldots , u_m$ of $\mathfrak{L}$ and $w_1, \ldots , w_q$ of L'' is given by

$$(53) \quad C = (\gamma_{ik}) , \qquad \gamma_{ik} = \sum_{j=1}^{n} \alpha_{ij} \beta_{jk} \quad (i = 1, \ldots , m;\ k = 1, \ldots , q) .$$

We define C to be the *product* AB. It is an $m \times q$ matrix which is the product of the $m \times n$ matrix A and the $n \times q$ matrix B. It is defined for every $m \times n$ matrix A and $n \times q$ matrix B, and we have defined it so that the following property holds:

LEMMA 2. *The matrix of a product of linear mappings is the product of the matrices of the factors.*

We also have the following property:

LEMMA 3. *Matrix multiplication is associative.*

For let S, T, and U be linear mappings such that ST and TU are defined. Then we have seen that $S(TU) = (ST)U$ and, indeed, $x[(ST)U] = x[S(TU)] = [(xS)T]U$. It follows that if A is the matrix of S, B of T, and C of U, then AB is the matrix of ST, BC of TU, $A(BC)$ of $S(TU)$, and $(AB)C$ of $(ST)U$. Since $(ST)U = S(TU)$, we have $A(BC) = (AB)C$.

We proceed to interpret equation (49) in terms of the concept of matrix product. Every element x of $\mathfrak{L} = u_1\mathfrak{F} + \cdots + u_m\mathfrak{F}$ determines a unique attached coordinate m-tuple $\underline{x} = (\xi_1, \ldots , \xi_m)$. Let $\mathfrak{L}' = v_1\mathfrak{F} + \cdots + v_n\mathfrak{F}$. Then every element y of $\mathfrak{L}'$ has a unique attached coordinate n-tuple $\underline{y} = (\eta_1, \ldots , \eta_n)$. Equation (49) then states that if S is a linear mapping of $\mathfrak{L}$ into $\mathfrak{L}'$, the coordinate vector of xS is determined in terms of that of x by

$$(54) \qquad \underline{xS} = \underline{x}A ,$$

where A is the matrix of S with respect to the given basis.

We may now derive an interpretation of Theorem 5. Let S map $\mathfrak{L}$ of dimension m over $\mathfrak{F}$ into $\mathfrak{L}'$ of dimension n over $\mathfrak{F}$. Suppose that S has rank r. Then

$$\mathfrak{L} = \mathfrak{N} + \mathfrak{L}_0 ,$$

where $\mathfrak{N}$ is the null space of S and S maps $\mathfrak{L}_0$ isomorphically onto the subspace $\mathfrak{L}S$ of S. We may then select a basis $u_1, \ldots, u_r$ of $\mathfrak{L}_0$ and a complementary basis $u_{r+1}, \ldots, u_m$ of $\mathfrak{N}$ such that $\mathfrak{L} = u_1\mathfrak{F} + \cdots + u_m\mathfrak{F}$. Similarly, we may select the elements $v_1 = u_1S, \ldots, v_r = u_rS$ to be a basis of $\mathfrak{L}S$, and select a complementary basis $v_{r+1}, \ldots, v_n$ so that $\mathfrak{L}' = v_1\mathfrak{F} + \cdots + v_n\mathfrak{F}$. Then $u_iS = v_i$ for $i = 1, \ldots, r$, and $u_kS = 0$ for $k = r + 1, \ldots, m$. We have proved the following result:

THEOREM 7. *Let* S *be a linear mapping of* $\mathfrak{L}$ *into* $\mathfrak{L}'$ *and let* r *be the rank of* S. *Then* $\mathfrak{L}$ *and* $\mathfrak{L}'$ *have bases such that the matrix of* S *with respect to these bases is given by*

$$\text{(55)} \qquad A = \begin{pmatrix} I_r & 0 \\ 0 & 0 \end{pmatrix} ,$$

where I_r *is the* r*-rowed identity matrix.*

We close this section with the statement of the following elementary properties:

LEMMA 4. *Let* A *be an* m × n *matrix,* B *and* C *be* n × q *matrices. Then* A(B + C) = AB + AC. *Similarly,* (B + C)A = BA + CA *if* B *and* C *are* m × n *matrices and* A *is an* n × q *matrix.*

LEMMA 5. *Let* A *be an* m × n *matrix and* B *be an* n × q *matrix. Then* (AB)′ = B′A′.

EXERCISES

1. Show that matrix multiplication is not commutative even when AB and BA both exist.

2. The *trace* of a square matrix A is defined to be the sum $\tau(A)$ of the diagonal elements of A. Show that if A is an $m \times n$ matrix and B is an $n \times m$ matrix, the formula $\tau(AB) = \tau(BA)$ holds.

9. The sign of a permutation. Let $\mathfrak{E}$ be the ring of all ordinary integers and $\mathfrak{J} = \mathfrak{E}[x_1, \ldots, x_n]$ be the ring of all polynomials in n independent indeterminates $x_1, \ldots, x_n$ over $\mathfrak{E}$. If

$$\text{(56)} \qquad f(x) = f(x_1, \ldots, x_n)$$

is any polynomial in $x_1, \ldots, x_n$ and

$$\text{(57)} \qquad P = \begin{pmatrix} 1 & 2 & \cdots & n \\ i_1 & i_2 & \cdots & i_n \end{pmatrix} ,$$

we define $x = (x_1, \ldots, x_n)$, $xP = (x_{i_1}, \ldots, x_{i_n})$, and

(58) $$[f(x)]P = f(xP) = f(x_{i_1}, \ldots, x_{i_n}) .$$

Thus $[f(x)]P$ is the result of replacing x_1 by x_{i_1}, x_2 by $x_{i_2}, \ldots, x_n$ by x_{i_n} in $f(x)$.

It should now be clear that the mapping

(59) $$f(x) \rightarrow f(xP)$$

is an automorphism of $\mathfrak{J}$ over $\mathfrak{E}$ and that the set Σ_n of all permutations P determines a subgroup of the automorphism group over $\mathfrak{E}$ (that is, of the automorphisms of $\mathfrak{J}$ leaving $\mathfrak{E}$ fixed) of $\mathfrak{J}$. Hence

(60) $$[af(x)]P = a[f(x)P]$$

for every a of $\mathfrak{E}$, and

(61) $$[f(x)g(x)]P = [f(x)P] \cdot [g(x)P] = f(xP)g(xP) .$$

Also

(62) $$[f(x)](PQ) = [f(xP)]Q = f[x(PQ)] .$$

THEOREM 8. *Let* $h(x) = (x_1 - x_2)(x_1 - x_3) \cdots (x_1 - x_n)(x_2 - x_3)$ $\cdots (x_{n-1} - x_n)$. *Then* $h(xP) = \sigma(P)h(x)$, *where* $\sigma(P) = \pm 1$ *is called the sign of* P.

A permutation will be called *even* if $\sigma(P) = 1$ and *odd* if $\sigma(P) = -1$. Every cycle may be expressed as the product

(63) $$(1\ 2 \ldots r) = (12)(23) \cdots (r - 1\ r)$$

of transpositions. Then every permutation P is expressible as a product of transpositions. We shall prove that

(64) $$h(xT) = -h(x)$$

for any transposition T. Theorem 8 will then follow from equations (61) and (62).

To prove equation (64), we observe that

$$h(x) = \prod_{i<j} h_{ij}(x) ,$$

where $h_{ij}(x) = x_i - x_j$. Let $T = (rs)$, so that $[h_{rs}(x)]T = -h_{rs}(x)$. The factors $x_i - x_j$ with $i \neq r, s$ and $j \neq r, s$ are unaltered by T. The remaining factors may be grouped into pairs of factors involving r and s such that the two factors are either simply interchanged by T or are interchanged and *both* changed in sign. Hence $h(x) = (x_r - x_s)k(x)$, where $[k(x)]T = k(x)$ and $[h(x)]T = -h(x)$, as desired.

The set of all even permutations forms a subgroup Γ_n of Σ_n. We call Γ_n the *alternating group*. It has index 2 in Σ_n, since, if P is odd, the product $P(12)$ is even, $\Sigma_n = \Gamma_n \cup \Gamma_n(12)$. Hence Γ_n is a normal subgroup of Σ_n.

10. Determinants. Let A be an $n \times n$ matrix,

$$A = (a_{ij}) \qquad (i, j = 1, \ldots, n). \tag{65}$$

We consider the product

$$f = a_{11} \cdots a_{nn} \tag{66}$$

of the diagonal elements of A. Write

$$fP = a_{1i_1} \cdots a_{ni_n}, \tag{67}$$

where P is any permutation (57). Then fP has one factor in every row and every column of A. Moreover, every product of n factors with exactly one factor in each row and column of A is a product fP. We form the sum

$$|A| = \sum_{P \text{ in } \Sigma_n} \sigma(P)(fP). \tag{68}$$

It is a sum of $n!$ terms, called the *determinant* of the matrix A. This function on $M_{n,n}$ to $\mathfrak{F}$ has the following properties:

LEMMA 6. *The determinant of a matrix* A *is equal to the determinant of its transpose* A$'$.

LEMMA 7. *Let* B *be obtained from* A *by interchanging two rows (columns) of* A. *Then* $|B| = -|A|$.

LEMMA 8. *Let* B *be obtained from* A *by multiplying any row (column) of* A *by* a *in* F. *Then* $|B| = a|A|$.

LEMMA 9. *Let* B *be obtained from* A *by adding a multiple of the* j*th row (column) of* A *to the* i*th row (column) of* A, *where* $i \neq j$. *Then* $|B| = |A|$.

LEMMA 10. *Let* A *have two equal rows (columns). Then* $|A| = 0$.

LEMMA 11. *Let* A *and* B *be* n*-rowed square matrices. Then* $|AB| = |A| \cdot |B|$.

Every r-rowed square submatrix of an $m \times n$ matrix A has a determinant called an r-rowed *minor* of A. Every element a_{ij} of an n-rowed square matrix A has a complementary submatrix A_{ij} whose determinant is an $(n-1)$-rowed *minor* of A. Define

$$\Delta_{ij} = (-1)^{i+j}|A_{ji}| \qquad (i, j = 1, \ldots, n) \tag{69}$$

and call this element the *cofactor* of a_{ij}. Then we have the properties stated as follows:

LEMMA 12. *The determinant* $|A|$ *has the expansions*

(70) $$|A| = \sum_{j=1}^{n} a_{ij}\Delta_{ji} = \sum_{j=1}^{n} \Delta_{ij} a_{ji} \qquad (i = 1, \ldots, n) .$$

Also

(71) $$\sum_{j=1}^{n} a_{ij}\Delta_{jk} = \sum_{j=1}^{n} \Delta_{ij} a_{jk} = 0 \quad (i \neq k;\ i, k = 1, \ldots, n) .$$

We shall not try to derive these properties of matrices. Proofs may be found in L. E. Dickson's *New First Course in the Theory of Equations* and in many other elementary texts. A derivation using the first expansion of equation (70) for $i = 1$ as the definition of $|A|$ may be found in the author's *College Algebra.* The proofs of all properties except that of Lemma 10 are valid for arbitrary fields. Lemma 10 requires a special argument when $\mathfrak{F}$ has characteristic 2, and this argument may be found on page 53 of the author's *Modern Higher Algebra.*

EXERCISES

1. Use Lemma 12 to determine the determinant of any n-rowed triangular matrix $A = (a_{ij})$.

2. Use Lemmas 8 and 9 to reduce the following matrices A to triangular form, and give the value of $|A|$ in each case:

$$(a)\ A = \begin{pmatrix} 1 & -1 & 2 \\ 3 & -2 & 4 \\ 0 & 2 & -3 \end{pmatrix}, \qquad (f)\ A = \begin{pmatrix} 2 & 1 & 3 \\ 4 & -11 & 0 \\ -4 & 2 & 1 \end{pmatrix},$$

$$(b)\ A = \begin{pmatrix} 4 & 2 & -2 \\ 2 & 1 & 4 \\ -2 & 4 & -8 \end{pmatrix}, \qquad (g)\ A = \begin{pmatrix} 3 & -1 & -2 \\ 4 & 0 & 1 \\ 2 & 5 & 3 \end{pmatrix},$$

$$(c)\ A = \begin{pmatrix} 2 & -1 & 0 & 1 \\ -3 & 0 & 1 & -2 \\ 1 & 1 & -1 & 1 \\ 2 & -1 & 5 & 0 \end{pmatrix}, \qquad (h)\ A = \begin{pmatrix} 1 & 0 & -1 & 2 \\ 2 & 1 & -2 & 3 \\ 4 & 3 & 0 & 6 \\ -1 & 1 & 4 & 3 \end{pmatrix},$$

$$(d)\ A = \begin{pmatrix} -4 & 1 & 0 & 1 \\ -2 & 0 & 2 & 1 \\ 0 & 2 & -3 & 0 \\ -7 & 2 & 0 & 2 \end{pmatrix}, \qquad (i)\ A = \begin{pmatrix} 1 & 0 & -1 & 1 \\ 0 & -1 & 2 & 1 \\ 1 & 0 & -1 & 2 \\ 2 & 1 & -1 & 0 \end{pmatrix},$$

$$(e)\ A = \begin{pmatrix} 1 & 2 & 0 & -1 \\ 2 & 3 & -1 & 0 \\ 0 & -1 & 2 & 4 \\ -1 & 0 & 4 & -1 \end{pmatrix}, \qquad (j)\ A = \begin{pmatrix} 1 & 2 & -3 & 4 \\ 1 & 0 & -1 & 9 \\ 3 & -1 & 1 & 0 \\ -1 & 1 & 0 & 2 \end{pmatrix}.$$

11. Non-singular matrices. If A is any square matrix, we define the *adjoint* of A to be the matrix

$$\text{adj } A = (\Delta_{ij}) \qquad (i, j = 1, \ldots, n), \tag{72}$$

where the Δ_{ij} are the cofactors of the elements of A. Then Lemma 12 is equivalent to the equation

$$A\,(\text{adj } A) = (\text{adj } A)A = |A|I\,, \tag{73}$$

where I is the n-rowed identity matrix. If $|A| \neq 0$, then A has a unique inverse,

$$A^{-1} = |A|^{-1}\,(\text{adj } A)\,, \tag{74}$$

such that

$$AA^{-1} = A^{-1}A = I\,. \tag{75}$$

Conversely, let A^{-1} exist. Then $AA^{-1} = I$ and $|AA^{-1}| = |A|\,|A^{-1}| = |I| = 1$ by Lemma 11. Then $|A| \neq 0$.

LEMMA 13. *A square matrix* A *has an inverse and is called a* non-singular matrix *if and only if* $|\text{A}| \neq 0$.

The set of all non-singular $n \times n$ matrices forms a group with respect to matrix multiplication. Note that

$$(AB)^{-1} = B^{-1}A^{-1}\,. \tag{76}$$

A linear transformation S of a finite-dimensional vector space $\mathfrak{L}$ over F is said to be non-singular if S is an automorphism over $\mathfrak{F}$ of $\mathfrak{L}$. Then the mapping $xS \to x$ is S^{-1}.

THEOREM 9. *A linear transformation* S *is non-singular if and only if its matrix* A *is non-singular.*

For if A is non-singular, the transformation T with matrix A^{-1} has the property that $\underline{x}(\underline{ST}) = \underline{xS}A^{-1} = (xA)A^{-1} = \underline{x}I = \underline{x}$, and so $x(ST) = x$ and ST is the identity transformation. Then S and T must both be one-to-one mappings of $\mathfrak{L}$ into $\mathfrak{L}$. Conversely, let S be non-singular and A be its matrix. Then S^{-1} must exist and has a matrix B such that $AB = I$. Hence A is non-singular.

12. The effect of a change of basis. Let $\mathfrak{L} = u_1\mathfrak{F} + \cdots + u_m\mathfrak{F} = v_1\mathfrak{F} + \cdots + v_m\mathfrak{F}$. Then

$$u_i = \sum_{j=1}^{m} \pi_{ij}\, v_j,\; v_j = \sum_{k=1}^{m} \rho_{jk} u_k\,, \tag{77}$$

and hence

$$u_i = \sum_{k=1}^{m} \sum_{j=1}^{m} (\pi_{ij}\rho_{jk})\, u_k . \tag{78}$$

It follows that if

$$P = (\pi_{ij}), \quad R = (\rho_{jk}) \quad (i, j, k = 1, \ldots, m), \tag{79}$$

then

$$PR = I . \tag{80}$$

If $x = \xi_1 u_1 + \cdots + \xi_m u_m$ so that the vector x has the coefficient m-tuple $\underline{x} = (\xi_1, \ldots, \ldots, \xi_n)$, then

$$x = \eta_1 v_1 + \cdots + \eta_m v_m = \sum_{i,\, j=1}^{m} (\xi_i \pi_{ij})\, v_j .$$

It follows that *a change of basis with matrix P* replaces the coordinate vector $\underline{x}$ by

$$\underline{\underline{x}} = \underline{x}P . \tag{81}$$

THEOREM 10. *Let* $\mathfrak{L} = u_1\mathfrak{F} + \cdots + u_m\mathfrak{F}$, $\mathfrak{L}' = u_1'\mathfrak{F} + \cdots + u\mathfrak{F}_n'$, *and* S *be a* linear *mapping of* $\mathfrak{L}$ *into* $\mathfrak{L}'$ *with matrix* A. *Then a change of basis of* $\mathfrak{L}$ *with matrix* P *and a change of basis of* $\mathfrak{L}'$ *with matrix* Q *replaces* A *by* $P^{-1}AQ$.

For our hypothesis states that $\underline{xS} = \underline{x}A$. It also introduces the coordinate vector $\underline{\underline{x}} = \underline{x}P$ for all x of $\mathfrak{L}$ and the coordinate vector $\underline{\underline{x}}' = \underline{x}'Q$ for all x' of $\mathfrak{L}'$. Then $\underline{\underline{xS}} = \underline{xSQ} = \underline{x}AQ = \underline{\underline{x}}P^{-1}AQ$, as desired.

Two $m \times n$ matrices A and B are said to be *equivalent in* $\mathfrak{F}$, and we write $A \simeq B$, if there exist non-singular matrices P and Q such that $PAQ = B$. Theorem 10 implies that $A \simeq B$ if and only if A and B are the matrices of the same linear mapping S with respect to some pair of bases. Since the rank of S has been defined independently of A, we may define it to be the rank of A. Combining this with Theorem 7, we have the following result:

THEOREM 11. *Two* $m \times n$ *matrices are equivalent in* $\mathfrak{F}$ *if and only if they have the same rank. Every matrix of rank* r *is equivalent in* $\mathfrak{F}$ *to*

$$\begin{pmatrix} I_r & 0 \\ 0 & 0 \end{pmatrix} . \tag{82}$$

13. Elementary transformations over $\mathfrak{J}$. Let A be an $m \times n$ matrix with elements in an integral domain $\mathfrak{J}$. Then we define

$$R_{i,\,\alpha}(A) \tag{83}$$

to be the $m \times n$ matrix obtained from A by multiplying the ith row of A by a *unit* α of $\mathfrak{J}$. We also define

$$R_{i,\,j,\,\lambda}(A) \tag{84}$$

to be the matrix obtained from A by adding the product of the jth row of A by any element λ of $\mathfrak{J}$ to the ith row of A. The mappings $A \rightarrow R_{i,\,\alpha}(A)$ and $A \rightarrow R_{i,\,j,\,\lambda}(A)$ are called the *elementary row transformations*. Note that $R_{i,\,1}(A) = R_{i,\,j,\,0}(A) = A$, so that the identity mapping is an elementary row transformation. Also, if $\alpha\beta = 1$, then $R_{i,\,\beta}[R_{i,\,\alpha}(A)] = A$. Since $R_{i,\,j,\,-\lambda}[R_{i,\,j,\,\lambda}(A)] = A$, we see that the inverse of an elementary row transformation is also an elementary row transformation.

The column transformations

$$A \rightarrow C_{i,\,\alpha}(A), \qquad A \rightarrow C_{i,\,j,\,\lambda}(A) \tag{85}$$

are defined similarly. It should be evident that

$$[R_{i,\,\alpha}(A)]' = C_{i,\,\alpha}(A'), \qquad [R_{i,\,j,\,\lambda}(A)]' = C_{i,\,j,\,\lambda}(A') \,. \tag{86}$$

Any finite product of elementary row transformations is a transformation on the set $\mathfrak{M}$ of all $m \times n$ matrices over $\mathfrak{J}$, called a *row equivalence transformation*. Any finite product of elementary column transformations is a transformation on $\mathfrak{M}$ called a *column equivalence transformation*. The row equivalence transformations on $\mathfrak{M}$ then form a group $\mathfrak{R}(\mathfrak{M})$, and the column equivalence transformations form a group $\mathfrak{C}(\mathfrak{M})$. The elements of $\mathfrak{R}(\mathfrak{M})$ commute with those of $\mathfrak{C}(\mathfrak{M})$, and the row and column equivalence transformations generate a group called the *equivalence group* over $\mathfrak{J}$. Thus we say that A is equivalent to B and write $A \cong B$ if A can be carried into B by a finite number of elementary row and column transformations. Since a field $\mathfrak{F}$ is also an integral domain, it will be necessary later to show that this new definition of equivalence in the field case is equivalent to the old.

The following result is quite trivial:

LEMMA 14. *Let* $A_i = (\alpha_{ij})$, $B = (\beta_{jk})$ *where* $i = 1, \ldots, m$; $j = 1, \ldots, n$; $k = 1, \ldots, q$, *so that the* j*th row of* B *is* $b_j = (\beta_{j1}, \ldots, \beta_{jq})$. *Then the* i*th row of* AB *is* $\alpha_{i1}b_1 + \cdots + \alpha_{in}b_n$. *Also the* j*th column of* A *is*

$$a^{(j)} = \begin{pmatrix} \alpha_{1j} \\ \cdot \\ \cdot \\ \cdot \\ \alpha_{mj} \end{pmatrix}, \tag{87}$$

and the k*th column of* AB *is* $a^{(1)}\beta_{1k} + \cdots + a^{(n)}\beta_{nk}$.

As a consequence of Lemma 14 we have

LEMMA 15. *Let* R *be a row equivalence transformation. Then* $R(A) \cdot B = R(AB)$. *If* C *is a column equivalence transformation, then* $A \cdot C(B) = C(AB)$.

It suffices to prove this result for elementary transformations. We first let $R = R_{i,\alpha}$. The tth row of $R_{i,\alpha}(A)$ is that of A and the tth row of $R_{i,\alpha}(AB)$ is that of AB for $t \neq i$. It follows that the tth row of $R_{i,\alpha}(A)B$ coincides with that of $R_{i,\alpha}(AB)$. The ith row of $R_{i,\alpha}(AB)$ is

$$\alpha \sum_{j=1}^{m} \alpha_{ij} b_j = \sum_{j=1}^{n} (\alpha\alpha_{ij})\, b_j ,$$

and this is the ith row of $R_{i,\alpha}(A)B$. In exactly the same way we need only compare the ith row of $R_{i,j,\lambda}(AB)$ with that of $[R_{i,j,\lambda}(A)]B$. The former is

$$\Sigma\alpha_{ik}b_k + \lambda\Sigma\alpha_{jk}b_k = \Sigma(\alpha_{ik} + \lambda\alpha_{jk})b_k ,$$

and our result is proved. The corresponding property for column transformations follows from equations (86).

It should now be clear that $R_{i,\alpha}(A)$ is the product

$$R_{i,\alpha}(A) = D_{i,\alpha}A , \tag{88}$$

where $D_{i,\alpha}$ is the matrix $R_{i,\alpha}(I_m)$. Similarly,

$$R_{i,j,\lambda}(A) = D_{i,j,\lambda}A , \tag{89}$$

where $D_{i,j,\lambda} = R_{i,j,\lambda}(I_m)$. The matrices $D_{i,\alpha}$ and $D_{i,j,\lambda}$ are called *elementary transformation* matrices. Any finite product of elementary transformation matrices is called an *elementary* matrix. Thus we have the following result:

LEMMA 16. *An* $m \times n$ *matrix* A *with elements in an integral domain* $\mathfrak{J}$ *is equivalent in* $\mathfrak{J}$ *to an* $m \times n$ *matrix* B *with elements in* $\mathfrak{J}$ *if and only if there exist elementary matrices* P *and* Q *such that* $PAQ = B$.

We note that $D_{i,\alpha} = D_{i,\beta}^{-1}$ if $\alpha\beta = 1$ and that $D_{i,j,-\lambda} = D_{i,j,\lambda}^{-1}$. If

$P = D_1 \cdots D_t$ for elementary transformation matrices D_i, we have $P^{-1} = D_t^{-1} \cdots D_1^{-1}$. Also $|PP^{-1}| = |P|\,|P^{-1}| = 1$, and we have the following result:

LEMMA 17. *Every elementary matrix has an inverse, and its determinant is a unit of* $\mathfrak{J}$.

If A is an $m \times n$ matrix with elements in $\mathfrak{J}$, the k-rowed minors of A are elements in $\mathfrak{J}$. Define

$$\Delta_k(A)$$

to be the ideal of $\mathfrak{J}$ spanned by these k-rowed minors. Here $k = 1, \ldots, \mu$, where μ is the lesser of m and n. Clearly, $\Delta_k(A) = 0$ if and only if all k-rowed minors of A are zero.

THEOREM 12. *Let* A *and* B *be* m $\times$ n *matrices with elements in* $\mathfrak{J}$ *such that* A *is equivalent in* $\mathfrak{J}$ *to* B. *Then* $\Delta_k(A) = \Delta_k(B)$ *for every* k.

It is sufficient to derive this property for the case where B is obtained from A by a single elementary row transformation. When $B = R_{i,\alpha}(A)$, the k-rowed minors of B which do not involve its ith row coincide with those of A and are in $\Delta_k(A)$. By Lemma 8 the minors d_k which do involve the ith row are replaced by αd_k, which is in $\Delta_k(A)$. Hence $\Delta_k(B) \subseteq \Delta_k(A)$. However, $A = R_{i,\beta}(B)$, where $\beta = \alpha^{-1}$, and so $\Delta_k(A) \subseteq \Delta_k(B)$ and $\Delta_k(A) = \Delta_k(B)$.

Assume now that $B = R_{i,j,\lambda}(A)$. Then by Lemma 9 the only minors of B which are altered in value are those k-rowed minors d which have a row which is a part of the ith row of A but do not have a row which is a part of the jth row of A. Let d be such a minor and $\bar{d}$ be the corresponding minor of B. Call the i row that row of d which is a part of the ith row of A. Expand $\bar{d}$ according to the i row and see that $\bar{d} = d \pm \lambda d_0$, where d_0 is either a k-rowed minor of A or the result of permuting the rows of a k-rowed minor of A. Then $\bar{d}$ is in $\Delta_k(A)$, and so again $\Delta_k(B) \subseteq \Delta_k(A)$. Since $A = R_{i,j,-\lambda}(B)$, we have $\Delta_k(A) \subseteq \Delta_k(B)$ and $\Delta_k(A) = \Delta_k(B)$. This completes our proof.

We shall close our general remarks on equivalence in an integral domain with the following property:

THEOREM 13. *Let* B *be obtained from* A *by permutations of the rows and (or) columns of* A. *Then* B *is equivalent to* A.

It suffices to show that the matrix B obtained by interchanging the ith and jth rows of A is equivalent to A. This follows from the fact that

$$B = D_{i,j,-1} D_{j,-1} D_{j,i,-1} D_{i,j,1} A\,.$$

14. Equivalence in $\mathfrak{F}$ and determinantal rank. Let us now consider any $m \times n$ matrix A with elements in a field $\mathfrak{F}$. The non-zero elements of $\mathfrak{F}$

are its units, and so the operation of multiplying any row of A by any non-zero element of $\mathfrak{F}$ is an elementary transformation. Let $A \neq 0$ so that A has a non-zero element. Permute the rows and columns of A so that this element is α_{11}. Multiply the first row of the resulting matrix by α_{11}^{-1} and obtain a matrix $A_{11} \cong A$ such that $A_{11} = (\beta_{ij})$ with $\beta_{11} = 1$. Subtract β_{i1} times the first row from the ith row for $i = 2, \ldots, m$ and then β_{1j} times the first column from the jth column for $j = 2, \ldots, n$. The result is a matrix of the form

$$\begin{pmatrix} 1 & 0 \\ 0 & A_1 \end{pmatrix},$$

where A_1 is an $(m - 1) \times (n - 1)$ matrix. After, at most, $m - 1$ or $n - 1$ such operations, we see that

$$PAQ = \begin{pmatrix} I_r & 0 \\ 0 & 0 \end{pmatrix}, \tag{90}$$

where P and Q are elementary matrices. By Theorem 11 the integer r is the rank of A. We now have the following conclusion:

THEOREM 14. *A matrix* P *is elementary if and only if* P *is non-singular.*

For let A be non-singular. Then equation (90) implies that there exist elementary matrices P and Q such that $PAQ = I$. Then $A = P^{-1}Q^{-1}$ is elementary. The converse is trivial.

Theorem 14 implies that when $\mathfrak{J} = \mathfrak{F}$ is a field, the definition of equivalence in terms of non-singular matrices and the definition in terms of elementary transformations are equivalent. We may also give a determinantal evaluation of the rank of a matrix as follows:

THEOREM 15. *An* m $\times$ n *matrix* A *has rank* r *if and only if* A *has an* r*-rowed non-zero minor and all* (r + 1)*-rowed minors of* A *are zero.*

For the matrix $PAQ = B$ of equation (90) clearly has $\Delta_k(B) = (1)$ for $k = 1, \ldots, r$ and $\Delta_k(B) = 0$ for $k > r$. By Theorem 12 we see that $\Delta_k(A) = (1)$ for $k = 1, \ldots, r$, and A must have an r-rowed non-zero minor, $\Delta_k(A) = 0$ for $k = r + 1$, all $(r + 1)$-rowed minors of A are zero. Conversely, if A has an r-rowed non-zero minor and all $(r + 1)$-rowed minors of A are zeros, we have $\Delta_r(A) = (1)$, $\Delta_{r+1}(A) = 0$, and r must be the rank.

The rank of a matrix is computed most easily by the use of elementary transformations, but it is not necessary to carry the matrix into the form (90). Indeed, we see that if A is the matrix of a linear mapping S of a space $\mathfrak{L} = u_1\mathfrak{F} + \cdots + u_m\mathfrak{F}$ into $\mathfrak{L}' = v_1\mathfrak{F} + \cdots + v_n\mathfrak{F}$, then $\underline{u_iS}$ is actually the ith row of A. Thus the m rows of the matrix A span an m-tuple representation of the image space $\mathfrak{L}S$. It follows that there exist r of the rows of A which form a basis of what we may now call $\mathfrak{L}S$ and that there exists an elementary matrix P so that

$$PA = \begin{pmatrix} A_1 \\ 0 \end{pmatrix},$$

where A_1 is an $r \times n$ matrix whose rows are linearly independent. It should also be clear that the rank of A is the number of linearly independent columns of A, since this *column rank* is equal to the determinantal rank of A' and hence to that of A.

EXERCISES

1. Compute the ranks of the following matrices by elementary row transformations:

$$(a) \begin{pmatrix} 5 & -4 & 4 & 2 \\ -2 & 0 & -8 & 5 \\ -1 & 2 & 2 & -3 \end{pmatrix}, \qquad (d) \begin{pmatrix} 1 & 3 & -2 \\ 2 & 5 & -2 \\ 1 & 1 & 6 \end{pmatrix},$$

$$(b) \begin{pmatrix} -4 & 1 & 0 & 1 \\ -2 & 0 & 2 & 1 \\ 0 & -2 & -3 & 0 \\ -7 & 2 & 0 & 2 \end{pmatrix}, \qquad (e) \begin{pmatrix} 1 & -2 & 1 & 2 \\ 2 & -4 & 2 & 4 \\ 2 & -3 & -1 & 2 \\ 4 & -7 & 1 & 6 \\ 2 & -3 & -1 & 2 \end{pmatrix},$$

$$(c) \begin{pmatrix} 1 & 2 & 4 & 0 & -2 \\ -2 & -3 & -1 & 1 & 0 \\ 0 & 1 & 7 & 1 & -4 \\ -2 & -2 & 6 & 2 & -4 \end{pmatrix}, \qquad (f) \begin{pmatrix} 3 & -1 & 2 & 1 \\ 1 & -4 & -6 & 1 \\ 7 & -11 & -6 & 1 \\ 11 & -8 & 2 & 3 \end{pmatrix}.$$

2. Compare the ranks of the matrices in Exercise 1, using elementary column transformations.

3. Determine a basis of the null space of the linear mapping $x = (x_1, \ldots, x_n) \to xA$ in each of the cases of Exercise 1.

4. Let $u_1 = (1\ -2\ -1\ 2)$, $u_2 = (2\ -4\ 1\ -2)$, $u_3 = (-1\ 2\ -2\ 4)$, $v_1 = (0\ 0\ 1\ -2)$, $v_2 = (3\ -6\ 0\ 1)$, $v_3 = (-1\ 2\ -2\ 1)$, and suppose that u_1, u_2, and u_3 span $\mathfrak{L}_1$ and that v_1, v_2, and v_3 span $\mathfrak{L}_2$. Determine a basis of the sum $(\mathfrak{L}_1, \mathfrak{L}_2)$.

5. If $x = (x_1, \ldots, x_n)$, where the x_i are independent indeterminates over a field $\mathfrak{F}$ and A is an n-rowed matrix such that $A = A'$ is symmetric, the expression $f(x) = xAx'$ is called a *quadratic form*. A quadratic form $g(x) = xBx'$ is said to be *equivalent* to $f(x)$ if there exists a non-singular matrix P such that $g(xP) = xPAP'x' = f(x)$. Show that, if $\mathfrak{F}$ has characteristic not 2, every

quadratic form xAx' is equivalent to a diagonal quadratic form zz', where $z = (x_1, \ldots, x_r, 0, \ldots, 0)$ and r is the rank of the matrix A.

6. If $x = (x_1, \ldots, x_m)$ and $y = (y_1, \ldots, y_n)$, the function $f(x, y) = xAy'$, defined for an m-by-n matrix, A is called a *bilinear* form. Two bilinear forms xAy' and $g(x, y) = xBy'$ are said to be *equivalent* if there exist non-singular matrices P and Q such that $g(xP, yQ) = xPBQ'y' = f(x, y) = xAy'$. Prove that every bilinear form is equivalent to zw', where $z = (x_1, \ldots, x_r, 0, \ldots, 0)$, $w = (y_1, \ldots, y_r, 0, \ldots, 0)$, and r is the rank of A.

7. Let x and y be as in Exercise 6, where $m = n$, $\mathfrak{F}$ has characteristic not 2, and $A = -A'$. Then the bilinear form $f(x, y) = xAy'$ is called a *skew-bilinear form*. Two skew-bilinear forms $f(x, y)$ and $g(x, y) = xBy'$ with $B = -B'$ are said to be *equivalent under cogredient transformations* if there exists a non-singular matrix P such that $g(xP, yP) = xPBP'y' = f(x, y) = xAy'$. Prove that every skew-bilinear form $f(x, y) = xAy'$ is equivalent to xEx', where

$$E = \begin{pmatrix} 0 & I_r & 0 \\ -I_r & 0 & 0 \\ 0 & 0 & 0 \end{pmatrix}.$$

Show, then, that every skew matrix has even rank $2r$ and that two skew-bilinear forms are equivalent under cogredient transformations if and only if they have the same rank.

15. Linear systems. A set of n linear equations

$$\sum_{i=1}^{m} x_i a_{ij} = y_j \qquad (j = 1, \ldots, n) \tag{91}$$

in m unknowns $x_1, \ldots, x_m$ is called a *linear system*. The a_{ij} are elements of a field $\mathfrak{F}$ called the *coefficients* of the system, and the y_j are elements of $\mathfrak{F}$ called the *constants*. The matrix $A = (a_{ij})$ is called the *matrix of the system*, and the matrix

$$A^* = \begin{pmatrix} A \\ y \end{pmatrix} \tag{92}$$

is called the *augmented* matrix of the system where $y = (y_1, \ldots, y_n)$. The system is representable by the matrix equation,

$$xA = y, \tag{93}$$

where $x_1 = (x, \ldots, x_m)$. Its solutions are those vectors x in the space $\mathfrak{L}$ of m-tuples which are mapped onto y by a linear mapping with matrix A.

THEOREM 16. *A linear system has a solution if and only if* A *and* A* *have the same rank* r. *If* x_0 *is any solution of the system, the set of all solutions is the set of all vectors* $x_0 + z$ *where* z *is any vector of the null space of* A.

For if $x_0A = y$ and $xA = y$, then $(x - x_0)A = y - y = 0$, and so $x = x_0 + z$, where z is in the null space of A. Conversely, if $x_0A = y$ and $zA = 0$, we have $xA = y$. To verify our condition for the existence of a solution, we use Theorems 10 and 11 to obtain non-singular matrices P and Q such that

$$P^{-1}AQ = \begin{pmatrix} I_r & 0 \\ 0 & 0 \end{pmatrix} . \tag{94}$$

Put $X = xP = (X_1, X_2)$ and $Y = yQ = (Y_1, Y_2)$, where X_1 and Y_1 are r-tuples. Then $xA = y$ if and only if $X(P^{-1}AQ) = Y$, that is,

$$X_1 = Y_1, \quad 0 = Y_2 . \tag{95}$$

But A^* has the same rank as

$$\begin{pmatrix} P^{-1} & 0 \\ 0 & 1 \end{pmatrix} A^*Q = \begin{pmatrix} P^{-1}AQ \\ Y \end{pmatrix} = \begin{pmatrix} I_r & 0 \\ 0 & 0 \\ Y_1 & Y_2 \end{pmatrix} . \tag{96}$$

It follows that A and A^* have the same rank if and only if $Y_2 = 0$, and this is precisely the condition for the existence of a solution obtained in equations (95).

A linear system is called a *homogeneous* system if $y_1, \ldots, y_n$ are all zero. Thus a homogeneous system is simply the system of equations $xA = 0$ for the vectors of the null space of A. The vector $x = 0$ is called the *trivial* solution of the system, and the system has non-trivial solutions if and only if $r < m$. Indeed, we may rephrase Theorem 16 as follows:

THEOREM 17. *A homogeneous system* xA = 0 *of* n *equations in* m *unknowns has a space of solutions of dimension* m − r *where* r *is the rank of* A. *The system always has a non-trivial solution if* m > n.

ILLUSTRATIVE EXAMPLE

Compute A^{-1} if

$$A = \begin{pmatrix} 1 & 2 & 1 \\ 1 & 3 & -1 \\ 1 & 4 & -2 \end{pmatrix} .$$

Solution: Consider the system of equations $xA = y$, that is,

$$\begin{aligned} x_1 + x_2 + x_3 &= y_1 , \\ 2x_1 + 3x_2 + 4x_3 &= y_2 , \\ x_1 - x_2 - 2x_3 &= y_3 . \end{aligned}$$

The solution of this system is $x = yA^{-1}$ if $|A| \neq 0$. We solve the system by elimination, first obtaining

$$\begin{aligned} y_1 - y_3 &= 2x_2 + 3x_3\,, \\ y_2 - 2y_3 &= 5x_2 + 8x_3\,. \end{aligned}$$

Then $5(y_1 - y_3) - 2(y_2 - 2y_3) = 5y_1 - 2y_2 - y_3 = 15x_3 - 16x_3 = -x_3$, and so $x_3 = -5y_1 + 2y_2 + y_3$. Then $2x_2 = y_1 - y_3 - 3(-5y_1 + 2y_2 + y_3) = 16y_1 - 6y_2 - 4y_3$ and $x_2 = 8y_1 - 3y_2 - 2y_3$. Also $x_1 = y_1 - x_2 - x_3 = y_1 - (8y_1 - 3y_2 - 2y_3) - (-5y_1 + 2y_2 + y_3) = -2y_1 + y_2 + y_3$, so that

$$A^{-1} = \begin{pmatrix} -2 & 8 & -5 \\ 1 & -3 & 2 \\ 1 & -2 & 1 \end{pmatrix}.$$

The solution should be verified by computing AA^{-1}.

EXERCISES

1. Compute A^{-1}, where A is given as follows:

$$(a)\ \begin{pmatrix} 1 & -1 & 3 \\ 3 & -2 & 7 \\ 1 & 3 & -3 \end{pmatrix}, \qquad (d)\ \begin{pmatrix} 2 & 1 & -1 & 0 \\ 1 & 2 & 0 & -1 \\ 2 & 3 & -1 & 0 \\ 0 & -1 & 2 & 4 \end{pmatrix},$$

$$(b)\ \begin{pmatrix} 1 & -1 & 2 \\ 3 & -2 & 4 \\ 0 & 2 & -3 \end{pmatrix}, \qquad (e)\ \begin{pmatrix} 1 & -1 & 0 & 2 \\ 0 & 1 & 1 & -1 \\ 2 & 1 & 2 & 1 \\ 3 & -2 & 1 & 6 \end{pmatrix},$$

$$(c)\ \begin{pmatrix} 3 & -1 & -2 \\ 4 & 0 & 1 \\ 2 & 5 & 3 \end{pmatrix}, \qquad (f)\ \begin{pmatrix} 1 & 0 & 1 & 0 \\ 2 & 2 & -5 & 0 \\ -2 & 1 & -5 & 2 \\ 1 & 0 & 1 & 1 \end{pmatrix}.$$

2. Solve the linear systems $Ax' = 0$ where $x = (x_1, \ldots, x_n)$ and A is one of the following matrices:

$$(a)\ \begin{pmatrix} 2 & -7 & -6 \\ 3 & 5 & -2 \\ 4 & -2 & -7 \end{pmatrix}, \qquad (c)\ \begin{pmatrix} 2 & 3 & -1 \\ 3 & 2 & -3 \\ 8 & 6 & -1 \\ 3 & 1 & 3 \end{pmatrix},$$

$$(b)\ \begin{pmatrix} 2 & 1 & 3 \\ 4 & 2 & -1 \\ 2 & 1 & 10 \end{pmatrix}, \qquad (d)\ \begin{pmatrix} 2 & 3 & 8 & 3 \\ 3 & 2 & 6 & 1 \\ -1 & -3 & -1 & 3 \end{pmatrix}.$$

3. Solve the linear systems $Ax' = y'$ for the following values of A and y:

(*a*) $A = \begin{pmatrix} 1 & -1 & 2 \\ 3 & -2 & 4 \\ 0 & 2 & -3 \end{pmatrix}$, $\quad y = (-2 \quad -5 \quad 2)$;

(*b*) $A = \begin{pmatrix} 1 & 1 & -5 \\ 1 & 2 & 1 \\ 1 & 3 & 6 \end{pmatrix}$, $\quad y = (26 \quad -4 \quad -29)$;

(*c*) $A = \begin{pmatrix} 1 & 0 & -1 & 1 \\ 0 & -1 & 2 & -1 \\ 1 & 0 & 1 & 2 \\ 2 & 1 & -1 & 0 \end{pmatrix}$, $\quad y = (-2 \quad 5 \quad 3 \quad -6)$;

(*d*) $A = \begin{pmatrix} -4 & 1 & 0 & 1 \\ -2 & 0 & 2 & 1 \\ 0 & 2 & -1 & 0 \\ -7 & 2 & 2 & 0 \end{pmatrix}$, $\quad y = (-10 \quad -4 \quad 1 \quad -15)$.

16. Equivalence in $\mathfrak{F}[x]$. Consider an $m \times n$ matrix A with elements in the integral domain $\mathfrak{J} = \mathfrak{F}[x]$ of all polynomials in an indeterminate x over $\mathfrak{F}$. Let d_1 be a polynomial of the lowest degree in the set $\mathfrak{N}$ of all elements of all matrices B equivalent in $\mathfrak{J}$ to A. By the use of $R_{i,\,a}$ we may take d_1 to be monic. We then prove

LEMMA 18. *The ideal* $\Delta_1(A) = (d_1)$.

For d_1 is an element of a matrix $B = (\beta_{ij})$ equivalent to A. By Theorem 13 we may take $d_1 = \beta_{11}$. Write

$$\beta_{i1} = \sigma_{i1} d_1 + \rho_{i1}\,, \tag{97}$$

where the degree of ρ_{i1} is less than the degree of d_1. Then the element in the ith row and first column of $R_{i,\,1,\,-\sigma_{i1}}(B)$ is ρ_{i1}. By the definition of d_1 we must have $\rho_{i1} = 0$. Hence d_1 divides every β_{i1}. Similarly, d_1 divides every β_{1j}. By using $R_{i,\,j,\,\lambda}$ we may assume that $\beta_{i1} = \beta_{1j} = 0$ for $i = 2, \ldots, m$ and $j = 2, \ldots, n$. Form $R_{i,\,1,\,1}(B) = G = (\gamma_{ij})$, where $\gamma_{i1} = d_1$ and $\gamma_{ij} = \sigma_{ij} d_1 + \rho_{ij}$. Then ρ_{ij} is an element of $C_{j,\,1,\,-\sigma_{ij}}(G)$ and so must be zero. Hence the element d_1 of B divides every element of B, and $(d_1) = \Delta_1(B) = \Delta_1(A)$, as desired.

Since $A \cong B$, where

$$B = \begin{pmatrix} d_1 & 0 \\ 0 & B_1 \end{pmatrix}, \tag{98}$$

we may carry out additional transformations on B which replace B_1 by

$$B_{11} = \begin{pmatrix} d_2 & 0 \\ 0 & B_2 \end{pmatrix}, \tag{99}$$

where $(d_2) = \Delta_1(B_{11})$. But then A is equivalent to

$$\begin{pmatrix} d_1 & 0 & 0 \\ 0 & d_2 & 0 \\ 0 & 0 & B_2 \end{pmatrix}, \tag{100}$$

and d_1 must divide d_2. After a finite sequence of such steps we arrive at a matrix,

$$C = \begin{pmatrix} D & 0 \\ 0 & 0 \end{pmatrix}, \quad D = \operatorname{diag}\{d_1, \ldots, d_r\}, \tag{101}$$

where $d_1, \ldots, d_r$ are monic polynomials such that d_i divides d_{i+1} for $i = 1, \ldots, r - 1$. Evidently, r is the rank of A. We also see that the only non-zero k-rowed minors of C are the minors $\rho_k = d_{i_1} \cdots d_{i_k}$, where $i_1 < i_2 < \cdots < i_k$. Then, since $j \leq i_j$ implies that d_j divides d_{i_j}, we see that $d_1 \cdots d_k$ divides every ρ_k. It follows that

$$\Delta_k(A) = (\delta_k), \tag{102}$$

where

$$\delta_k = \delta_k(x) = d_1 \cdots d_k. \tag{103}$$

Hence

$$d_k = \frac{\delta_k}{\delta_{k-1}} \qquad (k = 1, \ldots, r), \tag{104}$$

where we define $\delta_0 = 1$.

The polynomials $d_1, \ldots, d_r$ are called the *invariant factors* of A. By equation (104) and Theorem 12 we see that if A and B *are equivalent, they have the same invariant factors.* Conversely, if A and B have the same invariant factors, they are both equivalent to the matrix C of equations (101), and hence $A \cong B$. This yields the following result:

THEOREM 18. *Two* $m \times n$ *matrices with elements in* $\mathfrak{J} = \mathfrak{F}[x]$ *are equivalent in* $\mathfrak{J}$ *if and only if they have the same invariant factors* $d_1, \ldots, d_r$. *Every* $m \times n$ *matrix with invariant factors* $d_1, \ldots, d_r$ *is equivalent in* $\mathfrak{J}$ *to the matrix of equations* (101).

It sometimes happens that the process of reducing a matrix with polynomial elements to what is called diagonal form (i.e., to a form in which $a_{ij} = 0$ for $i \neq j$) yields a matrix

$$B = \begin{pmatrix} G & 0 \\ 0 & 0 \end{pmatrix}, \quad G = \text{diag}\,\{g_1, \ldots, g_r\}\,, \tag{105}$$

where we do *not* have the property that g_i divides g_{i+1}. The invariant factors are then obtained by the use of the following property:

LEMMA 19. *Let*

$$A = \begin{pmatrix} f & 0 \\ 0 & g \end{pmatrix}, \tag{106}$$

where $f = f(x)$ *and* $g = g(x)$ *are in* $\mathfrak{J} = \mathfrak{F}[x]$. *Then*

$$A \cong B = \begin{pmatrix} d & 0 \\ 0 & m \end{pmatrix}, \tag{107}$$

where $d = d(x)$ *is the g.c.d. of* f *and* g *and* m *is the least common multiple of* f *and* g.

For $f = df_1$, $g = dg_1$, $af_1 + bg_1 = 1$ for a and b in $\mathfrak{F}[x]$. Then $d = af + bg$, $m = df_1g_1 = f_1g$, and

$$A \cong \begin{pmatrix} f & 0 \\ af & g \end{pmatrix} \cong \begin{pmatrix} f & 0 \\ d & g \end{pmatrix} \cong \begin{pmatrix} d & g \\ f & 0 \end{pmatrix} \cong \begin{pmatrix} d & g \\ 0 & -f_1g \end{pmatrix} \cong \begin{pmatrix} d & 0 \\ 0 & m \end{pmatrix}, \tag{108}$$

as desired.

Lemma 17 states that if P is an elementary matrix with elements in $\mathfrak{J} = \mathfrak{F}[x]$, then $|P|$ is a non-zero element of $\mathfrak{F}$. The converse is also true, and we state the result as follows:

THEOREM 19. *A square matrix* A *with elements in* $\mathfrak{F}[x]$ *is elementary if and only if* $|A|$ *is a non-zero element of* $\mathfrak{F}$.

For PAQ has the form (101). Since $m = n = r$ when $|A| = \alpha \neq 0$ in $\mathfrak{F}$, we see that

$$PAQ = \begin{pmatrix} d_1 & & & & \\ & \cdot & & & \\ & & \cdot & & \\ & & & \cdot & \\ & & & & d_r \end{pmatrix}. \tag{109}$$

Then $|PAQ| = |P|\ |Q|\alpha = d_1 \cdots d_r = \beta$ in $\mathfrak{F}$. But $d_1, \ldots, d_r$ are monic polynomials whose product is in $\mathfrak{F}$, $d_1 = \cdots = d_r = 1$, $PAQ = I$, and $A = p^{-1}Q^{-1}$ is elementary.

EXERCISES

1. Use elementary transformations to compute the invariant factors of the following matrices:

(a) $$\begin{pmatrix} -x & 2x+1 & x-1 & x+1 \\ -x^2+x-1 & x^2+x+2 & x^2+3x-1 & x^2-x+2 \\ 2-x & x-1 & x+2 & x-2 \\ -3-2x & 3x+4 & x & 2x+4 \end{pmatrix},$$

(b) $$\begin{pmatrix} x^2 & x & 2x-1 & x+1 \\ x+2 & x+2 & 2x+1 & x+5 \\ 1 & 1 & x & 2 \\ x^2+1 & x+1 & 2x & x+3 \end{pmatrix},$$

(c) $$\begin{pmatrix} -x & -x^3+2x & -x^3+x^2+x & -x^4-x \\ 1 & x+x^2 & x^2 & x^3+1 \\ x+1 & x^3+3x^2+x & x^3+2x^2 & x^4+x^3+x+1 \\ x+2 & x^3+3x^2+2x & x^3+2x^2 & x^4+3x^3+x+2 \end{pmatrix},$$

(d) $$\begin{pmatrix} x-2 & 2x+3 & x^2-x+1 & x \\ x-1 & 3x+4 & x^2+x+2 & 2x+1 \\ x+2 & x & x^2+3x-1 & x-1 \\ 2x & 3x+4 & 2x^2+2x+1 & 2x \end{pmatrix},$$

(e) $$\begin{pmatrix} 2x-1 & x & x-1 & 1 \\ x & 0 & 1 & 0 \\ 0 & 1 & x & x \\ 1 & x^2 & 0 & 2x-2 \end{pmatrix}.$$

2. What are the invariant factors of

$$\begin{pmatrix} x^2+2x & 0 & 0 & 0 \\ 0 & (x+2)(x+1) & 0 & 0 \\ 0 & 0 & x^3+2x^2 & 0 \\ 0 & 0 & 0 & x^4+x^3 \end{pmatrix}?$$

3. Show that the following matrix is an elementary matrix:

$$\begin{pmatrix} x+1 & x^2+x+1 & x-2 & 1 \\ x+2 & x^2+2x+1 & x-2 & 1 \\ -1 & -x & 3-x & -1 \\ -2-x & -2x-x^2 & 4x-2-x^2 & 1-x \end{pmatrix}.$$

17. The ring $\mathfrak{M}_n$ over $\mathfrak{F}[x]$. The set of all $n \times n$ matrices with elements in $\mathfrak{J} = \mathfrak{F}[x]$ is easily seen to be a ring. Every element of $\mathfrak{M}_n$ is a matrix,

$$A = (\alpha_{ij}) , \tag{110}$$

where $\alpha_{ij} = \alpha_{ij}(x)$ is a polynomial in x. Let t be the maximum degree of all elements of A so that

$$\alpha_{ij}(x) = \alpha_{ij0}x^t + \cdots + \alpha_{ijt} , \tag{111}$$

where the coefficients α_{ijk} are in $\mathfrak{F}$. Then we may write

$$A = A_0x^t + \cdots + A_t , \tag{112}$$

where

$$A_k = (\alpha_{ijk}) \qquad (i, j = 1, \ldots , n). \tag{113}$$

It follows that $\mathfrak{M}_n$ over $\mathfrak{F}[x]$ is the ring $\mathfrak{M}_n[x]$ of all polynomials in x with coefficients in the ring $\mathfrak{M}_n$ of all $n \times n$ square matrices with elements in $\mathfrak{F}$. We may now derive the following vital result:

THEOREM 20. *Let* C = xI − A *and* D = xI − B, *where* A *and* B *are* n-*rowed square matrices with elements in* $\mathfrak{F}$. *Then* C *and* D *are equivalent in* $\mathfrak{J} = \mathfrak{F}$[x] *if and only if* B = Q⁻¹AQ, *where* Q *is a non-singular matrix with elements in* $\mathfrak{F}$.

For let $P(x)CQ(x) = D$, where $P(x)$ and $Q(x)$ are elementary matrices with elements in $\mathfrak{F}[x]$. Write

$$P(x) = (xI - B)P_0(x) + P, \quad Q(x) = Q_0(x)(xI - B) + Q , \tag{114}$$

as in Theorem 2.11, where P and Q have elements in $\mathfrak{F}$. Then

$$\begin{aligned} P(x)[(xI - A)]Q(x) &= (xI - B)P_0(x)(xI - A)Q(x) \\ &+ P\cdot(xI - A)Q_0(x)(xI - B) + P\cdot(xI - A)\cdot Q = xI - B . \end{aligned} \tag{115}$$

Now $P(x)$ has an inverse $S(x)$ in $\mathfrak{M}_n[x]$ and $Q(x)$ has an inverse $T(x)$ in $\mathfrak{M}_n[x]$, so that

$$(xI - A)Q(x) = S(x)(xI - B), \quad P(x)(xI - A) = (xI - B)T(x) . \tag{116}$$

Thus $P\cdot(xI - A) = (xI - B)[T(x) - P_0(x)(xI - A)]$ and so equations (115) and (116) imply that

$$(xI - B) - P\cdot(xI - A)\cdot Q = (xI - B)R(x)(xI - B) , \tag{117}$$

where

$$(118) \qquad R(x) = P_0(x)S(x) + T(x)Q_0(x) - P_0(x)(xI - A)Q_0(x) .$$

The degree of $(xI - B) - P\cdot(xI - A)\cdot Q$ in x is at most 1. The degree of $(xI - B)R(x)(xI - B)$ is at least 2 unless $R(x) = 0$. Hence $R(x) = 0$, and

$$(119) \qquad P\cdot(xI - A)\cdot Q = xI - B .$$

But then $PIQ = I, Q^{-1} = P$, and $Q^{-1}AQ = B$. Conversely, if $Q^{-1}AQ = B$, then $Q^{-1}(xI - A)Q = xI - B$, and the theorem is proved.

18. Similarity of square matrices. Every n-rowed square matrix A is the matrix of a linear transformation S on an n-dimensional vector space $\mathfrak{L}$ over $\mathfrak{F}$ with respect to a basis of $\mathfrak{L}$ over $\mathfrak{F}$. We apply Theorem 10 with $\mathfrak{L} = \mathfrak{L}'$. Then $P = Q$ in that theorem, and we see that A is replaced by $P^{-1}AP$. We say that an n-rowed square matrix B is *similar* to A if there exists a non-singular matrix P such that $P^{-1}AP = B$. The result just derived may then be stated as follows:

THEOREM 21. *Let* A *be the matrix of a linear transformation on a vector space* $\mathfrak{L}$. *Then a change of basis of* $\mathfrak{L}$ *replaces* A *by a similar matrix.*

If A is any n-rowed square matrix, the matrix

$$xI - A$$

is called the *characteristic* matrix of A. Theorem 20 may then be stated as follows:

THEOREM 22. *Two* n*-rowed square matrices* A *and* B *with elements in a field* $\mathfrak{F}$ *are similar if and only if their characteristic matrices have the same invariant factors.*

19. Characteristic and minimum functions. Every $n \times n$ matrix A generates a polynomial ring $\mathfrak{F}[A]$ consisting of all polynomials

$$h(A) = \alpha_0 A^\nu + \alpha_1 A^{\nu-1} + \cdots + \alpha_{\nu-1}A + \alpha_\nu \qquad (\alpha_i \text{ in } \mathfrak{F}).$$

Evidently $\mathfrak{F}[A]$ is a vector subspace over $\mathfrak{F}$ of the ring of all $n \times n$ matrices $\mathfrak{M}_n$ with elements in $\mathfrak{F}$. Since the dimension over $\mathfrak{F}$ of $\mathfrak{M}_n$ is n^2, the space $\mathfrak{F}[A]$ is finite-dimensional. It follows that there exists a non-zero polynomial $h(x)$ such that $h(A) = 0$.

Let $\mathfrak{N} = \mathfrak{N}(A)$ be the set of all polynomials $h(x)$ such that $h(A) = 0$. If $h(x)$ and $k(x)$ are in $\mathfrak{N}$, their sum $\lambda(x)$ has the property that $\lambda(A) = h(A) + k(A) = 0$. If $h(x)$ is in $\mathfrak{N}$ and $k(x)$ is in $\mathfrak{F}[x]$, then $\lambda(x) = h(x)k(x)$ is in $\mathfrak{N}$, since $\lambda(A) = h(A)k(A) = 0$. It follows that $\mathfrak{N}$ is an ideal of $\mathfrak{F}[x]$. But then

$$(120) \qquad \mathfrak{N} = (\phi) ,$$

where $\phi = \phi(x)$ is monic and in N, $\phi(A) = 0$, and $\phi(x)$ divides every $h(x)$ of N.

The polynomial $\phi(x)$ is called the *minimum function* of A. It is the monic polynomial of least degree in $\mathfrak{N}$.

The determinant $f(x) = |xI - A|$ is called the *characteristic determinant* or *characteristic function* of A. The equation $f(x) = 0$ is called the *characteristic equation* of A.

THEOREM 23. *Every matrix is a root of its characteristic equation.*

For $(xI - A)\ \text{adj}\ (xI - A) = f(x)I$. By Theorem 2.13 we see that $f(A) = 0$.

If A is any $n \times n$ matrix, the matrix $xI - A$ is a non-singular matrix. Indeed, $f(x) = |xI - A|$ is a monic polynomial of degree n. There then exist elementary matrices $P(x)$ and $Q(x)$ such that

$$P(x)[(xI - A)]Q(x) = \begin{pmatrix} d_1 & 0 & \cdots & 0 \\ 0 & d_2 & \cdots & 0 \\ \cdot & \cdot & \cdots & \cdot \\ 0 & 0 & \cdots & d_n \end{pmatrix}, \tag{121}$$

where $d_1, \ldots, d_n$ are monic polynomials in x which are the invariant factors of $xI - A$. Then $|P(x)|\ |Q(x)|f(x) = d_1 \cdots d_n$, where, by Theorem 19, $|P(x)|\ |Q(x)| = \alpha \neq 0$ is in $\mathfrak{F}$. It follows that

$$f(x) = d_1 \cdots d_n\,. \tag{122}$$

Thus *the characteristic determinant of* A *is the product of the invariant factors of* xI − A.

The polynomials $d_i = d_i(x)$ are so defined that d_i divides d_{i+1} for $i = 1, \ldots, n - 1$. We now prove

THEOREM 24. *The polynomial* $d_n(x)$ *is the minimum function of* A.

For $d_n(x) = \delta_n(x)[\delta_{n-1}(x)]^{-1}$, where $\delta_n(x) = f(x)$ and $\delta_{n-1}(x)$ is the g.c.d. of all $(n - 1)$-rowed minors of $xI - A$. Then $\delta_{n-1}(x)$ is the g.c.d. of the elements of adj $(xI - A)$, and so

$$\text{adj}\ (xI - A) = B(x)\delta_{n-1}(x)\,, \tag{123}$$

where the g.c.d. of the elements of $B(x)$ is 1. But then

$$d_n(x)I = B(x)(xI - A)\,. \tag{124}$$

It follows from Theorem 2.13 that $d_n(A) = 0$ and so $\phi(x)$ divides $d_n(x) = \psi(x)\phi(x)$. But $\phi(A) = 0$, $\phi(x)I = C(x)(xI - A)$ for $C(x)$ in $\mathfrak{M}_n[x]$, and $\psi(x)C(x)(xI - A) = B(x)(xI - A)$. By Theorem 2.11 we see that

$B(x) = \psi(x)C(x)$. Hence $\psi(x)$ divides all elements of $B(x)$, and $\psi(x)$ must be in $\mathfrak{F}$. Since $d_n(x)$ and $\phi(x)$ are both monic, we have $d_n(x) = \phi(x)$, as desired.

Equation (122) states that the sum of the degrees of $d_1(x), \ldots, d_n(x)$ is n. When all the $d_i(x)$ are linear, they must be equal to $x - \alpha$; the invariant factors of $xI - A$ and $xI - \alpha I$ are the same, $A = P^{-1}(\alpha I)P = \alpha I$. Hence the $d_i(x)$ are all linear only when A is a scalar matrix. In all other cases, at least one $d_i(x) = 1$. Thus $d_1(x) = 1$. We call the non-constant invariant factors of $xI - A$ its *non-trivial* invariant factors. The remaining invariant factors are equal to 1 and are called the *trivial* invariant factors of $xI - A$.

20. The companion matrix of a polynomial. An n-dimensional vector space $\mathfrak{L}$ over $\mathfrak{F}$ can be made into a ring by defining a product ab on $(\mathfrak{L}, \mathfrak{L})$ to $\mathfrak{L}$ such that

$$(125) \qquad (ab)c = a(bc), \qquad (\alpha a + \beta b)c = \alpha ac + \beta bc, \qquad a(\alpha b + \beta c) = \alpha(ab) + \beta(ac)$$

for every a, b, and c of $\mathfrak{L}$ and α and β of $\mathfrak{F}$. Such a ring is called a *linear associative algebra*. The transformation R_b,

$$(126) \qquad a \to ab = aR_b ,$$

is a linear transformation on $\mathfrak{L}$ for every b of $\mathfrak{L}$, called a *right multiplication*. The mapping

$$(127) \qquad b \to R_b$$

of $\mathfrak{L}$ onto the set $\mathfrak{L}'$ of all R_b is easily seen to be a homomorphism of $\mathfrak{L}$ onto an algebra $\mathfrak{L}'$ of linear transformations. Indeed, equations (125) imply that

$$(128) \qquad R_{bc} = R_bR_c, \quad R_{\alpha b + \beta c} = \alpha R_b + \beta R_c .$$

When $\mathfrak{L}$ has a unity element, mapping (127) is an isomorphism of the algebra $\mathfrak{L}$ and the algebra $\mathfrak{L}'$.

The following special case is of particular interest to us. Consider the polynomial

$$(129) \qquad \phi = \phi(x) = x^n + \alpha_1 x^{n-1} + \cdots + \alpha_n ,$$

where $\alpha_1, \ldots, \alpha_n$ are in a field $\mathfrak{F}$. Then the difference ring,

$$(130) \qquad \mathfrak{A} = \mathfrak{F}[x] - (\phi) ,$$

is an n-dimensional linear algebra. Indeed,

$$\mathfrak{A} = \mathfrak{F}[z] , \tag{131}$$

where

$$z = x + (\phi), \quad \phi(z) = 0 . \tag{132}$$

Then $\mathfrak{A}$ is isomorphic to the algebra of all right multiplications

$$R_h = \psi(R_z) , \tag{133}$$

where $h = \psi(z)$ is any polynomial of $\mathfrak{F}[z]$. Since $1, z, \ldots, z^{n-1}$ form a basis of $\mathfrak{A}$, the linear transformations $I, R_z, R_z^2, \ldots, R_z^{n-1}$ are linearly independent.

The algebra $\mathfrak{A} = \mathfrak{F} + z\mathfrak{F} + z^2\mathfrak{F} + \cdots + z^{n-1}\mathfrak{F}$, and we see that $1z = z$, $zz = z^2, \ldots, z^{n-2}z = z^{n-1}$, $z^{n-1}z = z^n = -a_n - a_{n-1}z - \cdots - a_1z^{n-1}$. It follows that the matrix of R_z is the *companion matrix*,

$$C_\phi = \begin{pmatrix} 0 & 1 & 0 & \cdots & 0 & 0 \\ 0 & 0 & 1 & \cdots & 0 & 0 \\ \cdot & \cdot & \cdot & \cdots & \cdot & \cdot \\ 0 & 0 & 0 & \cdots & 0 & 1 \\ -a_n & -a_{n-1} & -a_{n-2} & \cdots & -a_2 & -a_1 \end{pmatrix} . \tag{134}$$

But the linear independence of I and $R_z, \ldots, R_z^{n-1}$ implies that $I, C_\phi, C_\phi^2, \ldots, C_\phi^{n-1}$ are linearly independent. Since $\phi(z) = 0$, we know that $\phi(C_\phi) = 0$. But $\phi(x)$ has degree n, and so the linear independence just stated implies that $\phi(x)$ is the minimum function of C_ϕ. By equation (122) we have the following result:

THEOREM 25. *The characteristic function of* C_ϕ *is its minimum function* $\phi(x)$. *All other invariant factors of* $xI - C_\phi$ *are trivial.*

As a consequence of Theorem 25 we have the following result:

THEOREM 26. *Let* A *be an* n*-rowed square matrix and* $\phi_1(x), \ldots, \phi_t(x)$ *be the non-trivial invariant factors of* $xI - A$, *where we order them so that* $\phi_{i+1}(x)$ *divides* $\phi_i(x)$ *for* $i - 1, \ldots, t - 1$. *Then* A *is similar in* $\mathfrak{F}$ *to*

$$C = \operatorname{diag}\{C_{\phi_1}, \ldots, C_{\phi_t}\} . \tag{135}$$

The sum of the degrees of $\phi_1, \ldots, \phi_t$ is n by equation (122), so that the matrix C of equation (135) is an $n \times n$ matrix. By Theorem 25 there exist elementary matrices $P_i = P_i(x)$ and $Q_i = Q_i(x)$ such that

$$P_i(xI - C_{\phi_i})Q_i = \operatorname{diag}\{\phi_i, 1, \ldots, 1\} = \Delta_i . \tag{136}$$

Let

$$(137)\qquad P = \text{diag}\,\{P_1, \ldots, P_t\}, \quad Q = \text{diag}\,\{Q_1, \ldots, Q_t\}\,.$$

Then $|P| = |P_1| \cdots |P_t|$ and $|Q| = |Q_1| \cdots |Q_t|$ are in $\mathfrak{F}$ and not zero. Hence P and Q are elementary matrices. It follows that

$$(138)\qquad \begin{aligned} P(xI - C)Q &= \text{diag}\,\{P_1(xI - C_{\phi_1})Q_1, \ldots, P_t(xI - C_{\phi_t})Q_t\} \\ &= \text{diag}\,\{\Delta_1, \ldots, \Delta_t\} = \Delta\,. \end{aligned}$$

The matrix Δ is a diagonal matrix whose diagonal elements are $\phi_1, \ldots, \phi_t$ and $n - t$ ones. It follows that $xI - C$ and $xI - A$ have the same invariant factors and A and C are similar.

The matrix (135) is called the ***rational canonical form*** of A. It is determined by the invariant factors of $xI - A$. Conversely, a matrix C of form (135) with ϕ_i divisible by ϕ_{i+1} for $i = 1, \ldots, t - 1$ has $\phi_1, \ldots, \phi_t$ as the non-trivial invariant factors of $xI - C$ and so determines all matrices similar to C. It follows that two matrices in the rational canonical form are similar if and only if they are identical.

EXERCISES

1. Compute the invariant factors of $xI - A$ in the following cases:

$$(a)\ A = \begin{pmatrix} 1 & 2 & 6 & 0 \\ -1 & -1 & -2 & 0 \\ 0 & -1 & -2 & 0 \\ 0 & 0 & 0 & 2 \end{pmatrix}, \qquad (e)\ A = \begin{pmatrix} 0 & 2 & 1 & -3 \\ -2 & 1 & 0 & -2 \\ 2 & 0 & 1 & 2 \\ -1 & 0 & 0 & 0 \end{pmatrix},$$

$$(b)\ A = \begin{pmatrix} 2 & -2 & 0 \\ -2 & 1 & -2 \\ 0 & -2 & 0 \end{pmatrix}, \qquad (f)\ A = \begin{pmatrix} 1 & 1 & 0 & 0 & 0 \\ 0 & 1 & 1 & 0 & 0 \\ 0 & 0 & 1 & 0 & 0 \\ 0 & 0 & 0 & 1 & 1 \\ 0 & 0 & 0 & 0 & 1 \end{pmatrix},$$

$$(c)\ A = \begin{pmatrix} 2 & -1 & 0 \\ 1 & 0 & 0 \\ 1 & -1 & 1 \end{pmatrix}, \qquad (g)\ A = \begin{pmatrix} 0 & 1 & 1 \\ 1 & 0 & 1 \\ 1 & 1 & 0 \end{pmatrix},$$

$$(d)\ A = \begin{pmatrix} 0 & 1 & 0 & 0 \\ 0 & 0 & 1 & 0 \\ 0 & 0 & 0 & 1 \\ 1 & 2 & 3 & 4 \end{pmatrix}, \qquad (h)\ A = \begin{pmatrix} 1 & 1 & -1 \\ 0 & 0 & 0 \\ 1 & 1 & -1 \end{pmatrix}.$$

2. Give the rational canonical form of A if the non-trivial invariant factors of $xI - A$ are as follows:

(*a*) $x(x^2+1)^2(x^2-4)^2$, $x(x^2+1)(x-2)^2(x+2)$, x^2-4;

(*b*) $(x^2-1)^2x^3(x-2)$, $(x^3-x^2)^2$, x^2-x;

(*c*) $x^3(x-1)^2(x+1)^2$, $x(x-1)^2(x+1)$, $x(x-1)$, x;

(*d*) $x^5(x^2-1)^4(x+2)$, $x^3(x^2-1)^3$, $x^3(x-1)^2$, $(x-1)^2$;

(*e*) $x^4(x+1)^3(x-1)^2$, $x^3(x+1)^2(x-1)^2$, x^4-x^2, x^2-x;

(*f*) $x^2(x-1)^2(x+1)$, x^3-x^2, x^2.

3. Let A be a four-rowed rational square matrix such that $(A^2-4A+I)(A^2+I)=0$. Give all possible rational canonical forms for A.

21. Nilpotent matrices. An $n \times n$ matrix N is called a *nilpotent matrix of index* ν if $N^\nu = 0$, $N^{\nu-1} \neq 0$ where ν is an integer, and $\nu > 1$. The minimum function of N divides x^ν and so is a power of x. By the definition of ν we see that $\phi(x) = x^\nu$ is the minimum function of N.

The non-trivial invariant factors of $xI - N$ are divisors $\phi_i(x) = x^{\nu_i}$ of $\phi(x)$, and we may order the ν_i so that

$$\nu = \nu_1 \geq \nu_2 \geq \cdots \geq \nu_t . \tag{139}$$

We call the ν_i the indices of N and apply Theorem 26 to obtain the following result:

THEOREM 27. *Two nilpotent matrices are similar if and only if they have the same indices. Every nilpotent matrix* A *is similar to its rational canonical form,*

$$\mathrm{N} = \mathrm{diag}\,\{\mathrm{N}_1, \ldots, \mathrm{N}_t\}, \tag{140}$$

where N_i *is the* ν_i*-rowed matrix,*

$$\mathrm{N}_i = \begin{pmatrix} 0 & 1 & 0 & \cdots & 0 \\ 0 & 0 & 1 & \cdots & 0 \\ \cdot & \cdot & \cdot & \cdots & \cdot \\ 0 & 0 & 0 & \cdots & 1 \\ 0 & 0 & 0 & \cdots & 0 \end{pmatrix}, \tag{141}$$

and $\nu_1, \ldots, \nu_t$ *are the indices of* A.

22. The Jordan canonical form. Let S be a linear transformation on an n-dimensional vector space $\mathfrak{L}$ over a field $\mathfrak{F}$ and let A be the matrix of S with respect to a basis of $\mathfrak{L}$ over $\mathfrak{F}$. Then the matrices of S with respect to all other bases of $\mathfrak{L}$ have the form $P^{-1}AP$. It follows that $|P^{-1}AP| = |P^{-1}|\,|A|\,|P| = |A|$ is independent of the choice of a basis. We call $|A|$ the determinant of S and write $|A| = |S|$. The polynomial

$$f(x) = |xI - P^{-1}AP| = |P^{-1}(XI - A)P| = |xI - A| \tag{142}$$

is also independent of our choice of a basis. Then we can write

$$f(x) = |xI - A| = |xI - S| \tag{143}$$

and call $f(x)$ the characteristic determinant of S. Let us agree to write I both for the identity matrix and for the corresponding linear transformation.

An element α of $\mathfrak{F}$ is called a *characteristic root* of both S and A if $f(\alpha) = |\alpha I - A| = |\alpha I - S| = 0$. The characteristic roots of S are then the roots of the polynomial $f(x) = 0$. Let us assume that $\mathfrak{F}$ has the property that

$$f(x) = |xI - S| = (x - \alpha_1)^{n_1} \cdots (x - \alpha_t)^{n_t} \tag{144}$$

for $\alpha_1, \ldots, \alpha_t$ in $\mathfrak{F}$ and $\alpha_1, \ldots, \alpha_t$ all distinct. Then we say that α_i is a characteristic root of *multiplicity* n_i.

A subspace $\mathfrak{L}_1$ of $\mathfrak{L}$ is said to be *invariant under* S if x_1S is in $\mathfrak{L}_1$ for every x_1 of $\mathfrak{L}_1$. Then $\mathfrak{L}_1 = u_1\mathfrak{F} + \cdots + u_m\mathfrak{F}$, $\mathfrak{L} = u_1\mathfrak{F} + \cdots + u_m\mathfrak{F} + u_{m+1}\mathfrak{F} + \cdots + u_n\mathfrak{F}$, and the matrix A of S with respect to such a basis has the form

$$A = \begin{pmatrix} A_1 & 0 \\ A_2 & A_3 \end{pmatrix}, \tag{145}$$

where A_1 is an m-rowed square matrix. If $\mathfrak{L} \supset \mathfrak{L}_1 \supset 0$, where $\mathfrak{L}_1$ is then a proper invariant subspace of $\mathfrak{L}$, we say that S is reducible. The mapping $x_1 \to x_1S = x_1S_1$ is a linear transformation on $\mathfrak{L}_1$ with matrix A_1 called the *induced transformation*.

A vector $x \neq 0$ of $\mathfrak{L}$ is called a *characteristic vector* of S (and of A) if $xS = \alpha x$, where α is in $\mathfrak{F}$. Then $x(\alpha I - S) = 0$, and so $|\alpha I - S| = 0$. A characteristic vector spans a one-dimensional invariant subspace of $\mathfrak{L}$.

If $\mathfrak{L} = \mathfrak{L}_1 + \cdots + \mathfrak{L}_t$ is the direct sum of invariant subspaces $\mathfrak{L}_1, \ldots, \mathfrak{L}_t$ under S, we can select a basis of $\mathfrak{L}$ which is the union of bases of $\mathfrak{L}_1, \ldots, \mathfrak{L}_t$. The corresponding matrix of S has the form

$$A = \operatorname{diag}\{A_1, \ldots, A_t\}, \tag{146}$$

where A_i is the matrix of the induced linear transformation $x_i \to x_iS = x_iS_i$ on $\mathfrak{L}_i$.

We now define invariant subspaces of $\mathfrak{L}$ called the *characteristic subspaces* of $\mathfrak{L}$ under S. Define $\mathfrak{L}(a)$ to be the set of all vectors x of $\mathfrak{L}$ such that

$$x(S - aI)^k = 0 \tag{147}$$

for some integer $k \geq 1$. Evidently, $\mathfrak{L}(a)$ is an invariant subspace of $\mathfrak{L}$ under S. Moreover, if a is not a characteristic root of S, the transformation $S - aI$ is non-singular; equation (147) holds only for $x = 0$ and $\mathfrak{L}(a) = 0$.

THEOREM 28. *Let $\mathfrak{L}$ be an* n*-dimensional vector space over $\mathfrak{F}$ and* S *be a linear transformation of $\mathfrak{L}$ such that all the distinct characteristic roots $a_1 \cdots a_t$ of* S *are in $\mathfrak{F}$. Then*

$$\mathfrak{L} = \mathfrak{L}(a_1) + \cdots + \mathfrak{L}(a_t) \tag{148}$$

is the vector-space direct sum of its invariant characteristic subspaces $\mathfrak{L}(a_i)$. These subspaces have dimensions n_i, where n_i is the multiplicity of a_i. The induced transformations $x_i \to x_iS = x_iS_i$ have the form $S_i = a_iI_i + N_i$, where I_i is the identity transformation on $\mathfrak{L}_i$ and N_i is nilpotent.

For let $f(x) = (x - a_i)^{n_i}\phi_i(x)$ so that $\phi_i(x)$ is the product of the factors $(x - a_j)^{n_j}$ of $f(x)$ for $j \neq i$. Evidently, $\phi_i(x)(x - a_i)^{n_i}$ and $\phi_i(x)\phi_j(x)$ are both divisible by $f(x)$. Thus $\phi_i(S)(S - a_iI)^{n_i} - \phi_i(S)\phi_j(S) = 0$ for $i \neq j$. The g.c.d. of the set of polynomials $\phi_1(x), \ldots, \phi_t(x)$ is 1, and so there exist polynomials $\psi_1(x), \ldots, \psi_t(x)$ in $\mathfrak{F}[x]$ such that

$$1 = \psi_1(x)\phi_1(x) + \cdots + \psi_t(x)\phi_t(x) . \tag{149}$$

Put

$$B_i = \psi_i(S)\phi_i(S) . \tag{150}$$

Then $B_iB_j = 0$ for $i \neq j$. Also

$$I = B_1 + \cdots + B_t \tag{151}$$

by equation (149), and so $IB_i = B_i = B_i^2$. Define

$$\mathfrak{L}_i = \mathfrak{L}B_i . \tag{152}$$

Then, if x_i is in $\mathfrak{L}_i$, we have $x_i = yB_i = yB_i^2 = x_iB_i$ and $x_iB_j = yB_iB_j = 0$ for $i \neq j$. Since $I = B_1 + \cdots + B_t$, we have $\mathfrak{L} = (\mathfrak{L}_1, \ldots, \mathfrak{L}_t)$. If $x_1 + \cdots + x_t = 0$ for x_i in $\mathfrak{L}_i$, then $OB_i = x_iB_i = x_i = 0$. Hence

$$\mathfrak{L} = \mathfrak{L}_1 + \cdots + \mathfrak{L}_t \tag{153}$$

is a supplementary sum. Since $B_i(S - a_iI)^{n_i} = 0$, we see that $x_i(S - a_iI)^{n_i} = 0$, and so $\mathfrak{L}_i \subseteq \mathfrak{L}(a_i)$. Conversely, let $x(S - a_iI)^k = 0$ for some

k. Then $\mathfrak{Z}_i(x)\psi_i(x)$ is prime to $(x - \alpha_i)^k$, and so there exist polynomials $\lambda(x)$ and $\mu(x)$ in $\mathfrak{F}[x]$ such that $\lambda(x)\phi_i(x)\cdot\psi_i(x) + [\mu(x)](x - \alpha_i)^k = 1$. Then $\lambda(S)B_i + [\mu(S)](S - \alpha_i I)^k = I$, and $x = x\lambda(S)B_i$ is in $\mathfrak{L}_i$. Hence $\mathfrak{L}(\alpha_i) \subseteq \mathfrak{L}_i$, and $\mathfrak{L}(\alpha_i) = \mathfrak{L}_i$.

Let S_i be the induced transformation $x_i \to x_i S$ on $\mathfrak{L}_i$. Since $x_i(S - \alpha_i I)^{n_i} = x_i(S_i - \alpha_i I_1)^{n_i} = 0$, the transformation $S_i - \alpha_i I = N_i$ is nilpotent. We select a basis of $\mathfrak{L}$ consisting of the union of bases of $\mathfrak{L}_1, \ldots, \mathfrak{L}_t$ and obtain a corresponding matrix,

$$A = \operatorname{diag}\{A_1, \ldots, A_t\}, \tag{154}$$

where $A_i - \alpha_i I$ is nilpotent. Then

$$|xI - A| = |xI_1 - A_1| \cdots |xI_t - A_t|, \tag{155}$$

where the degree of $|xI_i - A_i|$ is the dimension m_i of $\mathfrak{L}_i$. Since $\alpha_i I_i - A_i$ is nilpotent, we see that $f_i(x) = |xI_i - A_i| = (x - \alpha_i)^{m_i}$; the dimension of $\mathfrak{L}_i$ is the multiplicity of α_i, as desired.

We now derive what is called the *Jordan canonical form* of A.

THEOREM 29. *Let* A *be an* n-*rowed square matrix with elements in a field* $\mathfrak{F}$, $f(x) = |xI - A| = (x - \alpha_1)^{n_1} \cdots (x - d_t)^{n_t}$, *where* $\alpha_1, \ldots, \alpha_t$ *are distinct and in* $\mathfrak{F}$. *Then* A *is similar in* $\mathfrak{F}$ *to*

$$\operatorname{diag}\{A_1, \ldots, A_t\}, \tag{156}$$

where

$$A_i = \operatorname{diag}\{A_{i1}, \ldots, A_{is_i}\}, \tag{157}$$

and

$$A_{ij} = \begin{pmatrix} \alpha_i & 1 & 0 & \cdots & 0 & 0 \\ 0 & \alpha_i & 1 & \cdots & 0 & 0 \\ \cdot & \cdot & \cdot & \cdots & \cdot & \cdot \\ 0 & 0 & 0 & \cdots & \alpha_i & 1 \\ 0 & 0 & 0 & \cdots & 0 & \alpha_i \end{pmatrix} \tag{158}$$

for $m_{ij} \times m_{ij}$ *matrices* A_{ij} *such that* $m_{i1} \geq m_{i2} \geq \cdots \geq m_{is_i}$. *Two matrices of forms* (156), (157), *and* (158) *are similar if and only if they are identical* up to a permutation among the A_i.

For we have seen that A is similar to a matrix of form (156), where $A_i = \alpha_i I_i + N_i$ and N_i is nilpotent. We use Theorem 27 to select a basis of $\mathfrak{L}_i$ so that N_i is given by $N_i = \operatorname{diag}\{N_{i1}, \ldots, N_{is_i}\}$, where N_{ij} is given by matrix (141). Then equation (158) holds, as desired. If A and B have form (156), they are similar if and only if they represent the same S. Then the characteristic subspaces must be the same, and the induced transformations S_i must be the same. The matrices A_i and B_i must be similar under a suitable rearrangement of the subscripts, and $A_i = \alpha_i I_i + N_i$ is similar to $B_i = \alpha_i I_i + M_i$ if and only if N_i is similar to M_i. But N_i and M_i are in their rational canonical forms and are similar if and only if they are identical.

EXERCISES

1. Let $f(x)$ be the characteristic function of a square matrix A with elements in a field $\mathfrak{F}$ such that equation (144) holds for α_i distinct and in $\mathfrak{F}$. Suppose that the non-trivial invariant factors of $xI - A$ are designated by $\phi_1(x)$, $\ldots$, $\phi_m(x)$, where $\phi_{i+1}(x)$ divides $\phi_i(x)$ for $i = 1, \ldots, m - 1$. Show that then $\phi_i(x) = (x - \alpha_1)^{e_{i1}} \cdots (x - \alpha_t)^{e_{it}}$, where $e_{ij} \geq e_{i+1,\,j}$ and $e_{ij} > 0$.

2. The polynomials $(x - \alpha_j)^{e_{ij}}$ are called the *elementary divisors* of $xI - A$. There are mt such polynomials, and those for which $e_{ij} = 0$ are equal to 1 and are called the *trivial elementary divisors* of $xI - A$. Show that the elementary divisors of $xI - A$ uniquely determine the invariant factors of $xI - A$ and hence that A and B are similar if and only if $xI - A$ and $xI - B$ have the same elementary divisors.

3. Give the elementary divisors of $xI - A$ in each of the cases in Exercise 2, Section 20.

4. What is the Jordan canonical form of a matrix A if $xI - A$ has prescribed elementary divisors?

5. Give the Jordan canonical form for each of the matrices in Exercise 3.

6. Let $A = A'$ be a real symmetric matrix. Show that the characteristic roots of A are all real. *Hint:* Show that if x is a complex characteristic vector of A and $\bar{x}$ is the conjugate complex vector, then $xA\bar{x}'$ is real, $x\bar{x}' > 0$, and $xA = \lambda x$, where λ is a characteristic root of A.

7. A matrix A is called an *orthogonal* matrix if $AA' = 1$. Prove that, if A is real and orthogonal, the absolute value of every characteristic root of A is 1.

8. Show that if A is a real symmetric matrix, there exists a real orthogonal matrix P such that PAP' is a diagonal matrix. Show that the rows of P may be taken to be characteristic vectors of A.

9. The characteristic function of a matrix is $(x^2 + 1)^3$. Give all matrices in rational canonical form which have this property.

10. Find a rational six-rowed square matrix A whose minimal polynomial is $(x^2 - 3)(x + 4)^2$ such that the elementary divisors of $xI - A$ are $x^2 - 3$, $(x + 4)^2$, $x + 4$, $x + 4$. Give the Jordan canonical form of A.

11. Determine whether or not the matrices

$$A = \begin{pmatrix} 0 & 1 & 0 \\ 0 & 0 & 2 \\ 3 & 4 & 0 \end{pmatrix}, \qquad B = \begin{pmatrix} 3 & 4 & 0 \\ 2 & 4 & 6 \\ 0 & 1 & 0 \end{pmatrix},$$

are similar in the field $\mathfrak{R}$ of all rational numbers. If they are regarded as matrices with elements in the field $\mathfrak{F}$ of 7 elements, are they similar?

12. Exhibit three 3×3 matrices A, B, C all having the characteristic function $(x+1)^3$ such that no two are similar.

13. Show that the matrix

$$\begin{pmatrix} 0 & 1 & 0 \\ 0 & 0 & 1 \\ -1 & 2 & -1 \end{pmatrix}$$

is not similar to a diagonal matrix in the field $\mathfrak{R}$ of all rational numbers but is similar to a diagonal matrix in the field of all real numbers.

14. Let A be a real n-rowed square matrix, $B = AA'$, and $B^n = I$. Show that the characteristic roots of B are all 1.

15. The characteristic roots of the symmetric matrix

$$A = \begin{pmatrix} 2 & -2 & 0 \\ -2 & 1 & -2 \\ 0 & -2 & 0 \end{pmatrix}$$

are $4, 1, -2$. Find an orthogonal matrix P such that PAP' is a diagonal matrix.

16. Find a non-singular matrix P such that PAP^{-1} is a diagonal matrix if

$$A = \begin{pmatrix} -1 & 8 & 4 \\ 8 & -1 & 4 \\ 4 & 4 & -7 \end{pmatrix}.$$

17. Let $f(u) = 3x^2 - 2y^2 + z^2 - w^2 + xy + 2xz - 6yz + 5xy + 3xw + 5yw + 4zw$ and $u = (x\ y\ z\ w)$. Find a symmetric matrix A such that $f(u) = uAu'$.

18. Use elementary transformations on the rows of A and the corresponding elementary transformations on the columns of A to find an integral matrix P such that PAP' is a diagonal matrix if

$$A = \begin{pmatrix} 4 & -6 & 2 & 0 \\ -6 & 3 & -4 & 0 \\ 2 & -4 & -1 & 1 \\ 0 & 0 & 1 & 0 \end{pmatrix}.$$

19. Let A be an n-by-n matrix and $A^t = 0$, where $t > n$. Prove that $A^n = 0$.

20. Let $\mathfrak{G}$ be the set of all 2×2 matrices A with elements in the field $\mathfrak{F}$ of 5 elements and such that $AA' = I$. Show that $\mathfrak{G}$ is a group and determine its order.

21. Let $A^2 = B^2 = 0$, where A and B are n-rowed square matrices. Show that A and B are similar if and only if they have the same rank.

22. Let

$$A = \begin{pmatrix} 0 & -1 & 0 & 0 \\ 1 & 0 & 0 & 0 \\ 0 & 0 & 0 & 1 \\ 0 & 0 & -1 & 0 \end{pmatrix}, \qquad B = \begin{pmatrix} 0 & 0 & 1 & 0 \\ 0 & 0 & 0 & 1 \\ -1 & 0 & 0 & 0 \\ 0 & -1 & 0 & 0 \end{pmatrix}.$$

Find the order and multiplication table of the group $\mathfrak{G}$ generated by A and B under matrix multiplications.

23. The characteristic roots of a polynomial. If A and B are the triangular matrices

(159) $$A = \begin{pmatrix} \alpha_{11} & \alpha_{12} & \cdots & \alpha_{1n} \\ 0 & \alpha_{22} & \cdots & \alpha_{2n} \\ \cdot & \cdot & \cdots & \cdot \\ 0 & 0 & \cdots & \alpha_{nn} \end{pmatrix}, \qquad B = \begin{pmatrix} \beta_{11} & \beta_{12} & \cdots & \beta_{1n} \\ 0 & \beta_{22} & \cdots & \beta_{2n} \\ \cdot & \cdot & \cdots & \cdot \\ 0 & 0 & \cdots & \beta_{nn} \end{pmatrix},$$

their sum and product have the form

(160) $$C = A + B = \begin{pmatrix} \gamma_{11} & \gamma_{12} & \cdots & \gamma_{1n} \\ 0 & \gamma_{22} & \cdots & \gamma_{2n} \\ \cdot & \cdot & \cdots & \cdot \\ 0 & 0 & \cdots & \gamma_{nn} \end{pmatrix}, \qquad D = AB = \begin{pmatrix} \delta_{11} & \delta_{12} & \cdots & \delta_{1n} \\ 0 & \delta_{22} & \cdots & \delta_{2n} \\ \cdot & \cdot & \cdots & \cdot \\ 0 & 0 & \cdots & \delta_{nn} \end{pmatrix},$$

where $\gamma_{ii} = \alpha_{ii} + \beta_{ii}$, $\delta_{ii} = \alpha_{ii}\beta_{ii}$. Also

(161) $$aA = \begin{pmatrix} a\alpha_{11} & a\alpha_{12} & \cdots & a\alpha_{1n} \\ 0 & a\alpha_{22} & \cdots & a\alpha_{2n} \\ \cdot & \cdot & \cdots & \cdot \\ 0 & 0 & \cdots & a\alpha_{nn} \end{pmatrix}.$$

It follows that if $\psi(x)$ is any polynomial in x, we have

(162) $$\psi(A) = \begin{pmatrix} \psi(\alpha_{11}) & \epsilon_{12} & \cdots & \epsilon_{1n} \\ 0 & \psi(\alpha_{22}) & \cdots & \epsilon_{2n} \\ \cdot & \cdot & \cdots & \cdot \\ 0 & 0 & \cdots & \psi(\alpha_{nn}) \end{pmatrix}.$$

Moreover, we have

(163) $$|xI - \psi(A)| = [x - \psi(\alpha_{11})] \cdots [x - \psi(\alpha_{nn})].$$

We are now able to obtain the following result:

THEOREM 30. *Let* $\psi(x)$ *be any polynomial in* $\mathfrak{F}[x]$ *and* A *be an* $n \times n$ *matrix whose characteristic roots are* $\alpha_1, \ldots, \alpha_n$. *Then the characteristic roots of* $\psi(A)$ *are* $\psi(\alpha_1), \ldots, \psi(\alpha_n)$.

For, by Theorem 29, we can find a matrix P such that $P^{-1}AP = B$, where B is in the form of equations (156)–(157), which is triangular and has $\alpha_1, \alpha_2, \ldots, \alpha_n$ down the main diagonal. Hence, as we have just shown, $\psi(B)$ has characteristic roots $\psi(\alpha_1), \ldots, \psi(\alpha_n)$. So

$$[x - \psi(\alpha_1)] \cdots [x - \psi(\alpha_n)] = |xI - \psi(B)| = |P^{-1}|\,|xI - \psi(B)|\,|P|$$
$$= |xI - P^{-1}\psi(B)P| = |xI - \psi(A)|\,.$$

But $|xI - \psi(A)|$ is the characteristic polynomial of $\psi(A)$.

An immediate consequence of Theorem 30 can be stated as follows:

THEOREM 31. *Let* $\phi(x)$ *be a polynomial of* $\mathfrak{F}[x]$ *and let* $\phi(x) = (x - \alpha_1) \cdots (x - \alpha_n)$, *where* $\alpha_1, \ldots, \alpha_n$ *are in a field* K. *Then the polynomial*

$$f(y) = [y - \psi(\alpha_1)] \cdots [y - \psi(\alpha_n)] \tag{164}$$

has coefficients in $\mathfrak{F}$ *for every polynomial* $\psi(x)$ *of* $\mathfrak{F}[x]$.

For let A be the companion matrix for $\phi(x)$. Then A has characteristic roots $\alpha_1, \alpha_2, \ldots, \alpha_n$. By Theorem 30 $\psi(A)$ has characteristic roots $\psi(\alpha_1), \ldots, \psi(\alpha_n)$. Hence

$$|yI - \psi(A)| = [y - \psi(\alpha_1)] \cdots [y - \psi(\alpha_n)] = f(y)\,.$$

But $|yI - \psi(A)|$ is a polynomial with coefficients in $\mathfrak{F}$, and hence also is $f(y)$.

24. References. The material presented in this chapter is a digest and improved presentation of material presented in chapter iv of the author's *Modern Higher Algebra* and chapters i–v of the author's *Introduction to Algebraic Theories*. The theory of quadratic forms is omitted because it will not be needed in later portions of the test. It may be found in chapter v of *Modern Higher Algebra* and chapter vi of the author's *Solid Analytic Geometry*.

CHAPTER IV

Theory of Algebraic Extensions

1. Simple extensions. A field $\mathfrak{K}$ has been called an *extension* of a field $\mathfrak{F}$ if $\mathfrak{F}$ is a subfield of $\mathfrak{K}$. Then $\mathfrak{K}$ is a vector space over $\mathfrak{F}$. When $\mathfrak{K}$ is an n-dimensional vector space over $\mathfrak{F}$, we say that $\mathfrak{K}$ *has finite degree* over $\mathfrak{F}$ and call n the *degree* of $\mathfrak{K}$ over $\mathfrak{F}$.

If k is an element of an extension $\mathfrak{K}$ of $\mathfrak{F}$, we have designated by $\mathfrak{F}[k]$ the integral domain of all polynomials in k with coefficients in $\mathfrak{F}$. It is a vector space over $\mathfrak{F}$. The quotient field of $\mathfrak{F}[x]$ is called a *simple* extension of $\mathfrak{F}$ and will be designated by $\mathfrak{F}(k)$. It consists of all rational functions of k with coefficients in $\mathfrak{F}$. We say that $\mathfrak{F}(k)$ is a *simple transcendental* extension of $\mathfrak{F}$ if k is an indeterminate over $\mathfrak{F}$. Since all rings $\mathfrak{F}[k]$ are then isomorphic, all simple transcendental extensions of $\mathfrak{F}$ are isomorphic.

When k is not an indeterminate over $\mathfrak{F}$, there is a polynomial $\psi(x) = x^t + \gamma_1 x^{t-1} + \cdots + \gamma_t$ with coefficients $\gamma_1, \ldots, \gamma_t$ in $\mathfrak{F}$ such that $\psi(k) = 0$. The set of all polynomials $\psi(x)$ such that $\psi(k) = 0$ is easily seen to be an ideal $\mathfrak{L}$ of $\mathfrak{F}[x]$. Then $\mathfrak{L}$ is a principal ideal (ϕ) of $\mathfrak{F}[x]$, where

$$(1) \qquad \phi = \phi(x) = x^n + \alpha_1 x^{n-1} + \cdots + \alpha_n \qquad (\alpha_1, \ldots, \alpha_n \text{ in } \mathfrak{F})$$

is a polynomial called the *minimum function of* k *over* $\mathfrak{F}$.

THEOREM 1. *Let $\mathfrak{K}$ be an extension of $\mathfrak{F}$ and* k *in $\mathfrak{K}$ be algebraic over $\mathfrak{F}$. Then the minimum function ϕ(x) of* k *over $\mathfrak{F}$ is an irreducible polynomial in $\mathfrak{F}$. The field $\mathfrak{F}$(k) = $\mathfrak{F}$[k] has finite degree* n *over $\mathfrak{F}$, where* n *is the degree of ϕ(x). Also $\mathfrak{F}$(k) is isomorphic to the difference ring $\mathfrak{F}[x] - (\phi)$.*

If $\psi(x)$ is any polynomial in x, we may write $\psi(x) = \theta(x)\phi(x) + \rho(x)$, where

$$(2) \qquad \rho(x) = \rho_0 + \rho_1 x + \cdots + \rho_{n-1} x^{n-1},$$

where $\rho_0, \ldots, \rho_{n-1}$ are in $\mathfrak{F}$. Then

$$(3) \qquad \rho(k) = \rho_0 + \rho_1 k + \cdots + \rho_{n-1} k^{n-1}.$$

Hence $1, k, \ldots, k^{n-1}$ span $\mathfrak{F}[k]$, and $\mathfrak{F}[k]$ is a finite-dimensional vector space over $\mathfrak{F}$. Now $\rho(k) = 0$ if and only if $\rho_0 = \rho_1 = \cdots = \rho_{n-1} = 0$, since $\phi(x)$ is the minimum function of k over $\mathfrak{F}$. Hence $\mathfrak{F}[k]$ is n-dimensional over $\mathfrak{F}$. The mapping

$$S: \qquad \rho(k) \to \rho(x) + (\phi)$$

is clearly a one-to-one linear mapping of $\mathfrak{F}[k]$ onto $\mathfrak{F}[x] - (\phi)$. It is an isomorphic mapping because $[\rho_1(k)\rho_2(k)]S = [\rho_3(k)]S$, where $\rho_3(x)$ is the remainder on division of $\rho_1(x)\rho_2(x)$ by $\phi(x)$, $[\rho_1(x) + (\phi)][\rho_2(x) + (\phi)] = [\rho_3(x) + (\phi)]$, and $[\rho_3(k)]S = \rho_3(x) + (\phi) = [\rho_1(k)]S \cdot [\rho_2(k)]S$. The ring $\mathfrak{F}[x] - (\phi)$ was seen in chapter ii to be a field if and only if $\phi(x)$ is irreducible. If $\phi(x) = \phi_1(x)\phi_2(x)$, where neither $\phi_1(x)$ nor $\phi_2(x)$ is in $\mathfrak{F}$, then $\phi(k) = \phi_1(k)\phi_2(k) = 0$, and neither $\phi_1(k)$ nor $\phi_2(k)$ is zero. This is impossible in the integral domain $\mathfrak{F}[k]$, and so $\phi(x)$ is irreducible, $\mathfrak{F}[k]$ is a field isomorphic to $\mathfrak{F}[x] - (\phi)$, and $\mathfrak{F}[k] = \mathfrak{F}(k)$.

Theorem 1 not only determines all simple algebraic extensions in the sense of isomorphism but actually proves that, if $\phi(x)$ is an irreducible polynomial of $\mathfrak{F}[x]$, there exists a field $\mathfrak{K} = \mathfrak{F}[k]$ where $\phi(k) = 0$. Indeed, $\mathfrak{K} = \mathfrak{F}[x] - (\phi)$. Note that then $x + (\phi) = k$. For $\phi(k) = \phi(x) + (\phi) = (\phi)$ is the zero element of $\mathfrak{K}$. A field $\mathfrak{F}[k]$ defined by an irreducible polynomial $\phi(x)$ will be called a *stem field* of $\phi(x)$.

2. Algebraic extensions of finite degree. A field $\mathfrak{K}$ is called an *algebraic extension* of a field $\mathfrak{F}$ if every element k of $\mathfrak{K}$ is algebraic over $\mathfrak{F}$. A field $\mathfrak{K}$ is said to be a *finite extension* of a field $\mathfrak{F}$ if $\mathfrak{K} = \mathfrak{F}(k_1, \ldots, k_t)$ is the field of all rational functions with coefficients in $\mathfrak{F}$ of the elements $k_1, \ldots, k_t$ of $\mathfrak{K}$. We call $\mathfrak{K}$ a *finite algebraic extension of* $\mathfrak{F}$ if $\mathfrak{K} = \mathfrak{F}(k_1, \ldots, k_t)$, where $k_1, \ldots, k_t$ are algebraic over $\mathfrak{F}$.

THEOREM 2. *A field $\mathfrak{K}$ is a finite algebraic extension of $\mathfrak{F}$ if and only if $\mathfrak{K}$ has finite degree* n *over $\mathfrak{F}$.*

For if $\mathfrak{K}$ has finite degree n over $\mathfrak{F}$, there are elements $u_1, \ldots, u_n$ in $\mathfrak{K}$ such that $\mathfrak{K} = u_1\mathfrak{F} + \cdots + u_n\mathfrak{F}$. Then $\mathfrak{K} = \mathfrak{F}[u_1, \ldots, u_n] = \mathfrak{F}(u_1, \ldots, u_n)$. Conversely, let $\mathfrak{K} = \mathfrak{F}[k_1, \ldots, k_t]$, where $k_1, \ldots, k_t$ are algebraic over $\mathfrak{F}$. Put $\mathfrak{F}_i = \mathfrak{F}_{i-1}[k_i]$, where $\mathfrak{F}_0 = \mathfrak{F}$ and $i = 1, \ldots, t$. By Theorem 1 the integral domain $\mathfrak{F}_1 = \mathfrak{F}[k_1] = \mathfrak{F}(k_1)$ has finite dimension n_1 over $\mathfrak{F}$. Assume that $\mathfrak{F}_{i-1}$ has dimension $\nu = n_{i-1}$ over $\mathfrak{F}$. Then $\mathfrak{F}_{i-1} = u_1\mathfrak{F} + \cdots + u_\nu\mathfrak{F}$. Since k_i is algebraic over $\mathfrak{F}$, it is necessarily algebraic over $\mathfrak{F}_{i-1}$ and $\mathfrak{F}_i = \mathfrak{F}_{i-1}(k_i)$ is a field of degree μ over $\mathfrak{F}_{i-1}$. Then $\mathfrak{F}_i = v_i\mathfrak{F}_{i-1} + \cdots + v_\mu\mathfrak{F}_{i-1}$ and is spanned over $\mathfrak{F}$ by the $\nu\mu$ elements u_iv_j; $\mathfrak{F}_i$ has finite dimension $n_i = \mu\nu$ over $\mathfrak{F}$. This proves that $\mathfrak{F}_t = \mathfrak{K} = \mathfrak{F}(k_1, \ldots, k_t) = \mathfrak{F}[k_1, \ldots, k_t]$ is a finite-dimensional vector space over $\mathfrak{F}$, as desired.

3. Subfields. We shall use the symbol

$$[\mathfrak{K} : \mathfrak{F}] \tag{4}$$

to represent the *degree* of $\mathfrak{K}$ over $\mathfrak{F}$. Every subfield of a field $\mathfrak{K}$ of degree n over $\mathfrak{F}$ is a subspace of a finite-dimensional space and so has finite dimension.

THEOREM 3. *Let $\mathfrak{K} \supseteq \mathfrak{L} \supseteq \mathfrak{F}$, where $\mathfrak{K}$, $\mathfrak{L}$, and $\mathfrak{F}$ are fields. Then $\mathfrak{K}$ has finite degree over $\mathfrak{F}$ if and only if $\mathfrak{K}$ has finite degree over $\mathfrak{L}$ and $\mathfrak{L}$ has finite degree over $\mathfrak{F}$. Moreover,*

$$[\mathfrak{K}:\mathfrak{L}][\mathfrak{L}:\mathfrak{F}] = [\mathfrak{K}:\mathfrak{F}] . \tag{5}$$

Theorem 3 states that the degree of a subfield $\mathfrak{L}$ of a field $\mathfrak{K}$ over $\mathfrak{F}$ divides the degree of $\mathfrak{K}$ over $\mathfrak{F}$. If $\mathfrak{K} \supseteq \mathfrak{L} \supseteq \mathfrak{F}$ and$[\mathfrak{K}:\mathfrak{F}] = n$, then $\mathfrak{L}:\mathfrak{F} = m$, and $\mathfrak{K}$ is spanned over $\mathfrak{L}$ by its basal elements over $\mathfrak{F}$, and so $[\mathfrak{K}:\mathfrak{L}] = q$. Then $\mathfrak{K} = w_1\mathfrak{L} + \cdots + w_q\mathfrak{L}$, $\mathfrak{L} = v_1\mathfrak{F} + \cdots + v_m\mathfrak{F}$, and it should be evident that the mq elements v_iw_j $(i = 1, \ldots, m; j = 1, \ldots, q)$ span $\mathfrak{K}$ over $\mathfrak{F}$. If

$$\sum_{1,j} a_{ij}w_j v_i = 0$$

for a_{ij} in $\mathfrak{F}$, then

$$0 = \sum_{j=1}^{q} a_j w_j ,$$

where the

$$a_j = \sum_{i=1}^{m} a_{ij} v_i$$

are in $\mathfrak{L}$. By the definition of $w_1, \ldots, w_q$ we see that $a_1 = \cdots = a_q = 0$. By the definition of the elements $v_1, \ldots, v_m$ it follows that the a_{ij} are all zero, and the mq elements v_iw_j are linearly independent in $\mathfrak{F}$. But then $\mathfrak{K}$ has degree mq over $\mathfrak{F}$, and equation (5) holds. Conversely, if $\mathfrak{K} = w_1\mathfrak{L} + \cdots + w_q\mathfrak{L}$ and $\mathfrak{L} = v_1\mathfrak{F} + \cdots + v_m\mathfrak{F}$, the elements w_jv_i span $\mathfrak{K}$ over $\mathfrak{F}$, and $[\mathfrak{K}:\mathfrak{F}]$ is finite.

As an immediate consequence we have:

COROLLARY. *Let $\mathfrak{K}$ have degree* n *over $\mathfrak{F}$ and* k *be in $\mathfrak{K}$. Then the degree of the minimum function of* k *over $\mathfrak{F}$ divides* n.

4. Splitting fields. Consider any polynomial $\phi(x)$ in an indeterminate x over $\mathfrak{F}$. Then a field $\mathfrak{K}$ over $\mathfrak{F}$ is said to *split* $\phi(x)$ if there exist elements $a_1, \ldots, a_n$ in $\mathfrak{K}$ such that

$$\phi(x) = (x - a_1) \cdots (x - a_n) . \tag{6}$$

We call $\mathfrak{K}$ a *splitting field* for $\phi(x)$ if $\mathfrak{K}$ splits $\phi(x)$ and $\mathfrak{K} = \mathfrak{F}(a_1, \ldots, a_n)$, where $a_1, \ldots, a_n$ are the roots in $\mathfrak{K}$ of $\phi(x)$. The subfields $\mathfrak{F}[a_i] = \mathfrak{F}(a_i)$ of $\mathfrak{K}$ will be called the stem fields of $\phi(x)$. (Stem fields were defined on p. 97 only for irreducible polynomials.) They need not be isomorphic over $\mathfrak{F}$. However, they are isomorphic when $\phi(x)$ is irreducible.

A portion of Theorem 1 may be generalized as follows: Let S be an isomorphism of a field $\mathfrak{F}$ onto a field $\mathfrak{F}'$. Let us use the same symbol x for an indeterminate over $\mathfrak{F}$ and over $\mathfrak{F}'$. Then the rings $\mathfrak{F}[x]$ and $\mathfrak{F}'[x]$ are isomorphic, and the mapping $a_i \to a_i S$ of each coefficient of $\phi(x) = x^n + a_1 x^{n-1} + \cdots + a_n$ maps $\phi(x)$ onto an image polynomial $\phi'(x) = x^n + (a_1 S)x^{n-1} + \cdots + a_n S$. It follows immediately that $\mathfrak{F}[x] - (\phi)$ is isomorphic to $\mathfrak{F}'[x] - (\phi')$. We state this result as follows:

THEOREM 4. *Let* S *be an isomorphic mapping of a field* $\mathfrak{F}$ *onto a field* $\mathfrak{F}' = \mathfrak{F}S$ *so that* S *maps every polynomial* $\phi = \phi(x)$ *of* $\mathfrak{F}[x]$ *onto an image polynomial* $\phi' = \phi'(x)$. *Let* $\phi(x)$ *be an irreducible polynomial of* $\mathfrak{F}[x]$ *so that* $\phi'(x)$ *is an irreducible polynomial of* $\mathfrak{F}'[x]$. *Then if* $\mathfrak{L} = \mathfrak{F}[k]$ *is a stem field of* $\phi(x)$ *and* $\mathfrak{L}' = \mathfrak{F}'[k']$ *is a stem field of* $\phi'(x)$, *the isomorphism* S *can be extended to be an isomorphism of* $\mathfrak{L}$ *onto* $\mathfrak{L}'$.

If $\phi(x)$ is any polynomial, there exists a stem field $\mathfrak{K}_1 = \mathfrak{F}[a_1]$ of an irreducible polynomial factor of $\phi(x)$. Then $\phi(x) = (x - a_1)\phi_1(x)$, where $\phi_1(x)$ is in $\mathfrak{K}_1[x]$. We adjoin a root a_2 of an irreducible factor of $\phi_1(x)$ and have $\phi(x) = (x - a_1)(x - a_2)\phi_2(x)$, where $\phi_2(x)$ is in $\mathfrak{K}_2[x]$ and $\mathfrak{K}_2 = \mathfrak{F}[a_1, a_2]$. After, at most, $n - 1$ such steps we obtain a splitting field $\mathfrak{N} = \mathfrak{F}[a_1, \ldots, a_n]$ of $\phi(x)$. We now prove the following result:

THEOREM 5. *Let* $\mathfrak{F}' = \mathfrak{F}S$, *as in Theorem* 4, $\phi(x)$ *be a polynomial in* $\mathfrak{F}[x]$, $\phi'(x)$ *be the image polynomial in* $\mathfrak{F}'[x]$, $\mathfrak{N}$ *be a splitting field over* $\mathfrak{F}$ *of* $\phi(x)$, *and* $\mathfrak{N}'$ *be a splitting field over* $\mathfrak{F}'$ *of* $\phi'(x)$. *Then* S *can be extended to be an isomorphism of* $\mathfrak{N}$ *onto* $\mathfrak{N}'$.

This result is true for polynomials $\phi(x)$ of degree $n = 1$, since then $\phi(x) = x - a$, $\phi'(x) = x - aS$, $\mathfrak{N} = \mathfrak{F}$, and $\mathfrak{N}' = \mathfrak{F}'$. Assume it true for polynomials of degree, at most, $n - 1$. We consider an irreducible factor $\psi(x)$ of $\phi(x)$ and let $\mathfrak{F}_1 = \mathfrak{F}(a_1)$ be a stem field in $\mathfrak{N}$ of $\psi(x)$. Similarly, we let $\mathfrak{F}_1' = \mathfrak{F}_1(a_1')$ be a stem field in $\mathfrak{N}'$ of $\psi'(x)$. By Theorem 4 we may extend S to be an isomorphism T of $\mathfrak{F}_1$ onto $\mathfrak{F}_1'$. Also $\phi(x) = (x - a_1)\phi_1(x)$, and $\phi'(x) = (x - a_1')\phi_1'(x)$, where T maps $\phi_1(x)$ onto $\phi_1'(x)$. But $\mathfrak{N}$ is a splitting field over $\mathfrak{F}_1$ of $\phi_1(x)$, $\mathfrak{N}'$ is a splitting field over $\mathfrak{F}_1'$ of $\phi_1'(x)$, $\phi_1(x)$ has degree $n - 1$, and so T may be extended to an isomorphism of $\mathfrak{N}$ onto $\mathfrak{N}'$, as desired.

If we take $\mathfrak{F} = \mathfrak{F}'$ and S to be the identity automorphism of $\mathfrak{F}$ in Theorem 5, we have the following result:

THEOREM 6. *Any two splitting fields over* $\mathfrak{F}$ *of a polynomial in* $\mathfrak{F}[x]$ *are isomorphic over* $\mathfrak{F}$.

An isomorphism S of a field $\mathfrak{L}$ over $\mathfrak{F}$ onto a field $\mathfrak{L}'$ over $\mathfrak{F}$ is called an *isomorphism over* $\mathfrak{F}$ if $aS = a$ for every a of $\mathfrak{F}$. An automorphism S of $\mathfrak{L}$

over $\mathfrak{F}$ onto $\mathfrak{L}$ is called an *automorphism over* $\mathfrak{F}$ if S is an isomorphism over $\mathfrak{F}$. Theorem 5 has the following important consequence:

THEOREM 7. *Let* $\mathfrak{N}$ *be a splitting field over* $\mathfrak{F}$ *of a polynomial* $\phi(x)$ *and* S *be an isomorphism over* $\mathfrak{F}$ *of a subfield* $\mathfrak{L}$ *over* $\mathfrak{F}$ *of* $\mathfrak{N}$ *onto a subfield* $\mathfrak{L}'$ *over* $\mathfrak{F}$ *of* $\mathfrak{N}$. *Then* S *may be extended to be an automorphism over* $\mathfrak{F}$ *of* $\mathfrak{N}$.

For $\mathfrak{N}$ is a splitting field over $\mathfrak{L}$ of $\phi(x)$ as well as a splitting field over $\mathfrak{L}'$ of $\phi'(x)$, where S clearly maps $\phi(x)$ onto $\phi'(x) = \phi(x)$. Our result then follows immediately from Theorem 5.

We close this section with an application of Theorem 3.

THEOREM 8. *Let* $\phi(x)$ *be an irreducible polynomial of* $\mathfrak{F}[x]$, $\phi(x) = (x - \alpha_1) \cdots (x - \alpha_n)$ *for* $\alpha_1, \ldots, \alpha_n$ *in a splitting field* $\mathfrak{N} = \mathfrak{F}[\alpha_1, \ldots, \alpha_n]$. *Then, if* $k = \psi(\alpha_1)$ *is any element of the stem field* $\mathfrak{F}[\alpha_1]$ *of* $\phi(x)$, *the polynomial*

$$(7) \qquad \lambda(x) = [x - \psi(\alpha_1)] \cdots [x - \psi(\alpha_n)] = [\mu(x)]^q ,$$

where $\mu(x)$ *is the minimum function over* $\mathfrak{F}$ *of* k, $n = mq$, *and* m *is the degree of* $\mathfrak{F}[k]$ *over* $\mathfrak{F}$.

For Theorem 3.31 implies that $\lambda(x)$ has coefficients in $\mathfrak{F}$ and $\lambda(k) = 0$. It follows that the minimum function over $\mathfrak{F}$ of k divides $\lambda(x)$. The polynomial $\mu[\psi(x)]$ has α_1 as a root and so is divisible by $\phi(x)$. Then $\mu[\psi(\alpha_i)] = 0$, and so every one of the roots of $\lambda(x)$ is a root of $\mu(x) = 0$.

Now $\lambda(x) = [\mu(x)]^q\lambda_0(x)$, where $\lambda_0(x)$ is either a non-constant polynomial prime to $\mu(x)$ or $\lambda_0(x) = 1$. Since $\lambda_0(x)$ must have a root in common with $\mu(x)$, it is divisible by $\mu(x)$, and the resulting contradiction implies that $\lambda_0(x) = 1$.

5. Composites. If $\mathfrak{L}$ and $\mathfrak{M}$ are two subfields of a field $\mathfrak{K}$, their *composite* in $\mathfrak{K}$ is the intersection $[\mathfrak{L}, \mathfrak{M}]$ of all subfields of $\mathfrak{K}$ which contain both $\mathfrak{L}$ and $\mathfrak{M}$. If $\mathfrak{K}$, $\mathfrak{L}$, and $\mathfrak{M}$ are all extensions of a field $\mathfrak{F}$, the field $[\mathfrak{L}, \mathfrak{M}]$ is a field over $\mathfrak{F}$ consisting of all rational functions with coefficients in $\mathfrak{F}$ of the elements of $\mathfrak{L}$ and $\mathfrak{M}$. If $f(x)$ is a polynomial of $\mathfrak{F}[x]$ and $\mathfrak{K}$ is a splitting field of $f(x)$, then $\mathfrak{K} = \mathfrak{F}(\alpha_1, \ldots, \alpha_n)$ is the composite of the stem fields $\mathfrak{F}(\alpha_i)$ in $\mathfrak{K}$ of $f(x)$.

If $\mathfrak{L}$ and $\mathfrak{M}$ are arbitrary fields, we define the *composites* of $\mathfrak{L}$ and $\mathfrak{M}$ to be the composites in $\mathfrak{K}$ of $\mathfrak{L}_0$ and $\mathfrak{M}_0$ for all fields $\mathfrak{K}$ with a subfield $\mathfrak{L}_0$ isomorphic to $\mathfrak{L}$ and a subfield $\mathfrak{M}_0$ isomorphic to $\mathfrak{M}$. Every composite of $\mathfrak{L}$ and $\mathfrak{M}$ is then isomorphic to a composite containing $\mathfrak{L}$. These composites are then all fields $\mathfrak{Z}$ over $\mathfrak{L}$ which contain a subfield $\mathfrak{M}_0$ isomorphic to $\mathfrak{M}$ and which are such that $\mathfrak{Z}$ is the composite in $\mathfrak{Z}$ of $\mathfrak{M}_0$ and $\mathfrak{L}$.

Let $f(x)$ be a polynomial in $\mathfrak{F}[x]$ and $\mathfrak{L}$ be a field over $\mathfrak{F}$. Then the composites of $\mathfrak{L}$ and a stem field $\mathfrak{M} = \mathfrak{F}[\alpha]$ of $f(x)$ are the stem fields over $\mathfrak{L}$

of $f(x)$ *considered as a polynomial* of $\mathfrak{L}[x]$. The composites of $\mathfrak{L}$ and a splitting field $\mathfrak{K}$ of $f(x)$ are all isomorphic to the essentially unique splitting field over $\mathfrak{L}$ of the polynomial $f(x)$ of $\mathfrak{L}[x]$.

THEOREM 9. *Let $\mathfrak{K}$ be algebraic of finite degree over $\mathfrak{F}$ and let $\mathfrak{K}$ contain a field $\mathfrak{L}$ of degree m over $\mathfrak{F}$ as well as a field $\mathfrak{M}$ of degree q over $\mathfrak{F}$. Then $[\mathfrak{L}, \mathfrak{M}]$ has degree $r \leq mq$ over $\mathfrak{F}$.*

For $\mathfrak{L} = u_1\mathfrak{F} + \cdots + u_m\mathfrak{F}$ and $\mathfrak{M} = v_1\mathfrak{F} + \cdots + v_q\mathfrak{F}$. Then $[\mathfrak{L}, \mathfrak{M}] = (v_1\mathfrak{L}, \ldots, v_q\mathfrak{L})$ has degree $t \leq q$ over $\mathfrak{L}$ and so has degree $r \leq mq$ over $\mathfrak{F}$. *Note* that $\mathfrak{C} = (v_1\mathfrak{L}, \ldots, v_q\mathfrak{L})$ is a ring containing $\mathfrak{L}$ and $\mathfrak{M}$ which is algebraic over $\mathfrak{F}$; it then follows from Theorem 1 that $\mathfrak{C}$ is a field, so $\mathfrak{C} = [\mathfrak{L}, \mathfrak{M}]$.

The composite $\mathfrak{C}$ of $\mathfrak{L}$ of degree m over $\mathfrak{F}$ and $\mathfrak{M}$ of degree q over $\mathfrak{F}$ is called the *direct product* of $\mathfrak{L}$ and $\mathfrak{M}$, and we write

$$\mathfrak{C} = \mathfrak{L} \times \mathfrak{M} \tag{8}$$

if $\mathfrak{C}$ has degree mq over $\mathfrak{F}$. It is easily shown to be unique in the sense of isomorphism.

THEOREM 10. *Let $\mathfrak{L}$ have degree m over $\mathfrak{F}$ and let $\mathfrak{M}$ have degree q over $\mathfrak{F}$, where m is prime to q. Then $[\mathfrak{L}, \mathfrak{M}] = \mathfrak{L} \times \mathfrak{M}$.*

For the degree r of $[\mathfrak{L}, \mathfrak{M}]$ is divisible by m and by q. Then mq divides r, and so $r \geq mq$. By Theorem 9 we know that $r \leq mq$, and so $r = mq$.

6. Binomial and trinomial equations. The roots of the equation $x^n = 1$ are called *nth roots of unity.* The nth roots of unity in a field form a multiplicative abelian group. When this group is cyclic, it is generated by an element called a *primitive* n*th root of unity.*

Let a be in a field $\mathfrak{F}$. Then the equation

$$x^n = a \tag{9}$$

is called a *binomial* equation. When n is a prime, we have the following result:

THEOREM 11. *Let p be a prime and a be in a field $\mathfrak{F}$. Then the polynomial $x^p - a$ is irreducible in $\mathfrak{F}$ if and only if the equation $x^p = a$ has no root in $\mathfrak{F}$.*

For assume, first, that $\mathfrak{F}$ has characteristic p. Then, if ξ is a root of $x^p = a$, we have $\xi^p = a$. By the binomial theorem, $(x - \xi)^p = x^p - \xi^p = x^p - a$. Hence all roots of $x^p = a$ are equal to ξ. If $f(x) = g(x)h(x)$, where $g(x)$ is a non-constant polynomial of degree $r < p$, the constant term of $g(x)$ is an element $(-1)^r\beta$ of $\mathfrak{F}$. The r roots of $g(x) = 0$ are all equal to ξ, and so $\xi^r = \beta$. But r is prime to p, $r\lambda + p\mu = 1$ for integers λ and μ; $\xi^{r\lambda} = \beta^\lambda = \xi^{1-p\mu} = \xi a^{-\mu}$; and $\xi = a^\mu\beta^\lambda$ is in $\mathfrak{F}$. Conversely, if $x^p = a$ has a root ξ in $\mathfrak{F}$, it has a factor $x - \xi$ and is reducible.

Assume, next, that $\mathfrak{F}$ has characteristic not p. If ξ and η are roots of $x^p = \alpha$, we have $(\xi\eta^{-1})^p = \alpha\alpha^{-1} = 1$ and so $\xi = \eta\omega$, where $\omega^p = 1$. It follows that the roots of $x^p = \alpha$ have the form $\xi, \xi\omega_2, \ldots, \xi\omega_p$, where $\omega_i^p = 1$. If $f(x) = g(x)h(x)$, where $g(x)$ is as above, we may assume that the roots of $g(x) = 0$ are $\xi, \xi\omega_2, \ldots, \xi\omega_r$. The constant term of $g(x)$ is an element $(-1)^r\beta$, where β is in $\mathfrak{F}$, and the product of the roots of $g(x)$ is $\beta = \xi^r\omega_2 \cdots \omega_r = \xi^r\omega$, where $\omega^p = 1$. As before, $r\lambda + p\mu = 1$, and so $\xi_r^\lambda = \omega^{-\lambda}\beta^\lambda = \xi^{1-p\mu} = \xi\alpha^{-\mu}$, and $\xi = \alpha^\mu\beta^\lambda\omega^{-\lambda}$. Then $\xi^p = (\alpha^\mu\beta^\lambda)^p = \alpha$ has the root $\alpha^\mu\beta^\lambda$ in $\mathfrak{F}$. As before, the converse is obvious.

A trinomial equation is an equation having three terms. We shall consider only a special case.

THEOREM 12. *Let* α *be in* $\mathfrak{F}$, *a field of characteristic* p. *Then the polynomial* $x^p - x - \alpha$ *is irreducible in* $\mathfrak{F}$ *if and only if the equation* $x^p = x + \alpha$ *has no root in* $\mathfrak{F}$.

For if ξ is a root of $x^p = x + \alpha$, we see that $(\xi + k)^p = \xi^p + k^p = \xi + \alpha + k$ for $k = 0, 1, \ldots, p - 1$. Hence the roots of $f(x) = x^p - x - \alpha = 0$ are $\xi, \xi + 1, \ldots, \xi + p - 1$. If $f(x) = g(x)h(x)$, where $g(x)$ has degree r and $0 < r < p$, the sum of the roots of $g(x) = 0$ is an element β in $\mathfrak{F}$. This sum is $r\xi + s$, where s is an integer. Then r has an inverse in $\mathfrak{F}$ and $r\xi + s = \beta$, $\xi = r^{-1}(\beta - s)$ is in $\mathfrak{F}$. The converse is trivial.

7. Separable polynomials and fields. The integral domain $\mathfrak{F}[x]$ is a vector space over $\mathfrak{F}$. There is a linear transformation D on $\mathfrak{F}[x]$ called the operation of *differentiation*. If

$$f(x) = \alpha_0x^n + \alpha_1x^{n-1} + \cdots + \alpha_n \quad (\alpha_0 \neq 0, \alpha_1, \ldots, \alpha_n \text{ in } \mathfrak{F}), \tag{10}$$

we define D as the mapping

$$f \to fD = f'(x) = \alpha_0nx^{n-1} + \alpha_1(n-1)x^{n-2} + \cdots + \alpha_{n-1} \tag{11}$$

of $\mathfrak{F}[x]$ into $\mathfrak{F}[x]$. It may easily be seen to be a linear transformation with the properties

$$(fg)' = fg' + f'g, \quad (f^k)' = kf^{k-1}f'. \tag{12}$$

A polynomial $f(x)$ of $\mathfrak{F}[x]$ is said to be *separable* if $f(x) = (x - \xi_1) \cdots (x - \xi_n)$ for *distinct* elements $\xi_1, \ldots, \xi_n$ in a splitting field $\mathfrak{K}$ of $f(x)$. When $f(x)$ is not separable, we say that $f(x)$ is *inseparable*. If $f(x) = (x - \alpha)^m g(x)$ and $g(\alpha) \neq 0$, we call α a root of *multiplicity* m of the polynomial $f(x)$ and the equation $f(x) = 0$.

LEMMA 1. *A polynomial* f(x) *is separable if and only if the greatest common divisor* d(x) *of* f(x) *and* f'(x) *is unity.*

For if $d(x) = 1$ and $f(x) = (x - \xi)^m g(x)$, we have $f'(x) = (x - \xi)^m g'(x) +$

$m(x - \xi)^{m-1}g(x) = (x - \xi)^{m-1}q(x)$. Thus $(x - \xi)^{m-1}$ divides $d(x)$, $m = 1$, all roots of $f(x)$ have multiplicity 1, and $f(x)$ is separable. Conversely, if $f(x)$ is separable and ξ is any root of $f(x) = 0$, we have $f(x) = (x - \xi)g(x)$, where $g(\xi) \neq 0$, $f'(x) = (x - \xi)g'(x) + g(x)$, and $f'(\xi) = g(\xi) \neq 0$. Then $d(\xi) \neq 0$ for every root ξ of $f(x)$. But the polynomial $d(x)$ divides $f(x)$, and every root of $d(x)$ is a root of $f(x)$, and $d(x) = 1$.

We apply this result to irreducible polynomials as follows:

THEOREM 13. *An irreducible polynomial* f(x) *is inseparable if any only if* f(x) = g(x^p), *where* p *is the characteristic of* $\mathfrak{F}$.

For the g.c.d. of $f(x)$ and $f'(x)$ is a monic divisor $d(x)$ of the irreducible polynomial $f(x)$. Then either $d(x) = 1$ or $d(x)$ is an associate of $f(x)$. However, the degree of $f'(x)$ is less than the degree of $f(x)$, and $f(x)$ divides $f'(x)$ if and only if $f'(x) = 0$. This occurs only when $\mathfrak{F}$ has characteristic p and $(n - i)a_i = 0$, p divides n, and p divides every i for which $a_i \neq 0$. Then $f(x)$ is a polynomial in $\mathfrak{F}[x^p]$.

We restrict our further attention to the study of algebraic extension fields $\mathfrak{K}$ of finite degree over $\mathfrak{F}$. An *element* k of $\mathfrak{K}$ is said to be *separable* over $\mathfrak{F}$ if there exists a separable polynomial $f(x)$ of $\mathfrak{F}[x]$ such that $f(k) = 0$. Since the minimum function of k over $\mathfrak{F}$ divides $f(x)$, it must also be separable. Thus an element k of $\mathfrak{K}$ is separable over $\mathfrak{F}$ if and only if the minimum function of k over $\mathfrak{F}$ is a separable irreducible polynomial. If k is not separable over $\mathfrak{F}$, we say that k is *inseparable.*

A *field* $\mathfrak{K}$ of finite degree over $\mathfrak{F}$ is said to be *separable* over $\mathfrak{F}$ if every element of $\mathfrak{K}$ is separable over $\mathfrak{F}$. By Theorem 13 every element of $\mathfrak{K}$ is separable over $\mathfrak{F}$ when $\mathfrak{F}$ has characteristic zero.

THEOREM 14. *Every algebraic extension of finite degree of a field* $\mathfrak{F}$ *of characteristic zero is separable over* $\mathfrak{F}$.

If $\mathfrak{K}$ is not separable over $\mathfrak{F}$, we call $\mathfrak{K}$ an *inseparable* extension of $\mathfrak{F}$. Inseparable extensions can occur only for fields of characteristic p. The binomial theorem implies that

$$(k_1 + k_2)^p = k_1^p + k_2^p \tag{13}$$

for all elements k_1 and k_2 of $\mathfrak{K}$ of characteristic p. Since $(k_1k_2)^p = k_1^pk_2^p$, we see that the set $\mathfrak{K}^p$ of all the pth powers of the elements of $\mathfrak{K}$ is a subfield of $\mathfrak{K}$. The mapping

$$k \to k^p \tag{14}$$

is an isomorphic mapping of $\mathfrak{K}$ onto $\mathfrak{K}^p$, since $k_1^p = k_2^p$ if and only if $k_1^p - k_2^p = (k_1 - k_2)^p = 0$, and $k_1 - k_2 = 0$. We now define

$$\mathfrak{K}^{(p)} = [\mathfrak{K}^p, \mathfrak{F}] . \tag{15}$$

If $\mathfrak{K} = u_1\mathfrak{F} + \cdots + u_n\mathfrak{F}$, then $\mathfrak{K}^p = u_1^p\mathfrak{F}^p + \cdots + u_n^p\mathfrak{F}^p$. It follows, as in the proof of Theorem 9, that

$$(16) \qquad \mathfrak{K}^{(p)} = (u_n^p\mathfrak{F}, \ldots, u_1^p\mathfrak{F}),$$

so that $u_1^p, \ldots, u_n^p$ span $\mathfrak{K}^{(p)}$ over $\mathfrak{F}$. However, $u_1^p, \ldots, u_n^p$ need not be linearly independent in $\mathfrak{F}$.

LEMMA 2. *Let* $\mathfrak{K} \supseteq \mathfrak{L} \supseteq \mathfrak{F}$. *Then* $\mathfrak{K} = \mathfrak{K}^{(p)} = [\mathfrak{K}^p, \mathfrak{F}]$ *if and only if* $\mathfrak{K} = [\mathfrak{K}^p, \mathfrak{L}]$ *and* $\mathfrak{L} = [\mathfrak{L}^p, \mathfrak{F}]$.

For let $\mathfrak{K} = u_1\mathfrak{L} + \cdots + u_q\mathfrak{L}$ and $\mathfrak{L} = v_1\mathfrak{F} + \cdots + v_m\mathfrak{F}$. If $\mathfrak{K} = \mathfrak{K}^{(p)}$, then $\mathfrak{K}^p = u_1^p\mathfrak{L}^p + \cdots + u_q^p\mathfrak{L}^p$, $\mathfrak{L}^p = v_1^p\mathfrak{F}^p + \cdots + v_m^p\mathfrak{F}^p$, and $\mathfrak{L}^{(p)} = (v_1^p\mathfrak{F}, \ldots, v_m^p\mathfrak{F})$. Then $\mathfrak{K}^{(p)}$ is spanned over $\mathfrak{F}$ by the $n = mq$ products $u_i^pv_j^p$. Since $\mathfrak{K}$ has dimension n over $\mathfrak{F}$, if $\mathfrak{K} = \mathfrak{K}^{(p)}$, these products must be linearly independent in $\mathfrak{F}$, $v_1^p, \ldots, v_m^p$ must be linearly independent in $\mathfrak{F}$, $\mathfrak{L}^{(p)} = \mathfrak{L}$, and $\mathfrak{K}^{(p)} = u_1^p\mathfrak{L} + \cdots + u_q^p\mathfrak{L} = [\mathfrak{K}^p, \mathfrak{L}] = \mathfrak{K}$. Conversely, if $[\mathfrak{K}^p, \mathfrak{L}] = \mathfrak{K}$ and $\mathfrak{L} = [\mathfrak{L}^p, \mathfrak{F}] = \mathfrak{L}^{(p)}$, we see that $\mathfrak{K}^{(p)} = (u_1^p[\mathfrak{L}^p, \mathfrak{F}], \ldots, u_q^p[\mathfrak{L}^p, \mathfrak{F}]) = (u_1^p\mathfrak{L}, \ldots, u_q^p\mathfrak{L}) = [\mathfrak{K}^p, \mathfrak{L}] = \mathfrak{K}$, as desired.

We use this result to obtain the following criterion:

THEOREM 15. *An algebraic extension* $\mathfrak{K}$ *of degree* n *over a field* $\mathfrak{F}$ *of characteristic* p *is separable over* $\mathfrak{F}$ *if and only if* $\mathfrak{K} = \mathfrak{K}^{(p)}$.

We first let $\mathfrak{K}$ be separable over $\mathfrak{F}$. The theorem is true trivially if $n = 1$. Hence let it be true for fields of degree less than $n > 1$. If $\mathfrak{K}$ contains a subfield $\mathfrak{L}$ of degree m over $\mathfrak{F}$, where $n > m > 1$, then $\mathfrak{L}$ is separable over $\mathfrak{F}$, and so $\mathfrak{L} = \mathfrak{L}^{(p)}$. But our definitions imply that $\mathfrak{K}$ is separable over $\mathfrak{L}$, and so $\mathfrak{K} = [\mathfrak{K}^p, \mathfrak{L}]$. By Lemma 2 we see that $\mathfrak{K} = \mathfrak{K}^{(p)}$. There remains the case where every element k of $\mathfrak{K}$ which is not in $\mathfrak{F}$ generates $\mathfrak{K}$ over $\mathfrak{F}$. Then $\mathfrak{K} = \mathfrak{F}[k] = \mathfrak{F} + k\mathfrak{F} + \cdots + k^{n-1}\mathfrak{F}$, and $\mathfrak{K}^{(p)} = (\mathfrak{F}, k^p\mathfrak{F}, \ldots, k^{p(n-1)}\mathfrak{F}) = \mathfrak{F}[k^p]$. Then $\mathfrak{K} = \mathfrak{K}^{(p)}$ unless $k^p = a$ in $\mathfrak{F}$. This can occur only if k is inseparable over $\mathfrak{F}$, contrary to hypothesis.

Conversely, let $\mathfrak{K} = \mathfrak{K}^{(p)}$. Assume that $\mathfrak{K}$ contains an element k which is inseparable over $\mathfrak{F}$. Then the minimum function of k is a polynomial $\psi(x^p)$ of degree mp over $\mathfrak{F}$. The field $\mathfrak{L} = \mathfrak{F}[k]$ has degree mp over $\mathfrak{F}$, and $\mathfrak{H} = \mathfrak{F}[k^p]$ has degree m over $\mathfrak{F}$. Then $\mathfrak{L}^{(p)} = \mathfrak{F}[k^p] = \mathfrak{H} \neq \mathfrak{L}$, which is impossible by Lemma 2. This completes our proof.

THEOREM 16. *Let* $\mathfrak{K} = \mathfrak{F}(\mathrm{k})$, *where* k *is separable over* $\mathfrak{F}$. *Then* $\mathfrak{K}$ *is separable over* $\mathfrak{F}$.

For, otherwise, $\mathfrak{K}^{(p)} = \mathfrak{F}(k^p)$ is a proper subfield over $\mathfrak{F}$. By Theorem 11 the polynomial $x^p - k^p$ is either irreducible in $\mathfrak{K}^{(p)}$ or has a root in $\mathfrak{K}^{(p)}$. It cannot have a root in $\mathfrak{K}^{(p)}$, since then k would be in $\mathfrak{K}^{(p)}$ and we would have $\mathfrak{K}^{(p)} = \mathfrak{K}$. Hence $\mathfrak{K}$ has degree p over $\mathfrak{K}^{(p)}$, the degree n of $\mathfrak{K}$ over $\mathfrak{F}$ has the form $n = pm$, where m is the degree of $\mathfrak{K}^{(p)}$ over $\mathfrak{F}$.

If $\psi(x) = 0$ is the minimum function of k^p over $\mathfrak{F}$, the polynomial $\psi(x^p)$ has k as a root and degree $mp = n$, and $\psi(x^p)$ must be the minimum function of k, whereas k was assumed to be separable.

8. The Artin lemmas. The non-zero elements of a field $\mathfrak{N}$ form a multiplicative group, which we denote by $\mathfrak{N}^*$. If $\mathfrak{G}$ is any group and S is a homomorphism of $\mathfrak{G}$ into $\mathfrak{N}^*$, we call S a *character* of $\mathfrak{G}$. A set of characters $S_1, \ldots, S_n$ are said to be *dependent* if there exist elements $\alpha_1, \ldots, \alpha_n$ in $\mathfrak{N}$ which are not all zero and are such that

$$(gS_1)\alpha_1 + \cdots + (gS_n)\alpha_n = 0 \tag{17}$$

for every element g of $\mathfrak{G}$. If $S_1, \ldots, S_n$ are not dependent, we call them *independent.*

LEMMA 3. *If* n *characters are distinct, they are independent.*

For if $n = 1$, we see that gS_1 is in $\mathfrak{N}^*$ and is not zero, $\alpha_1(gS_1) = 0$ only if $\alpha_1 = 0$. We make the inductive assumption that all sets of m distinct characters are independent if $n > m \geq 1$. Let $S_1, \ldots, S_n$ be distinct and suppose that equation (17) holds for $(\alpha_1, \ldots, \alpha_n) \neq 0$. If any $\alpha_i = 0$, we observe that equation (17) implies the dependence of $m < n$ characters. Hence every $\alpha_i \neq 0$. Since $S_1 \neq S_n$, there exists an element h in $\mathfrak{G}$ such that $hS_1 \neq hS_n$. Replace g by gh in equation (17) and obtain $(gS_1)(hS_1)\alpha_1 + \cdots + (gS_n)(hS_n)\alpha_n = 0$. Multiply by $(hS_n)^{-1}$ and obtain

$$(gS_1)\beta_1 + \cdots + (gS_n)\beta_n = 0, \quad \beta_i = (hS_i)(hS_n)^{-1}\alpha_i \qquad (i = 1, \ldots, n). \tag{18}$$

Then $\beta_n = \alpha_n$, and we subtract the relation in equations (18) from that in equation (17) to obtain $0 = (gS_1)\gamma_1 + \cdots + (gS_{n-1})\gamma_{n-1}$, where $\gamma_i = \alpha_i - \beta_i$ are in $\mathfrak{N}$ and $\gamma_1 = \alpha_1 - (hS_1)(hS_n)^{-1}\alpha_1 \neq 0$. This contradicts our inductive hypothesis, and the lemma is proved.

An *isomorphism* S of a field $\mathfrak{N}$ into a field $\mathfrak{N}'$ maps the non-zero elements of $\mathfrak{N}$ onto the non-zero elements of a subfield of $\mathfrak{N}'$. Then S is a character of $\mathfrak{N}^*$, and we have the following result:

LEMMA 4. *Let* $S_1, \ldots, S_n$ *be* n *distinct isomorphisms of a field* $\mathfrak{N}$ *into a field* $\mathfrak{N}'$. *Then* $S_1, \ldots, S_n$ *are linearly independent over* $\mathfrak{F}$.

Consider a set Σ of n distinct isomorphisms of a field $\mathfrak{N}$ into a field $\mathfrak{N}'$. An element k of $\mathfrak{N}$ is said to be *fixed* under Σ if the images $kS_1, \ldots, kS_n$ of k are all equal. If k_1 and k_2 are fixed under Σ, their sum, difference, and product are also fixed under Σ. For $(k_1 + k_2)S_i = k_1S_i + k_2S_i$, $(k_1 - k_2)S_i = k_1S_i - k_2S_i$, and $(k_1k_2)S_i = (k_1S_i)(k_2S_i)$. If $k_2 \neq 0$, then $(k_1k_2^{-1})S_i = (k_1S_i)(k_2S_i)^{-1}$. Let us write $\mathfrak{N}_\Sigma$ for the set of all elements of $\mathfrak{N}$ which are fixed under Σ. Then we have proved the following result:

LEMMA 5. *The mapping*

$$\Sigma \rightarrow \mathfrak{N}_{\Sigma} \tag{19}$$

of sets Σ *of isomorphisms of* $\mathfrak{N}$ *into* $\mathfrak{N}'$ *onto corresponding sets of elements of* $\mathfrak{N}$ *fixed under* Σ *maps each* Σ *onto a subfield* $\mathfrak{N}_{\Sigma}$ *of* $\mathfrak{N}$ *called the* fixed field *of* $\mathfrak{N}$ *for* Σ.

We are now ready to prove a basic inequality.

LEMMA 6. *Let* Σ *be a set of* n *distinct isomorphisms* $S_1, \ldots, S_n$ *of* $\mathfrak{N}$ *into* $\mathfrak{N}'$. *Then* $[\mathfrak{N}:\mathfrak{N}_{\Sigma}] \geq n$.

For if our conclusion were false, we would have $\mathfrak{N} = u_1\mathfrak{F} + \cdots + u_m\mathfrak{F}$, where $\mathfrak{F} = \mathfrak{N}_{\Sigma}$ and $m < n$. The system of equations

$$(u_iS_1)x_1 + \cdots + (u_iS_n)x_n = 0 \qquad (i = 1, \ldots, m) \tag{20}$$

is a homogeneous linear system of m equations in n unknowns. Since $m < n$, we may use Theorem 3.16 to obtain a solution $x = (\xi_1, \ldots, \xi_n) \neq 0$ for $\xi_1, \ldots, \xi_n$ in $\mathfrak{N}'$. Every element k of $\mathfrak{N}$ is expressible in the form

$$k = a_1u_1 + \cdots + a_mu_m ,$$

where $a_1, \ldots, a_m$ are in $\mathfrak{F}$, and so

$$a_iS_1 = a_iS_2 = \cdots = a_iS_n . \tag{21}$$

Multiply the ith equation of system (20) by a_iS_1 and use equation (21) and the fact that S_i is an isomorphism to obtain $(u_ia_i)S_1 \cdot \xi_1 + \cdots + (u_ia_i)S_n \cdot \xi_n = 0$. But then we may add these equations and derive the relation

$$(kS_1)\xi_1 + \cdots + (kS_n)\xi_n = 0 . \tag{22}$$

This is a dependence of $S_1, \ldots, S_n$ and is impossible by Lemma 4.

We shall actually use Lemma 6 in the following special case:

LEMMA 7. *Let* Σ *be a set of* n *distinct automorphisms of a field* $\mathfrak{N}$. *Then* $[\mathfrak{N}:\mathfrak{N}_{\Sigma}] \geq n$.

9. Normal fields. The set $\mathfrak{G}$ of all automorphisms of a field $\mathfrak{N}$ forms a group which we have called the *automorphism group* of $\mathfrak{N}$. If $\mathfrak{H}$ is a finite subgroup of $\mathfrak{G}$, an element a of $\mathfrak{N}$ is fixed under $\mathfrak{H}$ if and only if $a = aS$ for every S of $\mathfrak{H}$. Then we have defined the mapping

$$\mathfrak{H} \rightarrow \mathfrak{N}_{\mathfrak{H}} \tag{23}$$

of the finite subgroups $\mathfrak{H}$ of $\mathfrak{G}$ onto the corresponding subfields $\mathfrak{N}_{\mathfrak{H}}$ of $\mathfrak{N}$, where *the image of* $\mathfrak{H}$ *is the fixed field of* $\mathfrak{N}$ *under* $\mathfrak{H}$. Moreover, when $\mathfrak{H}$ has order n, the degree of $\mathfrak{N}$ over $\mathfrak{N}_{\mathfrak{H}}$ is at least n.

We shall now map the subfields of $\mathfrak{N}$ onto subgroups of $\mathfrak{G}$. If $\mathfrak{F}$ is a subfield of $\mathfrak{N}$ and S is an automorphism of $\mathfrak{N}$ such that $a = aS$ for every element a of $\mathfrak{F}$, we call S an automorphism over $\mathfrak{F}$ of $\mathfrak{N}$. We then define the mapping

$$\mathfrak{F} \rightarrow \mathfrak{G}_{\mathfrak{F}} \tag{24}$$

of $\mathfrak{F}$ onto the set $\mathfrak{G}_{\mathfrak{F}}$ of all automorphisms over $\mathfrak{F}$ of $\mathfrak{N}$. It is trivial to see that $\mathfrak{G}_{\mathfrak{F}}$ is a subgroup of $\mathfrak{G}$. We call $\mathfrak{G}_{\mathfrak{F}}$ the *automorphism group of* $\mathfrak{N}$ *over* $\mathfrak{F}$. We now define our fundamental concept.

DEFINITION. *A field* $\mathfrak{N}$ *over* $\mathfrak{F}$ *is said to be* normal *over* $\mathfrak{F}$ *if* $\mathfrak{N}$ *has finite degree over* $\mathfrak{F}$ *and if* $\mathfrak{F}$ *itself is the fixed field of* $\mathfrak{N}$ *under the automorphism group* $\mathfrak{G}_{\mathfrak{F}}$ *of* $\mathfrak{N}$ *over* $\mathfrak{F}$.

The fact is that if $\mathfrak{N}$ is an extension of finite degree n over $\mathfrak{F}$, and $\mathfrak{G}_{\mathfrak{F}}$ is its automorphism group over $\mathfrak{F}$, then $\mathfrak{G}_{\mathfrak{F}}$ leaves $\mathfrak{F}$ fixed *but may also leave elements of* $\mathfrak{N}$ *not in* $\mathfrak{F}$ *fixed*. What we are stating is that, when $\mathfrak{N}$ is normal over $\mathfrak{F}$, an element k of $\mathfrak{N}$ has the property that $k = kS$ for every S in $\mathfrak{G}_{\mathfrak{F}}$ *if and only if* k *is in* $\mathfrak{F}$.

The automorphism group $\mathfrak{G}_{\mathfrak{F}}$ of a *normal* field $\mathfrak{N}$ over $\mathfrak{F}$ is called the *Galois group* of $\mathfrak{N}$ over $\mathfrak{F}$. Normal fields are sometimes called *Galois fields*. However, this terminology leads to confusion, since the term "Galois field" is sometimes used for finite fields. If the Galois group of $\mathfrak{N}$ over $\mathfrak{F}$ is a cyclic group, we call $\mathfrak{N}$ a *cyclic* field over $\mathfrak{F}$.

The following result is the key theorem in Artin's treatment of the Galois theory:

THEOREM 17. *Let* $\mathfrak{F} = \mathfrak{N}_{\mathfrak{H}}$ *be the fixed field of* $\mathfrak{N}$ *under a group* $\mathfrak{H}$ *consisting of the* n *automorphisms* $S_1 = I, S_2, \ldots, S_n$. *Then* n *is the degree of* $\mathfrak{N}$ *over* $\mathfrak{F}$.

For Lemma 7 states that $[\mathfrak{N}:\mathfrak{F}] \geq n$. Assume that $[\mathfrak{N}:\mathfrak{F}] > n$, so that $\mathfrak{N}$ contains elements $u_1, \ldots, u_{n+1}$ which are linearly independent in $\mathfrak{F}$. Then the system of equations

$$x_1(u_1S_i) + x_2(u_2S_i) + \cdots + x_{n+1}(u_{n+1}S_i) = 0 \qquad (i = 1, \ldots, n) \tag{25}$$

is a homogeneous linear system of n equations in $n + 1$ unknowns with coefficients u_jS_i in $\mathfrak{N}$. By Theorem 3.16 there exists a non-zero solution vector $x = (a_1, \ldots, a_n)$ with the a_i in $\mathfrak{N}$. Since the first equation of the system becomes $a_1u_1 + \cdots + a_{n+1}u_{n+1} = 0$, and the u_j are linearly independent, the a_i are not all in $\mathfrak{F}$.

Define the *length* of x to be the number of non-zero elements a_i. Select a solution vector x of minimum length r. By permuting the u_j if necessary, we may assume that $x = (a_1, \ldots, a_r, 0, \ldots, 0)$. Also $r > 1$, since otherwise $a_1u_1 = 0$, whereas $u_1, \ldots, u_{n+1}$ are linearly independent.

Clearly, $a_r^{-1}x$ is a solution vector of length r, and we may therefore assume that $a_r = 1$. Then equation (25) becomes

$$(26) \qquad a_1(u_1S_i) + \cdots + a_{r-1}(u_{r-1}S_i) + u_rS_i = 0 \quad (i = 1, \ldots, n).$$

Since $a_1, \ldots, a_{r-1}$ are not all in $\mathfrak{F}$, one of them, say a_1, may be assumed to be in $\mathfrak{N}$ but not in $\mathfrak{F}$. There is then an automorphism S_k which *moves* a_1, that is, which is such that

$$(27) \qquad b_1 = a_1 - a_1S_k \neq 0 .$$

Apply S_k to equation (26) to obtain

$$(28) \quad (a_1S_k)(u_1T_i) + \cdots + (a_{r-1}S_k)(u_{r-1}T_i) + u_rT_i = 0 \qquad (i = 1, \ldots, n),$$

where $T_i = S_iS_k$ for $i = 1, \ldots, n$. But $\mathfrak{H}$ is a group, and so $T_1, \ldots, T_n$ are distinct and are a permutation of the elements of $\mathfrak{H}$. It follows that that $y = (a_1S_k, \ldots, a_{r-1}S_k, 1, 0, \ldots, 0)$ is a solution vector of equation (25). Then $x - y = (b_1, \ldots, b_{r-1}, 0, \ldots, 0)$ is also a solution vector, where $b_j = a_j - a_jS_k$ for $j = 1, \ldots, r-1$ and $b_1 \neq 0$. This contradicts our definition of r.

If $\mathfrak{N}$ is normal of degree n over $\mathfrak{F}$, then $\mathfrak{F} = \mathfrak{N}_{\mathfrak{H}}$, where $\mathfrak{H} = \mathfrak{G}_{\mathfrak{F}}$. Then Theorem 17 implies the following result:

THEOREM 18. *Let $\mathfrak{N}$ be normal of degree* n *over $\mathfrak{F}$ and $\mathfrak{G}_{\mathfrak{F}}$ be the automorphism group of $\mathfrak{N}$ over $\mathfrak{F}$. Then* n *is the order of $\mathfrak{G}_{\mathfrak{F}}$.*

We also have the following result:

THEOREM 19. *Let $\mathfrak{F} = \mathfrak{N}_{\mathfrak{H}}$ be the fixed field of $\mathfrak{N}$ under a group $\mathfrak{H}$ of automorphisms of $\mathfrak{N}$. Then $\mathfrak{H} = \mathfrak{G}_{\mathfrak{F}}$ is the automorphism group of $\mathfrak{N}$ over $\mathfrak{F}$.*

For let $\mathfrak{H}$ have order n, so that $\mathfrak{N}$ has degree n over $\mathfrak{F}$. Then $\mathfrak{H} \supseteq \mathfrak{G}_{\mathfrak{F}}$. If $\mathfrak{H} \neq \mathfrak{G}_{\mathfrak{F}}$, the order of $\mathfrak{G}_{\mathfrak{F}}$ is $m > n$. We apply Lemma 6 with $\Sigma = \mathfrak{G}_{\mathfrak{F}}$ and see that $[\mathfrak{N}:\mathfrak{F}] \geq m > n$, a contradiction.

The following result is a corollary of Theorem 19:

THEOREM 20. *Let $\mathfrak{G}_1$ and $\mathfrak{G}_2$ be distinct groups of automorphisms of a field $\mathfrak{N}$. Then the fixed fields of $\mathfrak{N}$ under $\mathfrak{G}_1$ and $\mathfrak{G}_2$ are not the same.*

10. Characterizations of normality. We shall proceed to obtain two characterizations of the property of normality for fields $\mathfrak{N}$ of finite degree over $\mathfrak{F}$. The first of these may be stated as follows:

THEOREM 21. *A field $\mathfrak{N}$ of finite degree over $\mathfrak{F}$ is normal over $\mathfrak{F}$ if and only if $\mathfrak{N}$ is the splitting field over $\mathfrak{F}$ of a separable polynomial* f(x) *of* $\mathfrak{F}$[x].

Assume that $\mathfrak{N}$ is a splitting field of a separable monic polynomial $f(x)$ of $\mathfrak{F}[x]$. If $f(x) = x - a$, we have $\mathfrak{N} = \mathfrak{F}$. Then the only automorphism of $\mathfrak{N}$ leaving $\mathfrak{F} = \mathfrak{N}$ fixed is the identity automorphism I, and the fixed field for I is $\mathfrak{F}$, $\mathfrak{N}$ is normal over $\mathfrak{F}$. We make an induction on the degree n of $f(x)$ and assume that the splitting fields $\mathfrak{N}_0$ of all separable polynomials $f_0(x)$ of degrees $n - 1$ over any field $\mathfrak{F}_0$ are normal over $\mathfrak{F}_0$. Let $f(x)$ have degree n, and so $f(x) = (x - \alpha_1)f_1(x)$ for α_1 in $\mathfrak{N}$. By the hypothesis of our induction, the splitting field $\mathfrak{N}$ of the separable polynomial $f_1(x)$ is normal over $\mathfrak{F}(\alpha_1)$. Thus every element k of $\mathfrak{N}$ which is not in $\mathfrak{F}(\alpha_1)$ is moved by at least one automorphism over $\mathfrak{F}(\alpha_1)$ of $\mathfrak{N}$.

Our result is now true if $\mathfrak{F}(\alpha_1) = \mathfrak{F}$. On the other hand, when $\mathfrak{F}(\alpha_1) \neq \mathfrak{F}$, $f(x)$ has a factor $\phi(x)$ which is an irreducible polynomial of degree m of $\mathfrak{F}[x]$ and

$$\phi(x) = (x - \alpha_1) \cdots (x - \alpha_m) \tag{29}$$

for $\alpha_1, \ldots, \alpha_m$ in $\mathfrak{N}$ and all distinct. The stem fields $\mathfrak{F}(\alpha_1), \ldots, \mathfrak{F}(\alpha_m)$ are isomorphic by Theorem 4. Let S_i be the isomorphism which maps $\mathfrak{F}(\alpha_1)$ onto $\mathfrak{F}(\alpha_i)$ and leaves $\mathfrak{F}$ fixed. By Theorem 7 the isomorphism S_i can be extended to be an automorphism over $\mathfrak{F}$ of $\mathfrak{N}$, and we use the same notation S_i for this automorphism. Suppose that k in $\mathfrak{N}$ is left fixed by all automorphisms over $\mathfrak{F}$ of $\mathfrak{N}$. The automorphisms over $\mathfrak{F}(\alpha_1)$ will then leave k fixed, whence k is in $\mathfrak{F}(\alpha_1)$. Then

$$k = \beta_0 + \beta_1\alpha_1 + \cdots + \beta_{m-1}\alpha_1^{m-1} \tag{30}$$

for $\beta_0, \ldots, \beta_{m-1}$ in $\mathfrak{F}$, and we see that

$$k = kS_i = \beta_0 + \beta_1\alpha_i + \cdots + \beta_{m-1}\alpha_i^{m-1} \quad (i = 1, \ldots, m). \tag{31}$$

The polynomial $\psi(x) = \beta_{m-1}x^{m-1} + \cdots + \beta_1 x + \beta_0 - k$ has m distinct roots. By Theorem 2.26 we see that $\beta_0 = k$ is in $\mathfrak{F}$, and so $\mathfrak{N}$ is normal over $\mathfrak{F}$.

Conversely, let $\mathfrak{N}$ be normal over $\mathfrak{F}$. We first derive the following result:

LEMMA 8. *If $\mathfrak{N}$ is normal over $\mathfrak{F}$, it is separable over $\mathfrak{F}$. Every element of $\mathfrak{N}$ is a root of an equation with coefficients in $\mathfrak{F}$ and roots in $\mathfrak{N}$.*

For let $\mathfrak{G}_{\mathfrak{F}}$ be the automorphism group of $\mathfrak{N}$ over $\mathfrak{F}$, where $S_1 = I$, $S_2, \ldots, S_n$ are the elements of $\mathfrak{G}_{\mathfrak{F}}$, and n is the degree of $\mathfrak{N}$ over $\mathfrak{F}$. Let k be in $\mathfrak{N}$ and let $k = k_1, k_2, \ldots, k_r$ be the complete set of distinct elements in the set of n elements consisting of the images $k, kS_2, \ldots, kS_n$ of k under $\mathfrak{G}_{\mathfrak{F}}$. Since $\mathfrak{G}_{\mathfrak{F}}$ is a group, we see that $k_iS_j = kS_iS_j = k_q$ is one of the elements $k_1, \ldots, k_r$. However, $k_1, \ldots, k_r$ are distinct, and so $k_1S_j, \ldots, k_rS_j$ are distinct, and this set of r elements is merely a permutation of the elements $k_1, \ldots, k_r$. It follows that every automorphism of $\mathfrak{G}_{\mathfrak{F}}$ merely permutes the factors of

$$f(x) = (x - k_1) \cdots (x - k_r) .$$

Then the coefficients of $f(x)$ are not altered by the automorphisms of $\mathfrak{G}_{\mathfrak{F}}$, and the hypothesis that $\mathfrak{N}$ is normal over $\mathfrak{F}$ implies that $f(x)$ has coefficients in $\mathfrak{F}$ and roots all distinct and in $\mathfrak{N}$. This completes our proof that every element of $\mathfrak{N}$ is separable over $\mathfrak{F}$, and the proof of our lemma is complete.

To prove our theorem we assume that $\mathfrak{N} = u_1\mathfrak{F} + \cdots + u_n\mathfrak{F}$. By Lemma 8 each u_i is a root of a separable irreducible polynomial $f_i(x)$ of $\mathfrak{F}[x]$ such that each $f_i(x)$ factors into distinct linear factors in $\mathfrak{N}$. We form the product $f(x)$ of the *distinct* polynomials $f_i(x)$ and see that $f(u_i) = 0$ for $i = 1, \ldots, n$. If $f_i(x) \neq f_j(x)$ and $f_i(\alpha) = f_j(\alpha) = 0$, the g.c.d. of $f_i(x)$ and $f_j(x)$ is a monic polynomial $f_i(x)g(x) + f_j(x)h(x) = d(x)$ and $d(\alpha) = 0$. But $d(x)$ divides $f_i(x)$ and $f_j(x)$ and is not a constant, and $d(x)$ is an associate of both $f_i(x)$ and $f_j(x)$, which is impossible. Hence $f(x)$ is separable and clearly has a splitting field $\mathfrak{N}_0 \subseteq \mathfrak{N}$. But $\mathfrak{N}_0$ contains $u_1, \ldots, u_n$ and contains $\mathfrak{N} = u_1\mathfrak{F} + \cdots + u_n\mathfrak{F}$. Hence $\mathfrak{N} = \mathfrak{N}_0$, and our theorem is proved.

The characterization in Theorem 21 may be broadened as follows:

THEOREM 22. *A field $\mathfrak{N}$ is normal over $\mathfrak{F}$ if and only if $\mathfrak{N}$ is the splitting field of a polynomial* f(x) *of* $\mathfrak{F}$[x] *whose irreducible factors are separable.*

For let $f(x) = f_1(x) \cdots f_t(x)$, where the $f_i(x)$ are irreducible and separable polynomials of $\mathfrak{F}[x]$. Let $\mathfrak{N}_1$ be a splitting field over $\mathfrak{N}_0 = \mathfrak{F}$ of $f_1(x)$ and let $\mathfrak{N}_i$ be a splitting field over $\mathfrak{N}_{i-1}$ of $f_i(x)$ for $i = 1, \ldots, t$. We see that $\mathfrak{N}_t$ is a splitting field over $\mathfrak{F}$ of $f(x)$, and we take $\mathfrak{N} = \mathfrak{N}_t$. If k is in $\mathfrak{N}$ and $k = kS$ for every automorphism S over $\mathfrak{F}$ of $\mathfrak{N}$, then $k = kS$ for every automorphism S over $\mathfrak{N}_i$ of $\mathfrak{N}$. Also $\mathfrak{N}_i$ is normal over $\mathfrak{N}_{i-1}$ by Theorem 21. But then the hypothesis that k is in $\mathfrak{N}_i$ implies that k is in $\mathfrak{N}_{i-1}$ and hence that k is in $\mathfrak{F}$ and $\mathfrak{N}$ is normal over $\mathfrak{F}$. The converse follows from Theorem 21.

We are now ready to derive our final characterization of normality.

THEOREM 23. *Let $\mathfrak{N}$ be a field of finite degree over $\mathfrak{F}$. Then $\mathfrak{N}$ is normal over $\mathfrak{F}$ if and only if every element of $\mathfrak{N}$ is a root of a separable equation with coefficients in $\mathfrak{F}$ and roots in $\mathfrak{N}$.*

For Lemma 8 implies that if $\mathfrak{N}$ is normal over $\mathfrak{F}$, every element of $\mathfrak{N}$ has the required property. Conversely, let $\mathfrak{N} = u_1\mathfrak{F} + \cdots + u_n\mathfrak{F}$ and assume that every element k of $\mathfrak{N}$ is a root of a separable polynomial equation $f(x) = (x - k)(x - k_2) \cdots (x - k_t) = 0$, where $k_2, \ldots, k_t$ are in $\mathfrak{N}$ and $f(x)$ is in $\mathfrak{F}[x]$. Then each u_i is a root of a corresponding irreducible separable polynomial $f_i(x)$, and we see, as in the proof of Theorem 21, that $\mathfrak{N}$ is a splitting field of $f(x) = f_1(x) \cdots f_n(x)$. By Theorem 22 the field $\mathfrak{N}$ is normal over $\mathfrak{F}$.

11. The Galois group of an equation. Let $f(x)$ be a polynomial of $\mathfrak{F}[x]$ and $\mathfrak{N}$ be a splitting field over $\mathfrak{F}$ of the equation $f(x) = 0$. The Galois group of the equation $f(x) = 0$ is a permutation group on its roots in $\mathfrak{N}$. It is an isomorphic representation of the Galois group $\mathfrak{G}$ of $\mathfrak{N}$ over $\mathfrak{F}$ by permutations on the n roots of $f(x)$. *It is defined only for separable polynomials.*

Let $f(x) = (x - \xi_1) \cdots (x - \xi_n)$ for distinct ξ_i in $\mathfrak{N} = \mathfrak{F}(\xi_1, \ldots, \xi_n)$ and let $\mathfrak{G}$ be the Galois group of $\mathfrak{N}$ over $\mathfrak{F}$. Then the mappings

$$P_S: \qquad \xi_i \rightarrow \xi_i S$$

are permutations of the finite set $\xi_1, \ldots, \xi_n$ for every S of $\mathfrak{G}$. They are then a set of n permutations in the set Σ_n of all permutations on n letters. But

$$P_{ST} = P_S P_T \,, \tag{32}$$

and so the mapping

$$S \rightarrow P_S \tag{33}$$

is a homomorphic mapping of $\mathfrak{G}$ onto the set $\mathfrak{G}_0$ of n permutations P_S. If $P_S = P_T$, then $\xi_i S = \xi_i T$ for every ξ_i, $kS = kT$ for every k of $\mathfrak{N}$, whence $S = T$. It follows that mapping (33) maps $\mathfrak{G}$ isomorphically onto $\mathfrak{G}_0$, and so the set $\mathfrak{G}_0$ is a permutation group which we call the *Galois group* of the equation $f(x) = 0$.

A permutation group $\mathfrak{H}$ on n letters $\xi_1, \ldots, \xi_n$ is called a *transitive* group if any letter ξ_i can be carried to any other letter ξ_j by a permutation P_{ij} of $\mathfrak{H}$. It is sufficient to show that ξ_1 can be carried to any letter ξ_j by a permutation P_j of $\mathfrak{H}$. For if $\xi_i = \xi_1 P_i$ and $\xi_j = \xi_1 P_j$, then $\xi_j = \xi_i P_i^{-1} P_j$.

THEOREM 24. *Let* f(x) *be a separable polynomial of* $\mathfrak{F}$[x]. *Then the Galois group* $\mathfrak{G}_0$ *of* f(x) *is a transitive group if and only if* f(x) *is irreducible.*

For if $f(x)$ is irreducible and $\mathfrak{G}$ is the Galois group of a splitting field $\mathfrak{N}$ over $\mathfrak{F}$, the stem fields $\mathfrak{F}[\xi_i]$ of the equation $f(x) = 0$ are isomorphic, and Theorem 7 implies that there exists an automorphism S_i of $\mathfrak{N}$ over $\mathfrak{F}$ such that $\xi_1 S_i = \xi_i$. Then P_{S_i} carries ξ_1 to ξ_i, and $\mathfrak{G}_0$ is transitive. Conversely, if $\mathfrak{G}_0$ is transitive, there exists a permutation P_i carrying ξ_1 to ξ_i and hence an automorphism S_i of $\mathfrak{G}$ such that $\xi_1 S_i = \xi_i$. If $f(x)$ were reducible, it would have two distinct irreducible factors $f_1(x)$ and $f_2(x)$ such that $f_1(\xi_1) = 0$ and $f_2(\xi_i) = 0$, where $i \neq 1$. Then $[f_1(\xi_1)]S_i = f_1(\xi_i) = 0$, and the two distinct irreducible polynomials $f_1(x)$ and $f_2(x)$

would have a root in common. This is impossible, as we saw in the proof of Theorem 21.

12. The fundamental theorems of the Galois theory. Let $\mathfrak{N}$ be a normal extension of degree n over $\mathfrak{F}$ and let $\mathfrak{G}_{\mathfrak{F}}$ be the Galois group of $\mathfrak{N}$ over $\mathfrak{F}$. Then $\mathfrak{G}_{\mathfrak{F}}$ is a group of order n, that is,

$$[\mathfrak{N}:\mathfrak{F}] = (\mathfrak{G}_{\mathfrak{F}}:I)\,. \tag{34}$$

Let Γ be the set of all subgroups $\mathfrak{H}$ of $\mathfrak{G}_{\mathfrak{F}}$, and Δ be the set of all subfields $\mathfrak{L} \supseteq \mathfrak{F}$ of $\mathfrak{N}$. Then the mapping

$$\sigma: \qquad \mathfrak{H} \to \sigma(\mathfrak{H}) = \mathfrak{N}_{\mathfrak{H}}$$

of each subgroup $\mathfrak{H}$ of $\mathfrak{G}_{\mathfrak{F}}$ onto the fixed field $\mathfrak{N}_{\mathfrak{H}}$ of $\mathfrak{N}$ under $\mathfrak{H}$ is a mapping of Γ into Δ. The mapping

$$\tau: \qquad \mathfrak{L} \to \tau(\mathfrak{L}) = \mathfrak{G}_{\mathfrak{L}}$$

of every subfield $\mathfrak{L} \supseteq \mathfrak{F}$ of $\mathfrak{N}$ onto the automorphism group $\mathfrak{G}_{\mathfrak{L}}$ of $\mathfrak{N}$ over $\mathfrak{L}$ is a mapping of Δ into Γ. We shall say that $\mathfrak{L}$ *belongs* to $\mathfrak{H}$ if $\mathfrak{L} = \mathfrak{N}_{\mathfrak{H}}$ and that $\mathfrak{H}$ *belongs* to $\mathfrak{L}$ if $\mathfrak{H} = \mathfrak{G}_{\mathfrak{L}}$.

LEMMA 9. *Let $\mathfrak{N}$ be normal over $\mathfrak{F}$ and let $\mathfrak{L}$ be a subfield over $\mathfrak{F}$ of $\mathfrak{N}$. Then $\mathfrak{N}$ is normal over $\mathfrak{L}$.*

For every element k of $\mathfrak{N}$ is a root of a separable equation $f(x) = 0$ with coefficients in $\mathfrak{F}$ and roots in $\mathfrak{N}$. Since these coefficients are also in $\mathfrak{L}$, Theorem 23 implies that $\mathfrak{N}$ is normal over $\mathfrak{L}$.

Lemma 9 implies that $\mathfrak{G}_{\mathfrak{L}}$ is a Galois group. Thus τ maps every subfield of $\mathfrak{N}$ in Δ onto a Galois group $\mathfrak{G}_{\mathfrak{L}}$ in Γ. We are now ready to state the first fundamental theorem of the Galois theory.

THEOREM 25. *The mapping σ is a one-to-one mapping of* Γ *onto* Δ. *The mapping $\tau = \sigma^{-1}$ so that $\mathfrak{H}$ belongs to $\mathfrak{L}$ if and only if $\mathfrak{L}$ belongs to $\mathfrak{H}$. Then*

$$[\mathfrak{N}:\mathfrak{L}] = (\mathfrak{H}:\mathrm{I}), \qquad [\mathfrak{L}:\mathfrak{F}] = (\mathfrak{G}:\mathfrak{H})\,. \tag{35}$$

For if $\mathfrak{L}$ is any subfield over $\mathfrak{F}$ of $\mathfrak{N}$, we let $\mathfrak{H} = \mathfrak{G}_{\mathfrak{L}}$. Since $\mathfrak{N}$ is normal over $\mathfrak{F}$ and hence over $\mathfrak{L}$, our *definition* of normality implies that $\mathfrak{L} = \mathfrak{N}_{\mathfrak{H}}$. Hence σ maps Γ *onto* Δ. But Theorem 20 states that distinct subgroups of $\mathfrak{G}_{\mathfrak{F}}$ map onto distinct subfields of $\mathfrak{N}$, and so σ is a one-to-one mapping. If $\mathfrak{H}$ belongs to $\mathfrak{L}$, then we have seen that $\mathfrak{L} = \mathfrak{N}_{\mathfrak{H}}$ and $\mathfrak{L}$ belongs to $\mathfrak{H}$. Hence $\tau = \sigma^{-1}$. By equation (34) we have $[\mathfrak{N}:\mathfrak{L}] = (\mathfrak{G}_{\mathfrak{L}}:I)$. Since $[\mathfrak{N}:\mathfrak{F}] = [\mathfrak{N}:\mathfrak{L}][\mathfrak{L}:\mathfrak{F}] = (\mathfrak{G}_{\mathfrak{F}}:I) = (\mathfrak{G}_{\mathfrak{F}}:\mathfrak{G}_{\mathfrak{L}})(\mathfrak{G}_{\mathfrak{L}}:I)$, we have equations (35).

As an immediate consequence of Theorem 25 we have the following second fundamental theorem:

THEOREM 26. *Let $\mathfrak{N}$ be normal over $\mathfrak{F}$, $\mathfrak{L}_1$ and $\mathfrak{L}_2$ be subfields over $\mathfrak{F}$ of $\mathfrak{N}$, $\mathfrak{H}_1$ belong to $\mathfrak{L}_1$, and $\mathfrak{H}_2$ belong to $\mathfrak{L}_2$. Then $\mathfrak{L}_2 \supseteq \mathfrak{L}_1$ if and only if $\mathfrak{H}_1 \supseteq \mathfrak{H}_2$, and in this case*

$$(36) \qquad\qquad [\mathfrak{L}_2 : \mathfrak{L}_1] = (\mathfrak{H}_1 : \mathfrak{H}_2) .$$

For we know that $\mathfrak{N}$ is normal over $\mathfrak{L}_1$ and that the Galois group of $\mathfrak{N}$ over $\mathfrak{L}_1$ is $\mathfrak{H}_1$. We apply Theorem 25 to see that $\mathfrak{L}_2 \supseteq \mathfrak{L}_1$ if and only if $\mathfrak{H}_2 = \mathfrak{G}_{\mathfrak{L}_2}$ is a subgroup of $\mathfrak{G}_{\mathfrak{L}_1} = \mathfrak{H}_1$. Then equation (36) follows from equations (35).

Two subfields $\mathfrak{L}_1$ and $\mathfrak{L}_2$ over $\mathfrak{F}$ of a normal field $\mathfrak{N}$ over $\mathfrak{F}$ are called *conjugate* subfields if they are isomorphic over $\mathfrak{F}$. Then there is an isomorphism S leaving $\mathfrak{F}$ fixed such that $\mathfrak{L}_1 S = \mathfrak{L}_2$. By Theorem 7 we can extend S to be an automorphism over $\mathfrak{F}$ of $\mathfrak{N}$. Two subgroups $\mathfrak{H}_1$ and $\mathfrak{H}_2$ of a group $\mathfrak{G}$ are called *conjugate groups* of $\mathfrak{G}$ if there exists an inner automorphism $T \to S^{-1}TS$ of $\mathfrak{G}$ which maps $\mathfrak{H}_1$ onto $\mathfrak{H}_2$. In this case we write $\mathfrak{H}_2 = S^{-1}\mathfrak{H}_2 S$.

THEOREM 27. *Let $\mathfrak{N}$ be normal over $\mathfrak{F}$, $\mathfrak{L}_1$ and $\mathfrak{L}_2$ be subfields over $\mathfrak{F}$ of $\mathfrak{N}$, $\mathfrak{H}_1$ belong to $\mathfrak{L}_1$, and $\mathfrak{H}_2$ belong to $\mathfrak{L}_2$. Then $\mathfrak{L}_1$ is isomorphic over $\mathfrak{F}$ to $\mathfrak{L}_2$ if and only if $\mathfrak{H}_1$ and $\mathfrak{H}_2$ are conjugate groups. Indeed, there exists an automorphism S over $\mathfrak{F}$ of $\mathfrak{N}$ such that $\mathfrak{L}_2 = \mathfrak{L}_1 S$ if and only if $\mathfrak{H}_2 = S^{-1}\mathfrak{H}_1 S$.*

For if $\mathfrak{L}_1$ and $\mathfrak{L}_2$ are isomorphic over $\mathfrak{F}$, they have the same degree. By equations (35) we see that $(\mathfrak{H}_2 : I) = (\mathfrak{H}_1 : I)$. If $\mathfrak{L}_1 S = \mathfrak{L}_2$ for S in $\mathfrak{G}_{\mathfrak{F}}$, we know that $S^{-1}\mathfrak{H}_1 S$ and $\mathfrak{H}_2$ have the same order. Every element k_1 of $\mathfrak{L}_1$ is fixed under every automorphism T of $\mathfrak{H}_1$. Since every element of $\mathfrak{L}_2$ has the form $k_2 = k_1 S$ for k_1 in $\mathfrak{L}_1$, we see that $k_2 S^{-1}TS = k_1 TS = k_1 S = k_2$. Hence $\mathfrak{L}_2$ is fixed under $S^{-1}\mathfrak{H}_1 S$, $S^{-1}\mathfrak{H}_1 S \subseteq \mathfrak{H}_2$, and $S^{-1}\mathfrak{H}_1 S = \mathfrak{H}_2$. Conversely, if $\mathfrak{H}_2 = S^{-1}\mathfrak{H}_1 S$, we see that $\mathfrak{L}_1 S$ is fixed under $\mathfrak{H}_2$, and thus $\mathfrak{L}_1 S \subseteq \mathfrak{L}_2$. But $\mathfrak{L}_1 S$ is isomorphic to $\mathfrak{L}_1$ and so has the same degree as $\mathfrak{L}_1$: $\mathfrak{H}_1$ and $S^{-1}\mathfrak{H}_1 S$ have the same orders; $\mathfrak{L}_1$ and $\mathfrak{L}_2$ have the same degrees by equations (35); $\mathfrak{L}_1 S$ and $\mathfrak{L}_2$ have the same degrees; and $\mathfrak{L}_1 S = \mathfrak{L}_2$ is isomorphic to $\mathfrak{L}_1$.

Our final result is a characterization of normal subfields over $\mathfrak{F}$ of $\mathfrak{N}$.

THEOREM 28. *A subfield $\mathfrak{L}$ over $\mathfrak{F}$ of a normal field $\mathfrak{N}$ over $\mathfrak{F}$ is normal over $\mathfrak{F}$ if and only if the subgroup $\mathfrak{H}$ to which $\mathfrak{L}$ belongs is a noraml subgroup of the Galois group $\mathfrak{G}_{\mathfrak{F}}$ of $\mathfrak{N}$ over $\mathfrak{F}$. Then the Galois group of $\mathfrak{L}$ over $\mathfrak{F}$ is isomorphic to $\mathfrak{G}_{\mathfrak{F}}/\mathfrak{H}$.*

If $\mathfrak{L}$ is normal of degree q over $\mathfrak{F}$, we use Theorem 18 to see that the order of the automorphism group Σ of $\mathfrak{L}$ over $\mathfrak{F}$ is q. Then $\mathfrak{L}$ has q distinct automorphisms $\sigma_1 = I, \sigma_2, \ldots, \sigma_q$. By Theorem 7 these automorphisms may be extended to q automorphisms $S_1 = I, S_2, \ldots, S_q$ of $\mathfrak{N}$ over $\mathfrak{F}$. Then

$$xσ_i = xTS_i \qquad (i = 1, \ldots, q) \tag{37}$$

for every x of $\mathfrak{L}$ and T of $\mathfrak{H}$. If $\mathfrak{H}S_i = \mathfrak{H}S_j$ for $i \neq j$, then $S_j = TS_i$, where T is in $\mathfrak{H}$, $z\sigma_j = zTS_i = zS_i = z\sigma_i$ for every z of $\mathfrak{L}$, which is impossible. It follows that $\mathfrak{H}S_1, \ldots, \mathfrak{H}S_q$ are distinct. Since $[\mathfrak{L}:\mathfrak{F}] = (\mathfrak{G}_{\mathfrak{F}}:\mathfrak{H}) = q$, the cosets $\mathfrak{H}S_1, \ldots, \mathfrak{H}S_q$ form a complete set of cosets of $\mathfrak{H}$ under $\mathfrak{G}_{\mathfrak{F}}$; every S of $\mathfrak{G}_{\mathfrak{F}}$ is in such a coset, and $\mathfrak{L}S = \mathfrak{L}$ for every S of $\mathfrak{G}_{\mathfrak{F}}$. Then $S^{-1}\mathfrak{H}S = \mathfrak{H}$ by Theorem 27, and so $\mathfrak{H}$ is a normal subgroup of $\mathfrak{G}_{\mathfrak{F}}$. The mapping $\sigma_i \to \mathfrak{H}S_i$ has already been seen to be a one-to-one mapping of Σ onto $\mathfrak{G}_{\mathfrak{F}}/\mathfrak{H}$. Since $x\sigma_i\sigma_j = xS_iS_j$, we see that this mapping is an isomorphism. Conversely, if $S^{-1}\mathfrak{H}S = \mathfrak{H}$ for every S of $\mathfrak{G}_{\mathfrak{F}}$, we write $\mathfrak{G}_{\mathfrak{F}} = \mathfrak{H} \cup \mathfrak{H}S_2 \cup \cdots \cup \mathfrak{H}S_q$ and see that the mappings $x \to x\sigma_i = xS_i$ define q automorphisms of $\mathfrak{L}$ over $\mathfrak{F}$. These automorphisms are distinct. For an automorphism S in $\mathfrak{G}_{\mathfrak{F}}$ leaves $\mathfrak{L}$ fixed if and only if S is in $\mathfrak{H}$. Thus two automorphisms in $\mathfrak{G}_{\mathfrak{F}}$ define the same automorphism of $\mathfrak{L}$ if and only if they define the same coset. Since every automorphism of $\mathfrak{L}$ over $\mathfrak{F}$ can be extended to an automorphism of $\mathfrak{N}$ over $\mathfrak{F}$, we see that the group Σ of all automorphisms of $\mathfrak{L}$ over $\mathfrak{F}$ has order q.

If $\mathfrak{F}'$ is the fixed field of $\mathfrak{L}$ under Σ, we have $\mathfrak{L} \supseteq \mathfrak{F}' \supseteq \mathfrak{F}$. By Theorem 17 we have $[\mathfrak{L}:\mathfrak{F}'] = (\Sigma:I) = q = [\mathfrak{L}:\mathfrak{F}]$ by equations (35), and so $[\mathfrak{L}:\mathfrak{F}'] = [\mathfrak{L}:\mathfrak{F}]$, $\mathfrak{F}' = \mathfrak{F}$, and $\mathfrak{L}$ is normal over $\mathfrak{F}$.

EXERCISES

1. Use the proof of Theorem 28 to show that a field $\mathfrak{L}$ of finite degree q over $\mathfrak{F}$ is normal over $\mathfrak{F}$ if and only if the automorphism group over $\mathfrak{F}$ of $\mathfrak{L}$ has order q.
2. Let $f(x)$ be an irreducible separable polynomial and let $\mathfrak{L}$ be a stem field of $f(x)$. Show that $\mathfrak{L}$ is normal over $\mathfrak{F}$ if and only if $\mathfrak{L}$ is a splitting field of $f(x)$.

13. Simple extensions. Since the Galois groups of normal fields have been connected with permutation groups on the roots of equations, it should be interesting to observe that a normal field of degree n over $\mathfrak{F}$ is a simple extension of $\mathfrak{F}$, and its Galois group can then be represented as a transitive group on n letters. We shall actually show that every separable extension is simple. We begin our derivation as follows:

THEOREM 29. *A field $\mathfrak{K}$ of degree* n *over $\mathfrak{F}$ is a simple extension of $\mathfrak{F}$ if and only if there is only a finite number of subfields $\mathfrak{L}$ over $\mathfrak{F}$ of $\mathfrak{K}$.*

The case where $\mathfrak{F}$ is a finite field is quite trivial and will follow from Theorem 5.4. *Assume henceforth that $\mathfrak{F}$ is an infinite field.*

Suppose, first, that $\mathfrak{K} = \mathfrak{F}(y)$, where $f(x) = 0$ is the minimum function of y over $\mathfrak{F}$. If $\mathfrak{K} \supseteq \mathfrak{L} \supseteq \mathfrak{F}$ and $g(x)$ is the minimum function over $\mathfrak{L}$ of y, the polynomial $g(x)$ has a finite number of coefficients $\alpha_1, \ldots, \alpha_m$ in $\mathfrak{L}$ and $\mathfrak{L} \supseteq \mathfrak{L}' = \mathfrak{F}(\alpha_1, \ldots, \alpha_m) \supseteq \mathfrak{F}$. But $g(x)$ is irreducible in $\mathfrak{L}$ and must be irreducible in $\mathfrak{L}'$. But then $[\mathfrak{K}:\mathfrak{L}'] = [\mathfrak{K}:\mathfrak{L}]$ is equal to the degree of $g(x)$, and so $[\mathfrak{L}:\mathfrak{F}] = [\mathfrak{L}':\mathfrak{F}]$, and $\mathfrak{L} = \mathfrak{L}'$. Hence $\mathfrak{L}$ is uniquely determined by $g(x)$. However, $g(x)$ divides $f(x)$, and $f(x)$ has only a finite number of divisors in $\mathfrak{K}[x]$. Thus there is only a finite number of possible intermediate fields $\mathfrak{L}$.

Conversely, suppose that there is only a finite number of fields $\mathfrak{L}$ such that $\mathfrak{K} \supseteq \mathfrak{L} \supseteq \mathfrak{F}$. Let h and k be in $\mathfrak{K}$ and $g_\lambda = h + \lambda k$ for λ in $\mathfrak{F}$. Then $\mathfrak{F}(g_\lambda)$ is a subfield of $\mathfrak{K}$ containing $\mathfrak{F}$ for every λ of $\mathfrak{F}$. Since $\mathfrak{F}$ has infinitely many elements and there is only a finite number of distinct fields $\mathfrak{F}(g_\lambda)$, there must exist two distinct elements λ and μ in $\mathfrak{F}$ such that $\mathfrak{L} = \mathfrak{F}(g_\lambda) = \mathfrak{F}(g_\mu)$. Then $g_\mu = h + \mu k$ and $g_\lambda = h + \lambda k$ are both in $\mathfrak{L}$, and so $\mathfrak{L}$ contains $(\mu - \lambda)k = g_\mu - g_\lambda$; hence k and $h = g_\lambda - \lambda k$. Then $\mathfrak{F}(h, k) \subseteq \mathfrak{F}(g)$ for $g = g_\lambda$, $\mathfrak{F}(g) \subseteq \mathfrak{F}(h, k)$, and $\mathfrak{F}(g) = \mathfrak{F}(h, k)$. We select an element k in $\mathfrak{K}$ such that the simple subfield $\mathfrak{L} = \mathfrak{F}(k)$ has maximal degree. Then $\mathfrak{L} = \mathfrak{K}$. For otherwise there exists an element h in $\mathfrak{K}$ such that h is not in $\mathfrak{L}$, $\mathfrak{L}(h) \neq \mathfrak{L}$, and $\mathfrak{L}(h) = \mathfrak{F}(h, k) = \mathfrak{F}(g)$ has degree over $\mathfrak{F}$ greater than the degree of $\mathfrak{L}$, contrary to hypothesis.

We are now ready to derive our result on separable extensions.

THEOREM 30. *Every separable field of finite degree over $\mathfrak{F}$ is simple over $\mathfrak{F}$.*

For a separable field $\mathfrak{K}$ of finite degree over $\mathfrak{F}$ is an extension $\mathfrak{K} = \mathfrak{F}(k_1, \ldots, k_t)$ for separable elements $k_1, \ldots, k_t$ over $\mathfrak{F}$. Let $f_i(x)$ be the minimum function of k_i over $\mathfrak{F}$. By Theorem 22 the splitting field $\mathfrak{N} \supseteq \mathfrak{K} \supseteq \mathfrak{F}$ of $f(x) = f_1(x) \cdots f_t(x)$ is normal over $\mathfrak{F}$. By Theorem 25 the field $\mathfrak{N}$ has only a finite number of subfields over $\mathfrak{F}$. Then the subfield $\mathfrak{K}$ has the same property and is simple by Theorem 29.

EXERCISES

1. Let $\mathfrak{R}$ be the field of all rational numbers $f(x) = x^n + a_1x^{n-1} + \cdots + a_n$, where the a_i are integers. Prove the *Gauss Lemma*, which states that if $g(x) = x^m + b_1x^{n-1} + \cdots b_m$ is a factor of $f(x)$ with b_i in $\mathfrak{R}$, the b_i are integers.

2. Let p be a prime and $f(x) = x^{p-1} + x^{p-2} + \cdots + 1$. Prove that $f(x)$ is irreducible in $\mathfrak{R}$. *Hint:* Suppose that $f(x) = g(x)h(x)$, where $g(x)$ has leading coefficient 1 and other coefficients in $\mathfrak{R}$, the degree of $g(x)$ is $m > 0$, $(p - 1) - m > 0$. Then $g(x)$ and $h(x)$ have integral coefficients. $g(1)h(1) = f(1) = p$. Prove that $f(x)$ divides $g(x^2) \cdots (gx^{p-1}) = P(x)$, $P(1) = 1$, and $f(1)$ divides $P(1)$, which is impossible.

3. Let $f(x) = x^4 + x^3 + x^2 + x + 1$. Determine the automorphism group over $\mathfrak{R}$ of a splitting field of $f(x)$.

4. Determine the automorphism group over $\mathfrak{R}$ of a splitting field of $f(x)$ in the following cases.

$$a)\ f(x) = x^4 - 10x^2 + 5, \quad c)\ f(x) = x^4 + x^2 - 6,$$

$$b)\ f(x) = x^4 - 10x^2 + 4, \quad d)\ f(x) = x^4 + 4x^2 + 2.$$

5. Let p be a prime, t be a primitive fifth root of unity, $\mathfrak{K} = \mathfrak{R}(\sqrt[5]{p}.\, t)$. Determine the automorphism group over $\mathfrak{R}$ of $\mathfrak{K}$.

6. Let $\mathfrak{K}$ be an inseparable field of degree $3p$ over $\mathfrak{F}$, where p is a prime, and let $\mathfrak{K}$ contain no subfield properly containing $\mathfrak{F}$ and separable over $\mathfrak{F}$.

a) What is the characteristic of $\mathfrak{K}$?

b) What are the possible generators of $\mathfrak{K}$ over $\mathfrak{F}$?

c) What are the degrees of the proper subfield of $\mathfrak{K}$ over $\mathfrak{F}$?

7. Prove that $\mathfrak{R}(\sqrt{2}, \sqrt{3}) = \mathfrak{R}(\sqrt{2 - 3})$.

8. Determine all subfields of $\mathfrak{R}(\sqrt{2}, \sqrt{3})$ and use the theorems of this chapter to show that your result is correct.

9. Let $\mathfrak{K}$ be a field of characteristic 7 and degree 147 over a subfield $\mathfrak{F}$.

a) What are the possible degrees over $\mathfrak{F}$ of a maximal separable subfield over $\mathfrak{F}$ of $\mathfrak{K}$?

b) If $\mathfrak{K} = \mathfrak{F}(a)$, where $a^{147} = b$ and b is a non-zero element of $\mathfrak{F}$, what are the possible groups of automorphisms over $\mathfrak{F}$ of $\mathfrak{K}$?

10. Let $\mathfrak{L}$ be the field of 5 elements and $\mathfrak{F} = \mathfrak{L}(t)$ be the field of all rational functions of an indeterminate t over $\mathfrak{L}$. Let $\mathfrak{N}$ be a splitting field over $\mathfrak{F}$ of the polynomial $(x^5 - x - t^2)(x^2 - u)$, where u is a primitive fourth root of unity. Determine the automorphism group of $\mathfrak{N}$ over $\mathfrak{F}$.

11. *a*) Let p be a prime, $\mathfrak{F}$ be a field whose characteristic is not p, $w^p = 1$, $\mathfrak{K} = \mathfrak{F}(w)$. What are the possible degrees of $\mathfrak{K}$ over $\mathfrak{F}$?

b) Determine the Galois group of $\mathfrak{K} = \mathfrak{F}(w)$ if $\mathfrak{F}$ is the field $\mathfrak{R}$ of all rational numbers and $p = 5, 7, 11$, or 19.

c) Let $\mathfrak{F} = \mathfrak{R}(u) \neq \mathfrak{R}$, where $\mathfrak{F}$ is a proper subfield of $\mathfrak{R}(w)$. Determine the Galois group of $\mathfrak{K}$ over $\mathfrak{F}$ in each of the cases of problem *b*.

d) Let $\mathfrak{K} = \mathfrak{R}(w_1, w_2)$, where w_1 and w_2 are primitive and $w_1^{ii} = w_2^{19} = 1$. Determine the Galois group of $\mathfrak{K}$ over $\mathfrak{R}$.

12. *a*) Let $y^p = a$ in $\mathfrak{F}$, where p is a prime, and let $\mathfrak{K} = \mathfrak{F}(y)$. Prove that $\mathfrak{K}$ has degree p over $\mathfrak{F}$ if and only if $a \neq b^p$ for b in $\mathfrak{F}$. Give the two proofs necessary.

b) Let the degree $(\mathfrak{K}:\mathfrak{F})$ of $\mathfrak{K}$ over $\mathfrak{F}$ satisfy $p > n > 1$ in problem *a*. What are the possible values of $(\mathfrak{K}:\mathfrak{F})$? Give numerical answers for $p = 13$. What can be said about the characteristic of $\mathfrak{F}$?

c) Let $\mathfrak{K} = F(y, z)$, where $y^p = a$, $z^p = b$, and $a \neq 0$, $b \neq 0$ are in $\mathfrak{F}$. Show that if $\mathfrak{F}$ has characteristic not p, then $(\mathfrak{K}:\mathfrak{F}) = p^2$ if and only if $a, b, ab^2, \ldots, ab^{p-1}$ are all not the pth powers of elements of $\mathfrak{F}$. Why is the result false in the case where $\mathfrak{F}$ has characteristic p?

d) Let $\mathfrak{K}$ be defined as in problem *c* and $p^2 > (\mathfrak{K}:\mathfrak{F}) > p$, $\mathfrak{K}_1 = \mathfrak{F}(y)$,

$(\mathfrak{K}_1:\mathfrak{F}) = p$. Give the values of $(\mathfrak{K}:\mathfrak{F})$ in terms of an integer defined in Exercise 11. *Hint:* Show that $\mathfrak{K}_2 = \mathfrak{F}(z) = \mathfrak{F}(z_0 w)$, where $w^p = 1$ and z_0 is in $\mathfrak{K}_1$.

e) What are the degrees of the following fields over the field $\mathfrak{R}$ of all rational numbers, where $\sqrt[p]{a}$ is the real pth root in all cases?

(i) $\mathfrak{R}(\sqrt{2}, \sqrt{3})$, (vi) $\mathfrak{R}(\sqrt[5]{2}, \sqrt[5]{-2})$,

(ii) $\mathfrak{R}(\sqrt{2}, \sqrt{-2})$, (vii) $\mathfrak{R}(\sqrt[5]{2}, \sqrt[5]{-3})$,

(iii) $\mathfrak{R}(\sqrt{2}, \sqrt[3]{3})$, (viii) $\mathfrak{R}(\sqrt[5]{-3}, \sqrt{288})$,

(iv) $\mathfrak{R}(\sqrt[3]{2}, \sqrt{3})$, (ix) $\mathfrak{R}(\sqrt[5]{2}, \sqrt[3]{3})$,

(v) $\mathfrak{R}(\sqrt[3]{54}), \sqrt[3]{3})$, (x) $\mathfrak{R}(\sqrt{3} - \sqrt[3]{2})$.

f) Determine the Galois group of the smallest normal extension of the fields in (iii) and (iv).

g) Which of the fields in problem *e* are normal over $\mathfrak{R}$?

13. *a*) Determine the Galois group of a splitting field over $\mathfrak{R}$ of the polynomial $(x^3 - 2)(x^3 + 3)$.

b) Let $\sqrt[3]{3}$ be real, $\mathfrak{F} = \mathfrak{R}(\sqrt[3]{3})$. Give the Galois group over $\mathfrak{F}$ of a splitting field of $x^3 - 54$.

14. *a*) Let $\mathfrak{P}$ be the field of five elements, $\mathfrak{F} = \mathfrak{P}(t)$, where t is an indeterminate over $\mathfrak{P}$. Give the degrees over $\mathfrak{F}$ of the fields $\mathfrak{K}_1 = \mathfrak{F}(\sqrt{t}, \sqrt{t+1})$, $\mathfrak{K}_2 = \mathfrak{F}(\sqrt[5]{t}, \sqrt[5]{t+1})$, $\mathfrak{K}_3 = \mathfrak{F}(\sqrt[5]{t^2} + t, \sqrt[5]{t^3})$.

b) Prove that the polynomial $x^5 - x - t^2$ is irreducible in $\mathfrak{F}$ and find the Galois group of a splitting field.

15. *a*) Let $\mathfrak{F}$ be a field of characteristic p, $\mathfrak{K} = \mathfrak{F}(y, z)$, where $y^p = y + a$, $z^p = z + b$ for non-zero elements a and b in $\mathfrak{F}$. Prove that $(\mathfrak{K}:\mathfrak{F}) \neq p^2$ if and only if there exists an integer n and an element c in $\mathfrak{F}$ such that $b - na = c^p - c$.

b) Use the criterion in problem *a* to determine $(\mathfrak{K}:\mathfrak{F})$ in the following cases where $\mathfrak{F} = \mathfrak{P}(t)$, as in Exercise 14. Determine the degrees of $\mathfrak{F}(y)$ and $\mathfrak{F}(z)$ in each case.

(i) $a = t$, $b = t^5 + t$; (iii) $a = t^2$, $b = t^5 + 2t^2 - t$;

(ii) $a = t$, $b = t^5 + t^2$; (iv) $a = t^2 + t$, $b = t^5 + 3t^{10}$.

c) Determine the automorphism group of $\mathfrak{K}$ over $\mathfrak{F}$ where $\mathfrak{F} = \mathfrak{P}(t)$, as in Exercise 14, and $\mathfrak{K}$ is a splitting field of $f(x)$ in each of the following cases:

(i) $x^3 - t$, (v) $(x^3 - t)(x^3 - t - 1)$,

(ii) $(x^3 - t)(x^5 - x - t)$, (vi) $x^5 - x - t^5 - t$,

(iii) $(x^5 - t)(x^5 - x - t)$, (vii) $x^7 - t$.

(iv) $(x^3 - t)(x^3 - t^2)$,

d) What is the degree of $\mathfrak{K} = \mathfrak{F}(u)$ over $\mathfrak{F} = P(t)$ if $u^3 = 2$ and t is an indeterminate over the field $\mathfrak{P}$ of 7 elements?

14. The characteristic function of a field. Let $\mathfrak{K}$ be separable of degree n over $\mathfrak{F}$. Then $\mathfrak{K} = \mathfrak{F}(z)$, where z is separable. The minimum function of z over $\mathfrak{F}$ is an irreducible polynomial $f = f(x)$ of $\mathfrak{F}[x]$ and

$$f(x) = (x - z_1) \cdots (x - z_n) \tag{38}$$

in a splitting field $\mathfrak{N} = \mathfrak{F}[z_1, \ldots, z_n)$ of $f(x)$. We may take $z = z_1$ and $\mathfrak{N} \supseteq \mathfrak{K}$.

The elements of $\mathfrak{K}$ are uniquely expressible in the form

$$k = \gamma(z) = \gamma_0 + \gamma_1 z + \cdots + \gamma_{n-1} z^{n-1} \quad (\gamma_0, \ldots, \gamma_{n-1} \text{ in } \mathfrak{F}). \tag{39}$$

If C is the companion matrix for $f(x)$, the mapping

$$k = \gamma(z) \to \gamma(C) = \gamma_0 I + \gamma_1 C + \cdots + \gamma_{n-1} C^{n-1} \tag{40}$$

is an isomorphic mapping of $\mathfrak{K}$ onto the field $\mathfrak{F}[C]$ of all polynomials in the matrix C. The characteristic function

$$f(x; k) = |xI - \gamma(C)| \tag{41}$$

is a polynomial in x of degree n called the *characteristic function of* k. We also call $f(x; k)$ the *characteristic function of the field* $\mathfrak{K}$.

The polynomial $f(x; k)$ has two important coefficients. The first of these is the negative of the *trace* (sum of the diagonal elements) *of the matrix* $\gamma(C)$. We use the notation

$$\sigma_{\mathfrak{K}/\mathfrak{F}}(k) \tag{42}$$

for this trace. Then $-\sigma_{\mathfrak{K}/\mathfrak{F}}(k)$ is the coefficient of x^{n-1} in the polynomial $f(x; k)$. We call $\sigma_{\mathfrak{K}/\mathfrak{F}}(k)$ the *trace of* k *in* $\mathfrak{K}$ *over* $\mathfrak{F}$. It is easy to see that

$$\sigma_{\mathfrak{K}/\mathfrak{F}}(ak) = a\sigma_{\mathfrak{K}/\mathfrak{F}}(k), \quad \sigma_{\mathfrak{K}/\mathfrak{F}}(h + k) = \sigma_{\mathfrak{K}/\mathfrak{F}}(h) + \sigma_{\mathfrak{K}/\mathfrak{F}}(k), \quad \sigma_{\mathfrak{K}/\mathfrak{F}}(a) = na \tag{43}$$

for every a of $\mathfrak{F}$ and h and k of $\mathfrak{K}$.

The second important coefficient is that of the constant term. It is $(-1)^n|\gamma(C)|$. We define

$$\nu_{\mathfrak{K}/\mathfrak{F}}(k) = |\gamma(C)| \tag{44}$$

for every k of $\mathfrak{K}$. It is a function on $\mathfrak{K}$ to $\mathfrak{F}$ called the *norm of* k *in* $\mathfrak{K}$ *over* $\mathfrak{F}$. It is a multiplicative function; and, in fact,

$$\nu_{\mathfrak{K}/\mathfrak{F}}(hk) = \nu_{\mathfrak{K}/\mathfrak{F}}(h)\nu_{\mathfrak{K}/\mathfrak{F}}(k), \quad \nu_{\mathfrak{K}/\mathfrak{F}}(a) = a^n \tag{45}$$

for every h and k of $\mathfrak{K}$ and a of $\mathfrak{F}$.

The matrix $\gamma(C)$ is the matrix of the linear transformation $x \to xk$ on the n-dimensional vector space $\mathfrak{K}$ over $\mathfrak{F}$. We extend the coefficient field to a field $\mathfrak{Z} = \mathfrak{F}(\xi_1, \ldots, \xi_n)$ isomorphic to $\mathfrak{N}$ over $\mathfrak{F}$ and obtain an n-dimensional vector space $\mathfrak{L} = \mathfrak{K}_{\mathfrak{Z}}$ over $\mathfrak{Z}$. Since the characteristic roots $\xi_1, \ldots, \xi_n$ of the matrix C are simple, the invariant subspaces $\mathfrak{L}_{\xi_i}$ are one-dimensional, and so C is similar in $\mathfrak{Z}$ to the matrix

$$C_0 = \text{diag}\,\{\xi_1, \ldots, \xi_n\}\,. \tag{46}$$

Then the mapping

$$k = \gamma(z) \to \gamma(C_0) \tag{47}$$

is an isomorphic mapping of $\mathfrak{K}$ onto $\mathfrak{F}[C_0]$. However, $|xI - \gamma(C)| = |xI - \gamma(C_0)|$, and so $\sigma_{\mathfrak{K}/\mathfrak{F}}(k) = \gamma(\xi_1) + \cdots + \gamma(\xi_n)$, and $\nu_{\mathfrak{K}/\mathfrak{F}}(k) = \gamma(\xi_1) \cdots \gamma(\xi_n)$. It follows immediately that

$$\sigma_{\mathfrak{K}/\mathfrak{F}}(k) = \gamma(z_1) + \cdots + \gamma(z_n), \quad \nu_{\mathfrak{K}/\mathfrak{F}}(k) = \gamma(z_1) \cdots \gamma(z_n). \tag{48}$$

Thus the trace of k in $\mathfrak{K}$ over $\mathfrak{F}$ is the sum of the roots in $\mathfrak{N}$ of the characteristic function of k, and the norm of k in $\mathfrak{K}$ over $\mathfrak{F}$ is the product of these roots. We shall use the following result later:

LEMMA 10. *Let $\mathfrak{K}$ be separable of degree* n *over $\mathfrak{F}$. Then there exists an element* k *in $\mathfrak{K}$ whose trace in $\mathfrak{K}$ over $\mathfrak{F}$ is not zero.*

For let $\sigma_{\mathfrak{K}/\mathfrak{F}}(k) = 0$ for every k. Then the matrices $I, C_0, \ldots, C^{n-1}$ all have zero trace. But the matrix

$$e_{11} = (C_0 - \xi_2 I) \cdots (C_0 - \xi_n I)[(\xi_1 - \xi_2) \cdots (\xi_1 - \xi_n)]^{-1} \tag{49}$$

has 1 in its first row and column and zeros elsewhere, and so its trace is 1. Since e_{11} is a polynomial in C_0 and is a linear combination of the matrices $I, C_0, \ldots, C_0^{n-1}$, all of which have zero trace, this is impossible.

EXERCISES

1. Let $\mathfrak{K}$ be separable of degree n over $\mathfrak{F}$ and $\mathfrak{K} \supset \mathfrak{L} \supset \mathfrak{F}$. Prove that if k is in $\mathfrak{K}$, then $\sigma_{\mathfrak{K}/\mathfrak{F}}(k) = \sigma_{\mathfrak{L}/\mathfrak{F}}[\sigma_{\mathfrak{K}/\mathfrak{L}}(k)]$.
2. Assume $\mathfrak{K} \supset \mathfrak{L} \supset \mathfrak{F}$, as in Exercise 1. Prove that $\nu_{\mathfrak{K}/\mathfrak{F}}(k) = \nu_{\mathfrak{L}/\mathfrak{F}}[\nu_{\mathfrak{K}/\mathfrak{L}}(k)]$.

15. The normal basis theorem. Let $\mathfrak{N}$ be a normal field of degree n over $\mathfrak{F}$ and let $S_1 = I, S_2, \ldots, S_n$ be the automorphisms over $\mathfrak{F}$ of $\mathfrak{N}$. Then a basis $u_1, \ldots, u_n$ of $\mathfrak{N}$ over $\mathfrak{F}$ is called a *normal basis* of $\mathfrak{N}$ if there exists an element u in $\mathfrak{N}$ such that

$$u_i = uS_i \qquad (i = 1, \ldots, n). \tag{50}$$

We shall show first that every cyclic field has a normal basis.

Consider a cyclic field $\mathfrak{K}$ of degree n over $\mathfrak{F}$ and let S generate its Galois group over $\mathfrak{F}$. Then $\mathfrak{K}$ is an n-dimensional vector space over $\mathfrak{F}$, and $I, S, \ldots, S^{n-1}$ are distinct automorphisms over $\mathfrak{F}$ of $\mathfrak{K}$. They are also linear transformations over $\mathfrak{F}$ of $\mathfrak{K}$, and Lemma 4 states that these linear transformations are linearly independent over $\mathfrak{F}$. Since $S^n = I$, the minimum function of S must be $x^n - 1$. Then $x^n - 1$ is also the characteristic function of the transformation S on an n-dimensional vector space. Hence the only non-trivial invariant factor of $xI - S$ is $f(x) = x^n - 1$. By Theorem 3.26 the field $\mathfrak{K}$ has a basis $u_1, \ldots, u_n$ over $\mathfrak{F}$ such that the matrix of S is the companion matrix of $f(x)$, that is,

$$\begin{pmatrix} 0 & 1 & 0 & \cdots & 0 \\ 0 & 0 & 1 & \cdots & 0 \\ \cdot & \cdot & \cdot & \cdots & \cdot \\ 0 & 0 & 0 & \cdots & 1 \\ 1 & 0 & 0 & \cdots & 0 \end{pmatrix}$$

But then $u_i S = u_{i+1}$ for $i = 1, \ldots, n$, that is, $u_i = u_1 S^{i-1}$ for $i = 1, \ldots, n$.

THEOREM 31. *Let $\mathfrak{K}$ be cyclic over $\mathfrak{F}$. Then $\mathfrak{K}$ has a normal basis.*

In chapter v we shall show that every field $\mathfrak{K}$ of finite degree over a finite field $\mathfrak{F}$ is cyclic over $\mathfrak{F}$. The existence of a normal basis for any normal field $\mathfrak{F}$ will then follow from Theorem 31 and our next result.

THEOREM 32. *Let $\mathfrak{N}$ be normal of degree* n *over an infinite field $\mathfrak{F}$. Then $\mathfrak{N}$ has a normal basis over $\mathfrak{F}$.*

For let $S_1 = I, \ldots, S_n$ be the automorphisms over $\mathfrak{F}$ of $\mathfrak{N}$. By Theorem 30 we may determine an element k such that $\mathfrak{N} = \mathfrak{F}(k)$. Let $f(x)$ be the minimum function over $\mathfrak{F}$ of k, so that

$$f(x) = (x - k)(x - kS_2) \cdots (x - kS_n) \tag{51}$$

in $\mathfrak{N}$. But then $f(x) = (x - kS_i)f_i(x)$, $f'(x) = (x - kS_i)f_i'(x) + f_i(x)$, and $f'(kS_i) = f_i(kS_i)$. It follows that the polynomial

$$g(x) = \frac{f(x)}{(x - k)\, f'(k)} \tag{52}$$

has the property that $g_i(kS_i) = 1$, where

$$g_i(x) = [g(x)]\, S_i = \frac{f(x)}{(x - kS_i)\, f'(kS_i)}\,. \tag{53}$$

Also $g_i(kS_j) = 0$ for $i \neq j$. Then the polynomial equation

$$g_1(x) + \cdots + g_n(x) = 1 \tag{54}$$

has virtual degree $n - 1$ and n distinct roots kS_i. Thus equation (54) is an identity. Also $g_i(x)g_j(x)$ is zero for $x = k$ and $kS_2, \ldots, kS_n$, and thus $f(x)$ divides $g_i(x)g_j(x)$ for $i \neq j$.

We now consider the matrix $C = C(x) = (\gamma_{ij})$, where $\gamma_{ij} = g_i(x)S_j$. Then $CC' = D = (\delta_{ik})$, where

$$(55) \qquad \delta_{ik} = \sum_{j=1}^{n} [g_i(x)\, S_j]\, [g_k(x)\, S_j]\, .$$

By equation (54) we see that $\delta_{ii} - 1$ is divisible by $f(x)$ for $i = 1, \ldots, n$. Also $f(x)$ divides $[g_i(x)S_j][g_k(x)S_j]$ for $i \neq k$, and so $f(x)$ divides δ_{ik} for $i \neq k$. Then the determinant $|D| = |C|^2 = 1 + f(x)q(x)$ is a non-zero polynomial in $\mathfrak{N}[x]$, and so $|C| = \gamma(x)$ is a non-zero polynomial of $\mathfrak{N}[x]$. There exists an element α in $\mathfrak{F}$ such that $\gamma(\alpha) \neq 0$. Thus the matrix

$$(56) \qquad C(\alpha) = (uS_iS_j) \qquad (i, j = 1, \ldots, n)$$

is non-singular if $u = g(\alpha)$. But if $a_1u + a_2uS_2 + \cdots + a_nuS_n = 0$ for $a_1, \ldots, a_n$ in $\mathfrak{F}$ and not all zero, we have $(\Sigma a_iuS_i)S_j = \Sigma a_i(uS_iS_j) = 0$. If $w = (a_1, \ldots, a_n) \neq 0$, this last equation states that $wC(\alpha) = 0$, whereas $C(\alpha)$ is non-singular. This completes our proof.

We may now apply Lemma 10 to obtain the following property of a normal basis:

THEOREM 33. *Every normal field* $\mathfrak{N}$ *over* $\mathfrak{F}$ *has a normal basis* u, $\mathrm{uS_2}, \ldots, \mathrm{uS_n}$ *where the trace of* u *is* 1.

For $\sigma_{\mathfrak{N}/\mathfrak{F}}(u) = \sigma_{\mathfrak{N}/\mathfrak{F}}(uS_2) = \cdots = \sigma_{\mathfrak{N}/\mathfrak{F}}(uS_n)$ by equation (48). By equation (43) we see that if $k = a_1u + a_2uS_2 + \cdots + a_nuS_n$, then $\sigma_{\mathfrak{N}/\mathfrak{F}}(k) = (a_1 + \cdots + a_n)\lambda$, where $\lambda = \sigma_{\mathfrak{N}/\mathfrak{F}}(u)$. If $\lambda = 0$, then $\sigma_{\mathfrak{N}/\mathfrak{F}}(k) = 0$ for every k of $\mathfrak{N}$ which contradicts Lemma 10. Hence $\lambda \neq 0$, and we take $v = \lambda^{-1}u$ and see that $vS_i = \lambda^{-1}(uS_i)$, $\sigma_{\mathfrak{N}/\mathfrak{F}}(v) = 1$, and v generates a normal basis of $\mathfrak{N}$ over $\mathfrak{F}$.

16. The trace theorem. If $\mathfrak{K}$ is a cyclic field of degree n over $\mathfrak{F}$ and k is in $\mathfrak{K}$, we have

$$(57) \qquad \sigma_{\mathfrak{K}/\mathfrak{F}}(kS - k) = 0$$

for every element k of $\mathfrak{K}$ where S generates the Galois group of $\mathfrak{K}$ over $\mathfrak{F}$.

THEOREM 34. *Let* $\mathfrak{K}$ *be cyclic over* $\mathfrak{F}$. *Then an element* g *of* $\mathfrak{K}$ *has zero trace if and only if* $\mathrm{g} = \mathrm{kS} - \mathrm{k}$ *for some* k *of* $\mathfrak{K}$.

For let $u, uS, \ldots, uS^{n-1}$ be a normal basis of $\mathfrak{K}$ over $\mathfrak{F}$, where we may take

$$(58) \qquad \sigma(u) = \sigma_{\mathfrak{K}/\mathfrak{F}}(u) = 1\, .$$

If $k = a_1u + a_2uS + \cdots + a_nuS^{n-1}$, then $kS = a_nu + a_1uS + \cdots + a_{n-1}uS^{n-1}$, and so $kS - k = \beta_1u + \beta_2uS + \cdots + \beta_nuS^{n-1}$, where

$$(59) \qquad \beta_1 = a_n - a_1, \quad \beta_2 = a_1 - a_2, \ldots, \quad \beta_n = a_{n-1} - a_n .$$

If we assume that $\beta_2, \ldots, \beta_n$ are given, then equations (59) determine $a_1, \ldots, a_{n-1}$ uniquely in terms of $\beta_2, \ldots, \beta_n$ and a_n, and the first equation imposes the restriction $a_n = a_1 + \beta_1$ on the a_i. But this restriction is $a_n = a_1 + \beta_1 = a_2 + \beta_1 + \beta_2 = \cdots = a_n + \beta_1 + \beta_2 + \cdots + \beta_n$, which can be satisfied if and only if $\beta_1 + \cdots + \beta_n = 0$. However, if $g = \beta_1u + \cdots + \beta_nuS^{n-1}$, then $\sigma(g) = \beta_1 + \cdots + \beta_n$, and our theorem is proved.

There is an analogous theorem on norms. It states that if $\mathfrak{K}$ is cyclic over $\mathfrak{F}$ with S generating its Galois group, then the norm $\nu_{\mathfrak{K}/\mathfrak{F}}(k) = 1$, for k in $\mathfrak{K}$, if and only if $k = (gS)g^{-1}$, where g is in $\mathfrak{K}$. We shall not need this result and will not derive it here. It may be found on page 200 of the author's *Modern Higher Algebra.*

17. References. An exposition of the theory of fields is given in chapters vii, viii, and ix of the author's *Modern Higher Algebra.* The exposition of the Galois theory given here is a modification of that presented in E. Artin's *Galois Theory* ("Notre Dame Mathematical Lectures," No. 2 [2d ed.]).

CHAPTER V

Finite Fields

1. Number of elements. A field which consists of a finite number of elements is called a *finite field.* We shall represent a finite field of q elements by the symbol $\mathfrak{F}_q$.

The unity element of a field $\mathfrak{F}$ generates a subfield of $\mathfrak{F}$ which we have called its *prime subfield.* The prime subfield of a finite field $\mathfrak{F}_q$ is necessarily a finite field and must be the field

$$\mathfrak{F}_p = \mathfrak{E}_p = \mathfrak{E} - (p) . \tag{1}$$

This is the difference ring of the ring $\mathfrak{E}$ of integers modulo (p), where p is the characteristic of $\mathfrak{F}_q$. We recall that the elements of $\mathfrak{E}_p$ may be represented by the integers

$$0, 1, \ldots, p - 1 , \tag{2}$$

where each integer a represents the class $a + (p)$ consisting of all integers of the form $a + \lambda p$. We also recall that for every a of $\mathfrak{E}_p$ we have the Fermat property

$$a^p = a , \tag{3}$$

since the set $\mathfrak{E}_p^*$ of all non-zero elements of $\mathfrak{E}_p$ is a group of order $p - 1$.

Every finite field $\mathfrak{K} = \mathfrak{F}_q$ is a vector space over its prime subfield $\mathfrak{E}_p$. Since $\mathfrak{K}$ is finite, it must have finite dimension n over $\mathfrak{E}_p$. Hence

$$\mathfrak{K} = u_1\mathfrak{E}_p + \cdots + u_n\mathfrak{E}_p , \tag{4}$$

that is, every element k of $\mathfrak{K}$ is *uniquely* expressible in the form

$$k = \xi_1 u_i + \cdots + \xi_n u_n , \tag{5}$$

where $\xi_1, \ldots, \xi_n$ are in $\mathfrak{E}_p$. Since $\xi_1, \ldots, \xi_n$ range independently over the p values in equation (2), there are p^n values of k.

THEOREM 1. *A finite field $\mathfrak{K}$ has $\mathrm{q} = \mathrm{p}^{\mathrm{n}}$ elements, where* p *is the characteristic of $\mathfrak{K}$ and* n *is the degree of $\mathfrak{K}$ over $\mathfrak{E}_{\mathrm{p}}$.*

2. Existence and uniqueness. The non-zero elements of any field $\mathfrak{K}$ form a multiplicative group $\mathfrak{K}^*$. If $\mathfrak{K} = \mathfrak{F}_q$, the group $\mathfrak{K}^*$ has order $\tau = q - 1$. By Theorem 1.10 we see that every element of $\mathfrak{K}^*$ satisfies the equation $x^\tau = 1$. But then we have the following property:

THEOREM 2. *Let* $\mathfrak{F}_q$ *be a finite field of* q *elements. Then every element of* $\mathfrak{F}_q$ *is a root of the equation*

$$(6) \qquad f(x) \equiv x^q - x = 0 .$$

We shall now prove the existence and uniqueness of $\mathfrak{F}_q$.

THEOREM 3. *The splitting field* $\mathfrak{K}$ *of equation* (6) *over* $\mathfrak{E}_p$ *is a finite field of* $q = p^n$ *elements. Every field* $\mathfrak{F}_q$ *is isomorphic to* $\mathfrak{K}$.

For $q = p^n = 0$ in $\mathfrak{E}_p$, and so $f'(x) = qx^{q-1} - 1 = -1$ has no root in common with $f(x)$. It follows that $f(x)$ is separable and has q distinct roots,

$$(7) \qquad a_1 = 0, \quad a_2 = 1, \ldots , a_q ,$$

in the splitting field $\mathfrak{K}$. If $a_i^q = a_i$ and $a_j^q = a_j$, then $(a_ia_j)^q = a_ia_j$. Hence any product $b_1 \cdots b_m$ of non-zero roots of $f(x) = 0$ is a non-zero root of $f(x) = 0$. Thus every element of $\mathfrak{K} = \mathfrak{E}_p(a_1, \ldots , a_q)$ is a linear function $k = \xi_2a_2 + \cdots + \xi_qa_q$, for $\xi_2, \ldots , \xi_q$ in $\mathfrak{E}_p$, and $\xi_i^p = \xi_i$. But then $k^q = \xi_2^qa_2^q + \cdots + \xi_q^qa_q^q = k$, and so *every element of* $\mathfrak{K}$ is a root of $f(x) = 0$. It follows that $\mathfrak{K}$ consists of exactly q elements, and so $\mathfrak{K} = \mathfrak{F}_q$. If $\mathfrak{F}_q'$ is any field of q elements, we may assume that $\mathfrak{F}_q'$ has the same prime subfield $\mathfrak{E}_p$ as $\mathfrak{K}$. By Theorem 2 we see that $\mathfrak{F}_q' \supseteq \mathfrak{K}' \supseteq \mathfrak{E}_p$, where $\mathfrak{K}'$ is a splitting field over $\mathfrak{E}_p$ of $f(x) = 0$. By the proof just given, $\mathfrak{K}'$ has q elements, and so $\mathfrak{K}' = \mathfrak{F}_q'$. By Theorem 4.6 all splitting fields of $f(x)$ are isomorphic, and our result is proved.

3. The cyclic group $\mathfrak{F}_q^*$. The set $\mathfrak{F}_q^*$ of all non-zero elements of $\mathfrak{F}_q$ is an abelian group of order $\tau = q - 1$. Let ϵ be the exponent of $\mathfrak{F}_q^*$. Then $x^\epsilon = 1$ for every x of $\mathfrak{F}^*$. But an equation of degree ϵ has at most ϵ roots in a field $\mathfrak{F}_q$, and the equation $x^\epsilon = 1$ has $q - 1$ distinct roots. Hence $\epsilon \geq \tau \geq \epsilon$, and so $\epsilon = \tau$. By Theorem 1.26 $\mathfrak{F}_q^*$ is a cyclic group, and we have the following result:

THEOREM 4. *Let* $\mathfrak{K} = \mathfrak{F}_q$, *where* $q = p^n = \tau + 1$. *Then* $\mathfrak{K} = \mathfrak{E}_p(y)$, *where* y *is a primitive* τth *root of unity, and the non-zero elements of* $\mathfrak{K}$ *are the powers* $1, y, y^2, \ldots , y^{\tau-1}$ *of* y.

The multiplicative order of any non-zero element k of $\mathfrak{K} = \mathfrak{F}_q$ is called the *period* of k. The period of k is then a divisor ρ of the order τ of $\mathfrak{F}_q^*$, and we shall say that *k belongs to ρ*. An element k is called a *primitive* element of $\mathfrak{F}_q$ if k belongs to τ. Then k is primitive if and only if $k = y^\mu$, where μ is prime to τ. The number of such exponents μ is the Euler ϕ-function, $\phi(\tau)$, and we state this result as follows:

THEOREM 5. *Let $\mathfrak{F}_q$ be a field of* $q = p^n$ *elements and* $\tau = q - 1$. *Then there are $\phi(\tau)$ primitive elements in $\mathfrak{F}_q$.*

4. Primitive roots modulo m. The theory of primitive roots modulo m is needed in the study of the degree of a finite field defined by a root of unity. We shall therefore consider the general case of a ring $\mathfrak{E}_m = \mathfrak{E} - (m)$, where $m > 1$ is an integer. We define $\mathfrak{E}_m^*$ to be the set of those residue classes $g + (m)$ defined by integers g which are prime to m. *Then $\mathfrak{E}_m^*$ is an abelian group of order* $\phi(m)$. If $\mathfrak{E}_m^*$ is a cyclic group and y is an integer such that $y + (m)$ generates $\mathfrak{E}_m^*$, we call y a *primitive root* modulo m. The cases where $\mathfrak{E}_m^*$ is cyclic are given in the following theorem:

THEOREM 6. *The group $\mathfrak{E}_m^*$ is cyclic if and only if* $m = 2, 4, p^n, 2p^n$, *where* p *is an odd prime. There is an odd primitive root δ modulo any odd prime* p *such that* $\delta^{p-1} - 1$ *is not divisible by* p^2. *Every such δ is a primitive root both modulo* p^n *and modulo* $2p^n$ *for every positive integer* n.

For if $m \neq 2^n, p^n, 2p^n$, we may write $m = ab$, where a is prime to b and $a > 2$, $b > 2$. Since $\phi(p^n) = p^{n-1}(p - 1)$ is even if p is odd or if $p = 2$ and $n > 1$, we see that $\phi(a)$ is even for every $a > 2$. But then the least common multiple of $\phi(a)$ and $\phi(b)$ is an integer $\gamma < \phi(ab)$. If δ is prime to m, we have $\delta^{\phi(a)} \equiv 1 \pmod{a}$ and $\delta^{\phi(b)} \equiv 1 \pmod{b}$, so that $\delta^\gamma \equiv 1 \pmod{a}$ and $\delta^\gamma \equiv 1 \pmod{b}$. But then $\delta^\gamma \equiv 1 \pmod{ab}$, the exponent of the abelian group $\mathfrak{E}_m^*$ is at most γ, and $\mathfrak{E}_m$ is not cyclic. Hence $m = p^n, 2p^n, 2^n$.

The groups $\mathfrak{E}_2^*$ and $\mathfrak{E}_4^*$ are cyclic and $\delta = -1$ for $m = 4$. If y is any odd integer, the formula

$$y^{2^k} \equiv 1 \pmod{2^{k+2}} \tag{8}$$

holds for $k = 1$, that is, $y^2 \equiv 1 \pmod{8}$ for all odd integers y. If it holds for any k, we have $y^{2^k} = 1 + q2^{k+2}$ and then $y^{2^{k+1}} = (y^{2^k})^2 = 1 + 2q\,2^{k+2} + q^2 2^{2k+4} = 1 + 2^{k+3}(q + 2^{k+1}q^2)$ and so congruence (8) holds for all integers k. But then the exponent of $\mathfrak{E}_m^*$ for $m = 2^n > 4$ is at most $2^{n-2} = (\frac{1}{2})\phi(2^n)$, and $\mathfrak{E}_m^*$ is not cyclic.

We assume now that $m = p^n$, where p is an odd prime and $n > 1$. Let us observe that if

$$a \equiv b \pmod{p^k}\,, \tag{9}$$

then $a = b + cp^k$, $a^p = b^p + b^{p-1}\,cp^{k+1} + \cdots + (cp^k)^p$, and so

$$a^p \equiv b^p \pmod{p^{k+1}}\,. \tag{10}$$

By Theorem 4 there exists a primitive root β modulo p. Then $\delta = \beta + ap$ is a primitive root modulo p for every integer a, and $\delta^p - \delta = (\beta + ap)^p - (\beta + ap) \equiv \beta^p - \beta - ap \pmod{p^2}$. Thus either $\beta^p - \beta \not\equiv 0 \pmod{p^2}$ and we take $a = 0$, or $\beta^p - \beta \equiv 0 \pmod{p^2}$ and $\delta^p - \delta \equiv ap \not\equiv 0 \pmod{p^2}$ if $1 \leq a \leq p - 1$. We have proved the existence of a primitive root δ modulo p such that

$$\delta^{p-1} = 1 + pd\,, \tag{11}$$

where $d \not\equiv 0 \pmod{p}$.

The binomial theorem implies that

$$(1 + p^i d)^p \equiv 1 + p^{i+1} d \pmod{p^{i+2}}. \tag{12}$$

The case $i = 1$ of congruence (12) is

$$\delta^{(p-1)p} \equiv 1 + p^2 d \pmod{p^3}.$$

By equation (11) this is the case $j = 1$ of the formula

$$\delta^{(p-1)p^j} \equiv 1 + p^{j+1} d \pmod{p^{j+2}}. \tag{13}$$

But from congruence (13) for a given value of j we have

$$\delta^{(p-1)p^{j+1}} \equiv (1 + p^{j+1} d)^p \pmod{p^{j+3}} \tag{14}$$

by equation (10), and we use congruence (12) with $i = j + 1$ to obtain congruence (13) for $j + 1$. This shows that congruence (13) holds for all values of j. But then, if $s = (p - 1)p^{n-2}$, we see that $\delta^s \equiv 1 + p^{n-1}d \not\equiv 1 \pmod{p^n}$.

Let t be the order of the residue class for δ modulo p^n. Then $\delta^t \equiv 1 \pmod{p}$, and so $p - 1$ divides t. But t divides $\phi(p^n) = p^{n-1}(p - 1)$, and so $t = p^k(p - 1)$, where $k \leq n - 1$. By the proof just given we see that $k = n - 1$, and so δ has order $\phi(p^n)$ modulo p^n, $\mathfrak{G}_m^*$ is cyclic if $m = p^n$ and p is any odd prime. Also one of δ and $\delta + p^n$ is odd, and both are primitive modulo p^n, so we may take δ to be odd. Now $\phi(2p^n) = \phi(2)\phi(p^n) = \phi(p^n)$, and, if t is the order of δ modulo $2p^n$, we see that $\delta^t \equiv 1 \pmod{p^n}$, t is divisible by $\phi(p^n) = \phi(2p^n)$, $t = \phi(2p^n)$, and δ is again primitive. This completes our proof.

We shall give a table of primitive roots for all odd primes $p < 500$ in Appendix I. We shall also give a brief sample table of the *indices* of integers in Appendix II. We observe that if δ is a primitive root modulo p, the elements of $\mathfrak{G}_p^*$ are powers of δ, and so

$$n \equiv \delta^{\nu(n)} \pmod{p}$$

for all integers $n = 1, 2, \ldots, p - 1$. The integer $\nu(n)$ is called the *index of* n *modulo* p *relative to* δ. It has the properties

$$\nu(ab) = \nu(a) + \nu(b), \quad \nu(n^k) \equiv k\nu(n) \quad (\text{mod } p - 1).$$

Let us now return to the theory of finite fields.

5. The Galois group of a finite field. If $\mathfrak{F}$ is any field of characteristic p, we have seen that the set $\mathfrak{F}^p$, consisting of the pth powers of the elements of $\mathfrak{F}$, is a subfield of $\mathfrak{F}$. The mapping

$$S: \qquad\qquad x \to xS = x^p$$

is an isomorphism of $\mathfrak{F}$ *onto* $\mathfrak{F}^p$ and must map a finite field $\mathfrak{F}$ onto itself. Thus S is an automorphism of $\mathfrak{F}$. By equation (3) we see that S is an automorphism over $\mathfrak{E}_p$ of $\mathfrak{F}$.

THEOREM 7. *The Galois group of a field* $\mathfrak{F}$ *of degree* n *over* $\mathfrak{E}_p$ *is the cyclic group generated by the automorphism* $x \to x^p$.

The order of the Galois group $\mathfrak{G}$ of $\mathfrak{F}$ over $\mathfrak{E}_p$ is n, and S generates $\mathfrak{G}$ if and only if S has order n. If S has order $m < n$ and $t = p^m$, we see that $xS^m = x^t = x$ for every x of $\mathfrak{F} = \mathfrak{F}_q$. The equation $x^t = x$ then has q distinct roots, which is impossible, since $t = p^m < q = p^n$.

Every cyclic group $[S]$ of order n has a unique (cyclic) subgroup $\mathfrak{H}$ of index m for every divisor m of n. Indeed, Theorem 1.24 states that $\mathfrak{H} = [S^m]$. The fixed field for $\mathfrak{H}$ is then a subfield $\mathfrak{L}$ of degree m over $\mathfrak{E}_p$ of $\mathfrak{K} = \mathfrak{F}_q$. Since $\mathfrak{L}$ is unique, we have the following result:

LEMMA 1. *Let* $\mathfrak{K}$ *be a field of degree* n *over* $\mathfrak{E}_p$. *Then a field* $\mathfrak{L}$ *of degree* m *over* $\mathfrak{E}_p$ *is isomorphic to a subfield over* $\mathfrak{E}_p$ *of* $\mathfrak{K}$ *if and only if* m *divides* n.

Lemma 1 implies the following theorem, of which it is a special case:

THEOREM 8. *Let* $\mathfrak{K}$ *be a field of degree* n *over* $\mathfrak{F}_q$. *Then a field* $\mathfrak{L}$ *of degree* m *over* $\mathfrak{F}_q$ *is isomorphic to a subfield over* $\mathfrak{F}_q$ *of* $\mathfrak{K}$ *if and only if* m *divides* n.

For let $\mathfrak{F} = \mathfrak{F}_q$ have degree ν over $\mathfrak{E}_p$, and so $p^\nu = q$. Then $\mathfrak{K}$ has degree $n\nu$ over $\mathfrak{E}_p$ by Theorem 4.3. If $\mathfrak{L}$ has degree m over $\mathfrak{F}_q$ and is isomorphic to a subfield over $\mathfrak{F}_q$ of $\mathfrak{K}$, then it is isomorphic over $\mathfrak{E}_p$ to a subfield of $\mathfrak{K}$, and so $m\nu$ divides $n\nu$, and m divides n. Conversely, if m divides n, the field $\mathfrak{K}$ contains a subfield $\mathfrak{L}'$ of degree m over $\mathfrak{F}$, and $\mathfrak{L}'$ is isomorphic to $\mathfrak{L}$ by Theorem 3.

We now restate Theorem 7 for relative fields, that is, for fields $\mathfrak{K}$ over $\mathfrak{F}_q$ rather than over $\mathfrak{E}_p$.

THEOREM 9. *Let* $\mathfrak{K}$ *be a field of degree* n *over* $\mathfrak{F}_q$. *Then the Galois group of* $\mathfrak{K}$ *over* $\mathfrak{F}$ *is the cyclic group generated by the automorphism* $x \to x^q$.

For $\mathfrak{K}$ is cyclic of degree $n\nu$ over $\mathfrak{E}_p$, where $q = p^\nu$. The Galois group of $\mathfrak{K}$ over $\mathfrak{F}$ is then the group of index ν leaving $\mathfrak{F}$ fixed. This is the νth power of S, where S is the automorphism $x \to x^p$, and we see clearly that S^ν is the automorphism $x \to x^{p^\nu}$; S^ν is precisely $x \to x^q$.

As a consequence of Theorem 9 we can obtain a criterion for determining the degree of a simple extension of a finite field.

THEOREM 10. *The field* $\mathfrak{K} = \mathfrak{F}(k)$ *has degree* m *over* $\mathfrak{F} = \mathfrak{F}_q$ *if and only if* m *is the least integer for which*

$$k^{q^m} = k\,. \tag{15}$$

For we may find a field $\mathfrak{W} \supseteq \mathfrak{K}$ such that the degree of $\mathfrak{W}$ over $\mathfrak{F}_q$ is an integer n divisible by m, where we define m as the least integer for which equation (15) holds. Then equation (15) states that k is in the field $\mathfrak{L}$ under the group $\mathfrak{H}$ generated by S^m. This group has index m, and so $\mathfrak{L}$ has degree m over $\mathfrak{F}$. If $\mathfrak{F}(k)$ has degree $\mu < m$ over $\mathfrak{F}$, then $k^{q^\mu} = k$ by Theorem 9, contrary to the definition of m.

6. Dedekind's formula. Theorem 8 on fields may be restated for irreducible polynomials as follows:

THEOREM 11. *Let* $\psi(x)$ *be an irreducible polynomial of degree* m *over* $\mathfrak{F} = \mathfrak{F}_q$ *and*

$$g(x) = x^r - x \qquad (r = q^n). \tag{16}$$

Then $\psi(x)$ *divides* g(x) *if and only if* m *divides* n.

It follows from Theorem 11 that $g(x)$ is divisible by all irreducible polynomials of degree m where m is any divisor of n. Moreover, $g(x) = x^r - x$ is a separable polynomial, and so each irreducible polynomial of degree m occurs exactly *once* in the factorization of $g(x)$ into irreducible polynomials, and we say that it is a *simple* factor of $g(x)$.

Let $\Lambda(x)$ be the product of all distinct irreducible polynomials whose degrees are *proper* divisors of n. Then $\Lambda(x)$ is the least common multiple of the polynomials

$$x^{\tau(\mu)} - 1 \qquad [\tau(\mu) = q^\mu - 1], \tag{17}$$

where μ ranges over all proper divisors of n. Evidently, $\Lambda(x)$ divides $g(x)$, and the quotient

$$\Gamma(x;\, n,\, q) = \frac{g(x)}{\Lambda(x)} \tag{18}$$

is the product of the distinct irreducible polynomials of degree n over $\mathfrak{F} = \mathfrak{F}_q$. We now introduce the notations for what is called DEDEKIND'S FORMULA.

Let $n = p_1^{e_1} \cdots p_s^{e_s}$, where $p_1, \ldots, p_s$ are the distinct prime factors of n. We let

$$\Sigma = (p_1, \ldots, p_s) \tag{19}$$

be the set consisting of the primes $p_1, \ldots, p_s$. If Σ_k is any subset consisting of k elements $p_{i_1}, \ldots, p_{i_k}$ of Σ, we define a corresponding quotient,

$$m(\Sigma_k) = \frac{n}{p_{i_1} \cdots p_{i_k}}, \tag{20}$$

of n by the product of the elements in Σ_k. There are $\sigma_{s,k}$ subsets Σ_k of Σ, where $\sigma_{s,k}$ *is the number of combinations of* s *objects taken* k *at a time.* We observe that $m(\Sigma_k)$ is a proper divisor of n for $k = 1, \ldots, s$. Let us define $m(\Sigma_0) = n$.

We define the symbol $[m]$ for all positive integers m by the formula

$$[m] = x^{q^m} - x, \tag{21}$$

where our basic coefficient field is $\mathfrak{F} = \mathfrak{F}_q$. Then

$$[n] = [m(\Sigma_0)] = g(x). \tag{22}$$

Let

$$\lambda_k(x) = \prod_{\Sigma_k \subseteq \Sigma} [m(\Sigma_k)]. \tag{23}$$

Then $\lambda_k(x)$ is a product of factors of form (21), with m a divisor of n, and

$$\lambda_0(x) = [m(\Sigma_0)] = g(x). \tag{24}$$

By Theorem 11 the degree of every irreducible factor of $\lambda_k(x)$ divides n and is a proper divisor of n if $k > 0$. The formula we shall now derive is due to Dedekind in the case $q = p$.

THEOREM 12. *Let $\mathfrak{F}$ be the field of* q *elements and* $\Gamma(x; n, q)$ *be the product of all irreducible polynomials of degree* n *over* $\mathfrak{F}$. *Let* $n = p_1^{e_1} \cdots p_s^{e_s}$ *and*

$$\Delta_0(x) = \prod_{0 \leq 2k \leq s} \lambda_{2k}(x), \tag{25}$$

$$\Delta_1(x) = \prod_{1 \leq 2k+1 \leq s} \lambda_{2k+1}(x). \tag{26}$$

Then

$$\Gamma(x; n, q) = \frac{\Delta_0(x)}{\Delta_1(x)}. \tag{27}$$

For we have already seen that every irreducible polynomial of degree n is a simple factor of $\lambda_0(x)$ and is not a factor of $\lambda_k(x)$ for $k > 0$. Let $h(x)$ be an irreducible polynomial divisor of $\Delta_0(x)\Delta_1(x)$ of degree $\mu < n$, so that μ is a proper divisor of n. Let $q_1, \ldots, q_t$ be the prime factors of n which occur to a higher exponent in n than they do in μ. Then, if $k > t$, the integer μ does not divide $m(\Sigma_k)$. Hence $h(x)$ does not divide $\lambda_k(x)$ for $k > t$. If $k \leq t$, we see that $m(\Sigma_k)$ is divisible by μ if and only if Σ_k is a subset of $\Sigma' = (q_1, \ldots, q_t)$. There are $\sigma_{t,k}$ subsets $\Sigma_k \subseteq \Sigma'$, and so $h(x)$ is a factor of multiplicity $\sigma_{t,k}$ of $\lambda_k(x)$. Hence $h(x)$ is a factor of multiplicity

$$\alpha = 1 + \sum_{2 \leq 2k \leq t} \sigma_{t,\,2k} \tag{28}$$

of $\Delta_0(x)$, and $h(x)$ is a factor of multiplicity

$$\beta = \sum_{1 \leq 2k+1 \leq t} \sigma_{t,\,2k+1} \tag{29}$$

of $\Delta_1(x)$. The expansion

$$\rho(x) = (1 + x)^t = 1 + \sigma_{t,1} x + \cdots + \sigma_{t,t} x^t \tag{30}$$

implies that α is the sum of the coefficients of the even powers of x in $\rho(x)$, and β is the sum of the coefficients of the odd powers of x in $\rho(x)$. Then $\rho(-1) = \alpha - \beta = (1 - 1)^t = 0$. Hence $h(x)$ has the same multiplicity in $\Delta_0(x)$ and in $\Delta_1(x)$ and has multiplicity zero in their quotient. This proves our theorem.

The degree of the function $\Gamma(x; n, q)$ in equation (27) is $n\nu(n, q)$, where

$$\nu(n, q) = \frac{1}{n}\left[q^n - \Sigma q^{n/p_1} + \Sigma q^{n/p_1 p_2} - \cdots + (-1)^s q^{n/p_1 \cdots p_s}\right]. \tag{31}$$

Thus equation (31) is a formula for the number of irreducible polynomials of degree n over $\mathfrak{F}_q$.

EXERCISES

1. Show that the three irreducible polynomials of degree 4 over $\mathfrak{F}_2$ are $x^4 + x + 1$, $x^4 + x^3 + 1$, and $x^4 + x^3 + x^2 + x + 1$ by factoring the quotient $(x^{16} - x)(x^4 - x)^{-1}$.

2. Let $\zeta^2 + \zeta + 1 = 0$, so that $\mathfrak{F}_2(\zeta)$ is a field $\mathfrak{F}_4$ of degree 2 over $\mathfrak{F}_2$. Determine the six irreducible quadratics over $\mathfrak{F}_4$ by the factorizations $x^4 + x + 1 = (x^2 + x + \zeta)(x^2 + x + \zeta^2)$, $x^4 + x^3 + 1 = (x^2 + \zeta x + \zeta)(x^2 + \zeta^2 x + \zeta^2)$, and $x^4 + x^3 + x^2 + x + 1 = (x^2 + \zeta x + 1)(x^2 + \zeta^2 x + 1)$.

7. Polynomials belonging to an exponent. An irreducible polynomial $f(x)$ of degree m over a finite field $\mathfrak{F}$ is said to *belong to the exponent* e if e is the least integer such that $f(x)$ divides $x^e - 1$.

THEOREM 13. *An irreducible polynomial* f(x) *of degree* m *over* $\mathfrak{F}_q$ *be-*

longs to e *if and only if every root of* f(x) = 0 *has period* e. *Then* e *divides* $q^m - 1$.

For let k be a root of $f(x) = 0$ so that $\mathfrak{F}(k)$ is a field of degree m over $\mathfrak{F}_q$ and $k^e = 1$. If ϵ is the period of k, we know that $e \geq \epsilon$. The mapping $x \rightarrow x^q$ is a generating automorphism of $\mathfrak{F}_q(k)$ over $\mathfrak{F}_q$ and $f(x) = (x - k_1) \cdots (x - k_m)$, where $k_i = kS^{i-1}$. Then $k_i^\epsilon = (k^\epsilon)S^{i-1} = 1$, and so every root of $f(x)$ is also a root of $x^\epsilon - 1$. Since $f(x)$ is separable, it divides $x^\epsilon - 1$, and so $\epsilon \geq e$, $\epsilon = e$. By Section 3 the period of every element of $\mathfrak{F}_q(k)$ is a divisor of $q^m - 1$, and so e divides $q^m - 1$.

The foregoing result may be amplified by the use of Theorem 10 as follows:

THEOREM 14. *Let* k *be a primitive* e*th root of unity in a field over* $\mathfrak{F}_q$. *Then the degree of* $\mathfrak{F}_q$(k) *over* $\mathfrak{F}_q$ *is the least integer* m *such that* $q^m \equiv 1$ (*mod* e). *Moreover,* $q^n \equiv 1$ (*mod* e) *if and only if* m *divides* n.

For Theorem 10 states that the degree of $\mathfrak{F}_q(k)$ over $\mathfrak{F}_q$ is the least integer m such that $k^\tau = 1$, where $\tau = q^m - 1$. But if k is a primitive eth root of unity, this value of m is precisely the least m such that $q^m \equiv 1$ (mod e). Indeed, m *is then the order of* q *as an element of the multiplicative group* $\mathfrak{E}^*$. But then, if $q^n \equiv 1$ (mod e), we have n divisible by m by Theorem 1.5.

It is now a simple matter to derive an expression for the number of *monic* irreducible polynomials of a given degree belonging to a given exponent in terms of the Euler ϕ-function.

THEOREM 15. *There are* $m^{-1}\phi(e)$ *monic irreducible polynomials of degree* m *over* $\mathfrak{F}_q$ *belonging to* e.

Theorem 15 is a consequence of the fact that field elements having the same period define the same field. For proof we let $\mathfrak{K}$ be a splitting field of $x^e - 1$ and let k in $\mathfrak{K}$ be a primitive eth root of unity. Then every eth root of unity in $\mathfrak{K}$ is a power of k by the fact that $\mathfrak{K}^*$ is a cyclic group and its subgroups are uniquely determined by their orders. Then, if h in $\mathfrak{K}$ has period e, we have $h = k^t$ for t prime to e, $k = h^s$ for s prime to e, $\mathfrak{F}(h) \subseteq \mathfrak{F}(k) \subseteq \mathfrak{F}(h)$, and $\mathfrak{F}(h) = \mathfrak{F}(k)$. Thus every primitive eth root of unity defines a monic irreducible polynomial over $\mathfrak{F}$ whose degree is the degree m of $\mathfrak{F}(k)$ over $\mathfrak{F}$. Each of these μ distinct polynomials has m distinct roots, all of which are elements of period e. Then there are μm primitive eth roots of unity in $\mathfrak{K}$. But every primitive eth root of unity is a power k^t, where t is prime to e, there are $\phi(e)$ such exponents, and $\mu = m^{-1}\phi(e)$, as desired.

We note that the fact that m divides $\phi(e)$ is due to Theorem 14, which states that m *is the group order of* q *in the ring* $\mathfrak{E}_e^*$. The order of $\mathfrak{E}_e^*$ is $\phi(e)$, and so m divides $\phi(e)$.

EXERCISES

1. Compute the order of 2 in the groups $\mathfrak{E}_9^*$, $\mathfrak{E}_{15}^*$.

2. Use Exercise 1 to determine the degree of $\mathfrak{F}_2(k)$, where k belongs to 9 and k belongs to 15.

3. Let y be an indeterminate over the field $\mathfrak{F}$ of q elements and $\mathfrak{J} = \mathfrak{F}_q[y]$. Show that the mapping $k \rightarrow k^q$ is an automorphism S over $\mathfrak{F}_q$ of $\mathfrak{J}$.

4. The following result is due to A. Gleason and R. Marsh. Let $f(x)$ be a polynomial of degree n in $\mathfrak{F}_q[x]$ and $f(x)$ be irreducible. Then $yf(S) = yg(y)$, where $g(y)$ clearly has degree $q^n - 1$. It then follows that $g(y)$ is irreducible if and only if $f(x)$ is primitive. Use this result to construct an irreducible polynomial of degree 6 over $\mathfrak{F}_2$ and one of degree 63 over $\mathfrak{F}_2$.

8. Polynomials belonging to a prime. The polynomial

$$x^{e-1} + x^{e-2} + \cdots + x + 1 \tag{32}$$

is irreducible in $\mathfrak{F} = \mathfrak{F}_q$ if and only if the residue class in $\mathfrak{E}_e$ defined by q has order $\phi(e)$. This can occur only when e is a prime and q is a primitive root modulo e.

We shall now obtain a result for the case where e is a prime and k is a primitive eth root such that $\mathfrak{F}(k)$ has even degree.

THEOREM 16. *Let* e *be a prime,* k *be a primitive* e*th root of unity,* $\mathfrak{K} = \mathfrak{F}(k)$ *have degree* $m = 2\mu$ *over* $\mathfrak{F}$. *Then the mapping* $k \rightarrow k^{-1}$ *induces an automorphism* T *over* $\mathfrak{F}$ *of* $\mathfrak{K}$, T *has order* 2, $\mathfrak{K}$ *has degree* 2 *over* $\mathfrak{L} = \mathfrak{F}(k + k^{-1})$, *and* $\mathfrak{L}$ *is the fixed field of* $\mathfrak{K}$ *under* T.

For Theorem 14 determines m as the least integer such that $q^m \equiv 1 \pmod{e}$. Then $q^\mu - 1$ is not divisible by e. Since e is a prime divisor of $q^m - 1 = (q^\mu - 1)(q^\mu + 1)$, we must have $q^\mu \equiv -1 \pmod{e}$. We now use Theorem 9 to see that the mapping $x \rightarrow x^q$ is a generating automorphism S of $\mathfrak{F}_q(k)$ over $\mathfrak{F}_q$. Then $xS^\mu = x^{q^\mu}$, and the fact that $k^e = 1$ and $q^\mu \equiv -1 \pmod{e}$ implies that $kS^\mu = k^{-1}$. Thus $T = S^\mu$ is an automorphism of $\mathfrak{K}$ over $\mathfrak{F}$ and is induced by $k \rightarrow k^{-1}$, since T is then the automorphism

$$T: \qquad \rho(k) = \rho_0 + \rho_1 k + \cdots + \rho_{m-1}k^{m-1} \rightarrow [\rho(k)]T$$
$$= \rho_0 + \rho_1 k^{-1} + \cdots + \rho_{m-1}k^{1-m}\,.$$

Since k is a root of the equation

$$x^2 - (k + k^{-1})x + 1 = 0\,, \tag{33}$$

we see that the degree of $\mathfrak{K}$ over $\mathfrak{L}_0 = \mathfrak{F}(k + k^{-1})$ is at most 2. Now $[\mathfrak{K}:\mathfrak{F}] = [\mathfrak{K}:\mathfrak{L}_0][\mathfrak{L}_0:\mathfrak{F}]$ and $\mathfrak{L}_0$ is a subfield of the fixed field $\mathfrak{L}$ of $\mathfrak{K}$ under T, $[\mathfrak{L}:\mathfrak{F}] = \mu$. It follows that $[\mathfrak{K}:\mathfrak{L}_0] = 2$, $[\mathfrak{L}_0:\mathfrak{F}] = \mu$, and $\mathfrak{L} = \mathfrak{L}_0$.

The foregoing result and the following consequence were first proved by W. A. Blankinship for the case $q = 2$.

THEOREM 17. *Let* k *be a primitive* e*th root of unity defining a field* $\mathfrak{F}_q(k)$ *of even degree* 2μ *over* $\mathfrak{F}_q$ *and let* e *be an odd prime. Then the period of* $1 + k^t$ *is* $e\delta_t$, *where* δ_t *is an integer prime to* e *for* $t = 1, 2, \ldots, e - 1$.

For the degree of $\mathfrak{F}(k + k^{-1})$ is μ, and so the period of $k + k^{-1}$ is a divisor δ_0 of $q^\mu - 1$. Since e does not divide $q^\mu - 1$, we know that δ_0 is prime to e. By Lemma 1.5 the period of $k(k + k^{-1}) = 1 + k^2$ is $e\delta_0$. Since $e = 2\epsilon - 1$ is odd, the integer ϵ is prime to e, and so $k_0 = k^\epsilon$ is a primitive eth root of unity. By the previous argument, $1 + k^{2\epsilon} = 1 + k$ has period $e\delta_1$, where δ_1 is prime to e. But this is then true for every primitive eth root of unity, and so $1 + k^t$ has period $e\delta_t$, where δ_t is prime to e for $0 < t < e$.

It should indeed be evident that if $\gamma(k + k^{-1})$ is any element of $\mathfrak{F}(k + k^{-1})$, the period of $k\gamma(k + k^{-1})$ is δe, where δ is prime to e. For example, the period of $k(k^t + k^{-t}) = k^{t+1} + k^{1-t}$ is $\lambda \cdot e$, where λ is prime to e.

EXERCISES

1. Find the first 10 primes e such that the polynomial $(x^e - 1)(x - 1)^{-1}$ is irreducible in $\mathfrak{F}_2$.
2. Find the degree over $\mathfrak{F}_2$ of the field $\mathfrak{F}_2(\xi)$, where ξ is a primitive seventh root of unity. *Hint:* Use Appendix I.
3. Find the first prime p such that $(x^{23} - 1)(x - 1)^{-1}$ is irreducible in $\mathfrak{F}_p$.
4. Let k be a primitive fifth root of unity over $\mathfrak{F}_2$. Find the period of $1 + k$. (Check your result by comparing with Appendix III.)
5. Prove that $x^{e-1} + x^{e+2} + \cdots + x + 1$ is irreducible in $\mathfrak{F}_q$ only when e is a prime. *Hint:* use Theorem 14.

9. A construction of irreducible polynomials. We shall show how certain irreducible polynomials may be derived from others. We begin by deriving the following lemma:

LEMMA 2. *Let* f(x) *be an irreducible polynomial of degree* m *over* $\mathfrak{F}_q$, $e = (q^m - 1)d^{-1}$ *be the integer to which* f(x) *belongs, and* π *be a prime divisor of* e *which does not divide* d. *Then* $f(x^\pi)$ *is irreducible over* $\mathfrak{F}_q$ *and belongs to* $e\pi$.

For $f(x)$ defines the field $\mathfrak{K} = \mathfrak{F}_q(k)$ of degree m over $\mathfrak{F}_q$, where k has period e. By Theorem 4.10 the equation $x^\pi = k$ either is irreducible in $\mathfrak{K}$ or has a root in $\mathfrak{K}$. By Exercise 4 of Section 1.14 we may take $k = h^d$, where h generates $\mathfrak{K}^*$. A root in $\mathfrak{K}$ of $x^\pi = k$ is a power h^α such that $h^{\alpha\pi} = k$, $h^{\alpha\pi - d} = 1$. Then $q^m - 1$ must divide $\alpha\pi - d$, which implies that π divides $\alpha\pi - d$, whereas π does not divide d. Then the equation $x^\pi = k$

defines the field $\mathfrak{Z} = \mathfrak{K}(z)$ of degree π over $\mathfrak{K}$, and $\mathfrak{Z}$ has degree πm over $\mathfrak{F}_q$. However, $z^\pi = k$, and so $\mathfrak{F}_q(z) \supset \mathfrak{K}$, and $\mathfrak{F}_q(z) = \mathfrak{K}(z)$ has degree $m\pi$ over $\mathfrak{F}_q$. Since z is a root of $f(x^\pi) = 0$ of degree $m\pi$, this equation must be the minimum function of z over $\mathfrak{F}_q$, and $f(x^\pi)$ is irreducible in $\mathfrak{F}_q$. If z has period σ, then $z^\sigma = z^{\sigma\pi} = k^\sigma = 1$ and e divides $\sigma = e\sigma_0$. But $z^{e\pi} = k^e = 1$, and so σ divides $e\pi$, and σ_0 divides π. If $\sigma_0 = 1$, then z has period e and is a power of k, which is impossible by the previous proof. Hence $\sigma_0 = \pi$, z has period $e\pi$, and $f(x^\pi)$ belongs to $e\pi$.

We shall apply Lemma 2 in the derivation of a generalization involving all the prime factors of e prime to d. The application involves only the observation that the hypothesis is preserved at every step and so will require an additional hypothesis.

THEOREM 18. *Let* $f_1(x), f_2(x), \ldots, f_\sigma(x)$ *be the* $\sigma = m^{-1}\phi(e)$ *distinct irreducible monic polynomials of degree* m *over* $\mathfrak{F}_q$ *belonging to the exponent*

$$e = (q^m - 1)d^{-1}, \tag{34}$$

and t *be an integer whose prime factors all divide* e *but not* d. *Assume also that* $t \not\equiv 0$ *(mod 4) if* $q^m \equiv -1$ *(mod 4). Then the polynomials* $f_1(x^t), \ldots, f_\sigma(x^t)$ *are a complete set of monic irreducible polynomials of degree* mt *over* $\mathfrak{F}_q$ *belonging to* et.

The result is trivially true if $t = 1$. Assume it true for all integers $t_0 < t$. Since the prime factors of t all divide e, we may write $e = p_1^{\alpha_1} \cdots p_s^{\alpha_s}$, $et = p_1^{\beta_1} \cdots p_s^{\beta_s}$, where $\beta_i \geq \alpha_i > 0$. Then, by Theorem 2.22, $\phi(e) = e(1 - p_1^{-1}) \cdots (1 - p_s^{-1})$, and $\phi(et) = et(1 - p_1^{-1}) \cdots (1 - p_s^{-1})$. Hence $e^{-1}\phi(e) = (et)^{-1}\phi(et)$. But then

$$(mt)^{-1}\phi(et) = (m^{-1}e)(et)^{-1}\phi(et) = (m^{-1}e)e^{-1}\phi(e) = \sigma\,; \tag{35}$$

and so Theorem 15 implies that the number of irreducible polynomials of degree mt belonging to et is exactly the same as the number of degree m belonging to e. We now write $t = \pi t_0$, where π is a prime. Our result follows immediately from Lemma 2 if $t = \pi$. Otherwise, $t_0 < t$, and we apply Lemma 2 to see that $f_1(x^\pi), \ldots, f_\sigma(x^\pi)$ are $(m\pi)^{-1}\phi(e\pi)$ irreducible polynomials of degree $m\pi$ belonging to $e\pi$. We now show that every prime factor of t_0 divides $e\pi$ and is prime to $d_0 = (q^{m\pi} - 1)(e\pi)^{-1}$. Indeed,

$$(q^{\pi m} - 1) = \gamma(q^m - 1), \qquad \gamma = q^{m(\pi-1)} + \cdots + q^m + 1\,. \tag{36}$$

Then $d_0 = (q^{m\pi} - 1)(e\pi)^{-1} = [(q^m - 1)e^{-1}]\gamma\pi^{-1} = d\gamma\pi^{-1}$. If π_0 is any prime factor of e which is prime to d, then π_0 divides $q^{m\pi} - 1 = \gamma(q^m - 1) = de\gamma$. Also π_0 divides d_0 if and only if π_0 divides $\gamma\pi^{-1}$. But $q^m \equiv 1 \pmod{\pi_0}$, $q^m \equiv 1 \pmod{\pi}$, and so $\gamma \equiv 0 \pmod{\pi}$, $\gamma \equiv \pi$ (mod

π_0). If $\pi_0 \neq \pi$, then $\gamma\pi^{-1} \equiv 1 \pmod{\pi_0}$. If $\pi_0 = \pi$, then $q^m \equiv (1 + \delta\pi) \pmod{\pi^2}$, where $0 \leq \delta < \pi$, and

$$q^{m\epsilon} \equiv (1 + \epsilon\delta\pi) \pmod{\pi^2} \quad (\epsilon = 0, 1, \ldots, \pi - 1).$$

Thus $\gamma \equiv \pi + \delta\pi\frac{1}{2}\pi(\pi - 1) \pmod{\pi^2}$, $\gamma\pi^{-1} \equiv 1 + \delta(\pi - 1)\frac{1}{2}\pi \pmod{\pi}$. But then $\gamma\pi^{-1}$ is not divisible by π unless $\pi = 2$. When $\pi = 2 = \pi_0$, we have $\gamma = q^m + 1$, and if $q^m + 1 \equiv 0 \pmod 4$, our hypothesis that π_0 does not divide d_0 would fail to be satisfied. This is the reason why we must assume that $q^m \equiv 1 \pmod 4$ if $t \equiv 0 \pmod 4$. But $q^m \equiv 1 \pmod 4$ implies that $\gamma \equiv 2 \pmod 4$, $\gamma\pi^{-1} \equiv 1 \pmod 2$, and so again π_0 is prime to d_0. We have thus shown that the hypotheses of our theorem are satisfied by $f_1(x^\pi), \ldots, f_\sigma(x^\pi)$ for t_0, and the hypothesis of our induction implies that $f_1(x^t), \ldots, f_\sigma(x^t)$ form a complete set of irreducible polynomials of degree mt belonging to et.

As a consequence of Theorem 18 we have the following result:

THEOREM 19. *Let* ρ *be a primitive element of* $\mathfrak{F}_q$, t *be an integer whose prime factors divide* q − 1, r *be any integer prime to* t, d *be the g.c.d. of* r *and* q − 1, q *be congruent to* 1 *modulo* 4 *if* 4 *divides* t. *Then the monic irreducible polynomials of degree* t *over* $\mathfrak{F}_q$ *which belong to* $t(q - 1)d^{-1}$ *are the binomials* $x^t - \rho^r$.

For the monic irreducible polynomials of degree 1 which belong to $(q - 1)d^{-1}$ are the binomials $x - \rho^r$, where r ranges over all integers $r_0 d$ with r_0 prime to $(q - 1)d^{-1}$. Then d is the g.c.d. of r and $q - 1$, and our result follows immediately from Theorem 18.

We note that Theorem 19 yields all binomials irreducible in $\mathfrak{F}_q$. For t and r must be relatively prime, since otherwise $x^t - \rho^r$ is trivially reducible. If t contains a prime factor π not a divisor of $q - 1$, the equation $x^\pi = \rho^r$ is reducible. For there exists an integer π_1 such that $\pi\pi_1 \equiv 1 \pmod{q - 1}$ and $(\rho^{\pi_1 r})^\pi = \rho^r$. But then $x^t - \rho^r = x^{\pi s} - \rho^r$ has $x^s - \rho^{\pi_1 r}$ as a factor.

10. The exceptional case. In this section we assume that $q^m \equiv -1 \pmod 4$. Then q is odd, $q^{2a} \equiv 1 \pmod 4$, and so m is odd, $q \equiv -1 \pmod 4$.

THEOREM 20. *Let* $f_1(x), \ldots, f_\sigma(x)$ *be the* $\sigma = m^{-1}\phi(e)$ *irreducible monic polynomials of odd degree* m *over* $\mathfrak{F}_q$ *belonging to an even exponent* $e = (q^m - 1)d^{-1}$; *let*

$$q = 2^u\tau - 1, \quad t = 2^v r \quad (u, v \geq 2), \tag{37}$$

where τ *and* r *are odd and all prime factors of* t *divide* e *but not* d; *and let* k *be the smaller of* u *and* v. *Then each of the polynomials* $f_i(x^t)$ *factors as a product of* 2^{k-1} *irreducible monic polynomials* $g_{ij}(x)$ *of degree* $mt2^{1-k}$ *over*

$\mathfrak{F}_q$. *The* $2^{k-1}\sigma$ *polynomials* $g_{ij}(x)$ *form a complete set of irreducible monic polynomials of degree* $mt2^{1-k}$ *belonging to* et.

For, by Theorem 18, the polynomials $f_{0i}(x) = f_i(x^r)$ form a complete set of $(mr)^{-1}\phi(er)$ monic polynomials of odd degree mr belonging to the even exponent er. Thus we have reduced the proof of our theorem to the case where $t = 2^v$.

If z is a primitive eth root of unity and e is even, every root of $x^2 = z$ is a primitive $(2e)$th root of unity. For the cyclic multiplicative group $\{x\}$ generated by x has order at most $2e$ and contains $\{z\}$ of order e as a subgroup. Thus the order of $\{x\}$ is either e or $2e$. If x has order e, then $x = z^a$, $x^2 = z^{2a} = z$, and $z^{2a-1} = 1$, whereas e is even. It follows by induction that the roots of $x^t = z$ are primitive (et)th roots of unity. Then all the roots of $f_i(x^t)$ belong to et. By the proof of Theorem 15 all primitive (et)th roots of unity generate fields of the same degree μ over $\mathfrak{F}_q$, and, in fact, μ is the least integer such that $q^\mu \equiv 1 \pmod{et}$. It follows that

$$f_i(x^t) = g_{i1}(x) \cdots g_{is}(x) \qquad (i = 1, \ldots, \sigma), \tag{38}$$

where the polynomials $g_{ij}(x)$ all have the same degree μ and are irreducible in $\mathfrak{F}_q$. Thus

$$s\mu = mt\,. \tag{39}$$

If θ is a root of $f_i(x^t) = 0$, then $\mathfrak{F}_q(\theta) \supseteq \mathfrak{F}_q(\theta^t)$ of degree m over $\mathfrak{F}_q$, and so m divides μ, $\mu = m\lambda$, and λ divides t and is a power of 2. Also $\lambda \neq 1$, since otherwise $q^m - 1 \equiv 0 \pmod{t}$ and $q^m \equiv 1 \pmod{4}$, contrary to hypothesis. Now $q^\mu - 1 = (q^m - 1)\delta = ed\delta$, where $\delta = 1 + q^m + \cdots + q^{(\lambda-1)m}$. Therefore, λ *is the least integer such that* t *divides* δ. We now compute λ.

Since q and m are odd, we see that $q^m + 1 = (q+1)(q^{m-1} - q^{m-2} + \cdots + q^2 - q + 1) = 2^u\tau\epsilon$, where ϵ is a sum of m odd (positive and negative) integers and is odd. Then $q^m = 2^u\xi - 1$, where ξ is odd, and we apply the binomial theorem to compute $q^\mu = (2^u\xi - 1)^\lambda$ and so obtain

$$\delta = \frac{q^\mu - 1}{q^m - 1} = \frac{2^u\xi}{2^u\xi - 2}\Big[-\lambda + \frac{\lambda(\lambda-1)}{2}\,2^u\xi \cdots \pm \sigma_{\lambda,\beta}\, 2^{u(\beta-1)}\xi^{\beta-1} \pm \cdots\Big], \tag{40}$$

where $\sigma_{\lambda,\beta}$ is the usual binomial coefficient. Since every term in the bracketed expression in equation (40) after the first term is divisible by a higher power of 2 than the first term, we see that t divides δ if and only if t divides $2^{u-1}\lambda$, that is, $2^{u-v-1}\lambda$ is an integer. When $u \geq v$, the least even integer λ for which this holds is $\lambda = 2 = 2^{1-v}t = 2^{1-k}t$. When $u < v$, then $k = u$, and $2^{u-v-1}\lambda$ is integral if and only if $2^{v+1-u} = 2^{1-k}t$ divides λ. It follows that

$$(41) \qquad \lambda = 2^{1-k}t, \quad \mu = mt2^{1-k},$$

in all cases, as desired. We are now ready to compute

$$(42) \qquad \sigma = \frac{\phi(e)}{m} = \frac{\phi(et)}{mt} = \frac{1}{2^{k-1}}\frac{\phi(et)}{\mu},$$

where we have used equation (35). Then $\mu^{-1}\phi(et) = 2^{k-1}\sigma$ is the number of monic irreducible polynomials of degree μ belonging to the exponent et by Theorem 15. Now $s\mu = sm\lambda = st2^{1-k}m = mt$, and so $s = 2^{k-1}$. This completes our proof.

11. Irreducible polynomials of even degree. We shall give a construction of irreducible polynomials of even degree t over any $\mathfrak{F}_q$ such that $q = 2^{\psi}\tau - 1$, where τ is odd and $\psi \geq 2$. Assume that all prime factors of t divide $q - 1$ and put

$$(43) \qquad \nu = \gamma t, \; \gamma = 2^{\psi-1}.$$

Then $2^i = 2\gamma$ divides ν. If ρ is a primitive root in $\mathfrak{F}_q$ and s is any integer prime to t, the polynomial $x - \rho^s$ belongs to $(q-1)d^{-1}$, where d is the g.c.d. of s and $q - 1$ and ν is prime to d. Apply Theorem 20 to see that $x^{\nu} - \rho^s$ is the product of γ irreducible polynomials of degree t in $\mathfrak{F}_q[x]$. We proceed to the determination of these polynomials.

Since γ and $\frac{1}{2}(q-1)$ are relatively prime, there exist integers α_0 and β_0 such that

$$(44) \qquad \gamma\alpha_0 - \tfrac{1}{2}(q-1)\beta_0 = 1.$$

Multiply equation (44) by the even integer $s + \frac{1}{2}(q-1)$ and obtain integers α and β such that

$$(45) \qquad 2\alpha\gamma - (q-1)\beta = s + \tfrac{1}{2}(q-1).$$

Since ρ is primitive, we have $\rho^{\delta} = -1$, where $\delta = \frac{1}{2}(q-1)$ and

$$(46) \qquad x^{\nu} - \rho^s \equiv x^{\gamma t} + \rho^{2\alpha\gamma}.$$

THEOREM 21. *The roots of the equation*

$$(47) \qquad \Phi(\xi) \equiv \xi^{\gamma} + \gamma \sum_{k=1}^{1/2\gamma-1} \frac{(\gamma-k-1)!}{k!\,(\gamma-2k)!}\,\xi^{\gamma-2k} + 2 = 0$$

are all in $\mathfrak{F}_q$. *Then we have the decomposition*

$$(48) \qquad x^{t\gamma} + \rho^{2a\gamma} = \prod_{j=1}^{\gamma} x^t - \xi_j \rho^a x^{1/2t} - \rho^{2a}$$

of $x^\nu - \rho^s$ *into irreducible factors* $x^t - \xi_j \rho^a x^{1/2t} - \rho^{2a}$ *of* $\mathfrak{F}_q[x]$, *where the* ξ_j *are the roots of* $\Phi(\xi) = 0$.

For the roots of the quadratic equation

$$(49) \qquad x^2 - \xi x - 1 = 0$$

are η and $-\eta^{-1}$. By Waring's Formula (L. E. Dickson, *First Course in the Theory of Equations*, p. 140), the sum of the γth powers of the roots of equation (49) is $\Phi(\xi)$. Thus the definition

$$(50) \qquad \xi \equiv \eta - \frac{1}{\eta}$$

implies that

$$(51) \qquad \Phi(\xi) = \eta^\gamma + \eta^{-\gamma} .$$

It follows that if $\xi_j = \eta_j - \eta_j^{-1}$ is a root of $\Phi(\xi) = 0$, we have

$$(52) \qquad \eta_j^{2\gamma} = -1 .$$

Since $q + 1 = 2\gamma\tau$, where τ is odd, we have

$$(53) \qquad \eta_j^{q+1} = -1, \quad \eta_j^q = -\eta_j^{-1} .$$

But then in $\mathfrak{F}_q(\xi_j)$ we have

$$(54) \qquad \xi_j^q = (\eta_j - \eta_j^{-1})^q = \eta_j^q - \eta_j^{-q} = -\eta_j^{-1} + \eta_j = \xi_j .$$

It follows that ξ_j must be in $\mathfrak{F}_q$. Then

$$(55) \qquad \Phi(\xi) = \prod_{j=1}^{\gamma} (\xi - \xi_j) = \eta^\gamma + \eta^{-\gamma}$$

is an identity. Substitute

$$(56) \qquad \eta = x^{(1/2)t}\rho^{-a}, \qquad \xi = \eta - \frac{1}{\eta} = \frac{x^t - \rho^{2a}}{x^{(1/2)t}\rho^a}$$

in equation (55), and clear fractions to obtain identity (48).

12. Applications. We shall apply the results of Section 8 to derive certain irreducible polynomials.

We first take $q = 4$. Then $\mathfrak{F}_4 = \mathfrak{F}_2(\omega)$, where $\omega^2 + \omega + 1 = 0$ and ω is a primitive cube root of unity. Apply Theorem 19 with $t = 3$ to see that the irreducible polynomials of degree 3 over $\mathfrak{F}_4$ which belong to 9 are $x^3 - \omega$ and $x^3 - \omega^2$. Their product $x^6 - (\omega + \omega^2)x^3 + 1 = x^6 + x^3 + 1$ is an irreducible polynomial of degree 6 over $\mathfrak{F}_2$ belonging to 9. Its octal form is 111, and it appears in the table of Appendix IV. Similarly, the polynomials of degree 9 over $\mathfrak{F}_4$ which belong to 27 are $x^9 - \omega$ and $x^9 - \omega^2$, and $x^{18} + x^9 + 1$ is an irreducible polynomial of degree 18 over $\mathfrak{F}_2$ belonging to 27.

We next take q = 5. Then we are allowed to take $t = 4 = q - 1$ and $\rho = 2$. Thus the irreducible polynomials of degree 4 over $\mathfrak{F}_5$ are $x^4 - 2$ and $x^4 - 2^3 = x^4 - 3$.

Take q = 7, $\rho = 5$. Then for $t = 2$ we obtain the irreducible quadratics $x^2 - 5$, $x^2 + 1$, and $x^2 - 3$ belonging to 12, 4, and 12, respectively. For $t = 3$ and $r = 1, 2, 4$, and 5, respectively, we obtain

$$x^3 - 5, \quad x^3 - 4, \quad x^3 - 2, \quad x^3 - 3\,,$$

irreducible in $\mathfrak{F}_7$ and belonging to 18, 9, 9, and 18.

We finally take q = 8. Then by Appendix III we can take $\mathfrak{F}_8 = \mathfrak{F}_2(\rho)$, where ρ is a primitive seventh root of unity and $\rho^3 = \rho + 1$. Take $t = 7$ and $r = 1, 2, 3, 4, 5$, and 6 to obtain the irreducible polynomials $x^7 - \rho$, $x^7 - \rho^2$, $x^7 - \rho^3$, $x^7 - \rho^4$, $x^7 - \rho^5$, and $x^7 - \rho^6$. The conjugates of ρ are ρ^2 and ρ^4, and the conjugates of ρ^3 are ρ^6 and $\rho^{12} = \rho^5$. Hence $(x^7 - \rho)(x^7 - \rho^2)(x^7 - \rho^4) = x^{21} - (\rho + \rho^2 + \rho^4)x^{14} + (\rho\rho^2 + \rho\rho^4 + \rho^2\rho^4)x^7 - 1 = x^{21} + x^7 + 1 = h(x)$, which is an irreducible polynomial of degree 21 over $\mathfrak{F}_2$ belonging to the exponent 49. The polynomial $(x^7 - \rho^3)(x^7 - \rho^6)(x^7 - \rho^5)$ has as roots the reciprocals of the roots of $h(x)$, and so is the polynomial $x^{21} + x^{14} + 1$, also belonging to 49.

To apply Theorem 18 we consider the case q = 2, m = 4. By Appendix IV the irreducible polynomials of degree 4 belonging to the exponent 15 are $x^4 + x + 1$ and $x^4 + x^3 + 1$. Then the irreducible polynomials of degree 12 over $\mathfrak{F}_2$ belonging to the exponent 45 are $x^{12} + x^3 + 1$ and $x^{12} + x^9 + 1$. The irreducible polynomials of degree 20 belonging to 75 are $x^{20} + x^5 + 1$ and $x^{20} + x^{15} + 1$. Finally, the irreducible polynomials of degree 60 belonging to 225 are $x^{60} + x^{15} + 1$ and $x^{60} + x^{45} + 1$.

We finally apply Theorem 21. Take q = 7 = $2^3 - 1$ *and* t = 4. Then we have $\nu = 16$, and we propose to decompose

$$x^{16} - 5^s \qquad (s = 1, 3, 5). \tag{57}$$

The equation

$$\Phi(\xi) = \xi^4 + 4\xi^2 + 2$$

has the roots $\xi = 1, -1, 3, -3$. Also

$$x^{16} - 5^{s} \equiv x^{16} + 5^{s+3} = x^{16} + 5^{2a}$$

$$(s + 3 = 2a = 4, 6, 8).$$

Since $5^{8a} \equiv 5^{2a}$ (mod 7), equation (48) becomes

$$(58) \qquad x^{16} + 5^{2a} \equiv \prod_{j=1}^{4} x^4 - \xi_j 5^a x^2 - 5^{2a}$$

over $\mathfrak{F}_7$. Then

$$x^{16} + 4 = (x^4 - x^2 - 4)(x^4 + x^2 - 4)(x^4 - 2x^2 - 4)(x^4 + 2x^2 - 4)\,,$$

$$x^{16} + 2 = (x^4 - 2x^2 - 2)(x^4 + 2x^2 - 2)(x^4 - 4x^2 - 2)(x^4 + 4x^2 - 2)\,,$$

$$x^{16} + 1 = (x^4 - x^2 - 1)(x^4 + x^2 - 1)(x^4 - 4x^2 - 1)(x^4 + 4x^2 - 1)\,,$$

and we have the decompositions desired.

EXERCISES

1. Construct an irreducible polynomial of degree 4 over $\mathfrak{F}_3$. Use the result to construct an irreducible polynomial of degree 8 over $\mathfrak{F}_3$.
2. Use the result of Example 1 to construct an irreducible polynomial of degree 16 over $\mathfrak{F}_3$.
3. Find an irreducible cubic over $\mathfrak{F}_{16}$. Use Appendix IV and compute an irreducible polynomial of degree 12 over $\mathfrak{F}_2$.
4. Find an irreducible quintic over $\mathfrak{F}_{16}$ and an irreducible polynomial of degree 20 over $\mathfrak{F}_2$.

13. Polynomials of degree p over $\mathfrak{F}_q$, $q = p^n$. In this section we derive the following basic result:

THEOREM 22. *The polynomial* $\lambda^p x^p - \lambda x - \beta$, $\lambda \neq 0$ *in* $\mathfrak{F}_q$, *is an irreducible polynomial in* $\mathfrak{F}_q$ *for* $q = p^n$ *if and only if the trace* $\sigma_{\mathfrak{F}_q/\mathfrak{F}_p}(\beta) \neq 0$.

For the polynomial $\lambda^p x^p - \lambda x - \beta$ is irreducible in $\mathfrak{F}_q$ if and only if $x^p - x - \beta$ is irreducible in $\mathfrak{F}_q[x]$. By Theorem 4.11 the polynomial $x^p - x - \beta$ is reducible if and only if the equation $x^p - x = \beta$ has a root γ in $\mathfrak{F}_q$. But the mapping $x \rightarrow x^p$ is a generating automorphism of $\mathfrak{F}_q$ over $\mathfrak{F}_p$, and our result is a direct consequence of Theorem 4.34.

We may now apply this result as follows:

THEOREM 23. *Let* $f(x)$ *be an irreducible polynomial of degree* m *over* $\mathfrak{F}_q$ *and* $q = p^n$,

$$(59) \qquad f(x) = x^m + \alpha_1 x^{m-1} + \cdots + \alpha_m \qquad (\alpha_i \text{ in } \mathfrak{F}_q).$$

Then, if $\alpha_1 + \alpha_1^p + \cdots + \alpha_1^{p^{n-1}} \neq 0$, *the polynomial* $f(x^p - x)$ *is an irreducible polynomial of degree* pm *over* $\mathfrak{F}_q$.

For let ξ be a root of $f(x) = 0$ and $\mathfrak{F} = \mathfrak{F}_p$, $\mathfrak{L} = \mathfrak{F}_q$, and $\mathfrak{K} = \mathfrak{F}_q(\xi)$. Then the roots of $f(x) = 0$ are $\xi, \xi^q, \ldots, \xi^{q^{m-1}}$ and $-\alpha_1 = \sigma_{\mathfrak{K}/\mathfrak{L}}(\xi)$. Then

$$(60)\qquad \sigma_{\mathfrak{K}/\mathfrak{F}}(\xi) = \sigma_{\mathfrak{L}/\mathfrak{F}}[\sigma_{\mathfrak{K}/\mathfrak{L}}(\xi)] = -\sigma_{\mathfrak{L}/\mathfrak{F}}(\alpha_1) \neq 0\,.$$

By Theorem 22 the polynomial $y^p - y - \xi$ is irreducible in $\mathfrak{K}$. It defines a field $\mathfrak{K}(\eta)$ of degree mp over $\mathfrak{F}_q$. Since $q = \eta^p - \eta$ is in $\mathfrak{F}_q(\eta)$, we see that $\mathfrak{F}_q(\eta) = \mathfrak{K}(\eta)$ has degree mp over $\mathfrak{F}_q$, $f(\eta^p - \eta) = 0$, η is a root of the polynomial $f(x^p - x)$ of degree mp in $\mathfrak{F}_q[x]$, and $f(x^p - x)$ is irreducible in $\mathfrak{F}_q$.

EXERCISES

1. Apply Theorem 22 to determine an irreducible quadratic over $\mathfrak{F}_4$. Use the result to determine an irreducible quartic over $\mathfrak{F}_2$.
2. Find an irreducible polynomial of degree 6 over $\mathfrak{F}_2$ by applying Theorem 23.

14. Dickson's theorem. L. E. Dickson derived the following result for $r = q$ on page 98 of the *Transactions of the American Mathematical Society*, Volume XII (1911).

THEOREM 24. *Let θ be a primitive element of $\mathfrak{F}_q$ for $q = p^n$, β be any element of $\mathfrak{F}_q$, and $r = p^m > 2$, where m divides n. Then the polynomial*

$$(61)\qquad f(x) = x^r - \theta x + \beta$$

is the product of a linear polynomial and an irreducible polynomial over $\mathfrak{F}_q$ of degree $r - 1$.

For $f'(x) = -\theta \neq 0$, and so $f(x)$ is separable. Since $r > 2$, we may let ξ and η be two distinct roots of $f(x) = 0$ in a splitting field. Then $\xi^r - \eta^r = (\xi - \eta)^r = \theta(\xi - \eta)$, and so $(\xi - \eta)^{r-1} = \theta$. Also $r - 1 = p^m - 1$ divides $p^n - 1$. By Theorem 19 the polynomial $x^{r-1} = \theta$ is irreducible in $\mathfrak{F}_q$ and defines a field $\mathfrak{F}_q(\xi - \eta)$ of degree $r - 1$ over $\mathfrak{F}_q$. But $\mathfrak{F}_q(\xi - \eta) \subseteq \mathfrak{F}_q(\xi, \eta)$, so that there is a root ξ of $f(x) = 0$ such that $\mathfrak{F}_q(\xi) \neq \mathfrak{F}_q$. Also $\mathfrak{F}_q(\xi)$ contains ξ^q. However, $(\xi^r - \theta\xi + \beta)^q = (\xi^q)^r - \theta^q\xi^q + \beta^q = (\xi^q)^r - \theta\xi^q + \beta = 0$, and so $\mathfrak{F}_q(\xi - \xi^q)$ has degree $r - 1$ over $\mathfrak{F}_q$. Hence the degree of $\mathfrak{F}_q(\xi)$ is an integer μ such that $r \geq \mu \geq r - 1$ and $r - 1$ divides μ. But $r > 2$ and $r - 1$ can divide μ only if $r - 1 = \mu$, $\mathfrak{F}_q(\xi)$ has degree $r - 1$, and our result is proved.

We observe that when $r = q$, it is easy to find the root in $\mathfrak{F}_q$ of equation (61). Indeed, if ξ is in $\mathfrak{F}$, we have $\xi^q = \xi$ and so $\xi^q = \xi\theta - \beta$ if and only if $\xi(1 - \theta) = -\beta$,

$$\xi = \beta(\theta - 1)^{-1}\,.$$

Then $x^q - \theta x + \beta - (\xi^q - \theta\xi + \beta) = (x^q - \xi^q) - \theta(x - \xi) = (x - \xi)Q(x)$, where

$$Q(x) = x^{q-1} - \xi x^{q-2} + \xi^2 x^{q-3} + \cdots + (-1)^{q-1}\xi^{q-1} - \theta\,, \tag{62}$$

and so equation (62) yields a polynomial of degree $q - 1$ irreducible in $\mathfrak{F}_q$.

For example, we may take $q = 7$ and $\theta = 5$. Then, if $\beta = 1$, we have $\xi = (5 - 1)^{-1} = 2$. Then in $\mathfrak{F}_7$ we have

$$Q(x) = x^6 - 2x^5 + 4x^4 - x^3 + 2x^2 - 4x - 4 \tag{63}$$

and have obtained an irreducible polynomial of degree 6.

We may also take $q = 4$, so that θ is a cube root of unity. Then $\theta^2 = 1 + \theta$ and $\theta - 1 = \theta^2$. Take $\beta = \theta^2$ and obtain $\xi = 1$, and hence

$$Q(x) = x^3 + x^2 + x + \theta^2 \tag{64}$$

is irreducible in $\mathfrak{F}_4$.

EXERCISES

1. Apply Theorem 24 to obtain an irreducible polynomial of degree 7 over $\mathfrak{F}_8$.
2. Apply Theorem 24 to obtain an irreducible polynomial of degree 3 over $\mathfrak{F}_{16}$.

15. Generation of irreducible polynomials. An irreducible polynomial $f(x)$ of degree n over $\mathfrak{F}_q$ is said to be *primitive* if it has a root θ which is a primitive element of $\mathfrak{F}_q(\theta)$. *Then all roots of* f(x) *are primitive.* Every non-zero element of $\mathfrak{F}_q(\theta)$ is a power

$$k = \theta^t\,, \tag{65}$$

of θ. The characteristic function

$$f_t(x) = f(x; \theta^t) \tag{66}$$

of θ^t is a polynomial of degree n with coefficients in $\mathfrak{F}_q$. If $\mathfrak{F}_q(\theta^t)$ has degree m over $\mathfrak{F}_q$, then $n = mr$ and $f_t(x) = [g_t(x)]^r$, where $g_t(x)$ is the minimum function over $\mathfrak{F}_q$ of θ^t, and its degree is m.

The polynomial $f_t(x)$ may be constructed in the following three ways:

I. *Construct the companion matrix* C_f *for* f(x). Then $f_t(x) = |xI - C_f^t|$. Since this involves the computation of the characteristic determinant of a power of a matrix, it may be impractical for large values of n.

II. The field $\mathfrak{F}_q(\theta)$ is a vector space $\mathfrak{K}$ with a basis $1, \theta, \ldots, \theta^{n-1}$ over $\mathfrak{F}_q$. Then $\theta^t = a_{11} + a_{12}\theta + \cdots + a_{1n}\theta^{n-1}$, where the a_{1j} are in $\mathfrak{F}$. *Compute the products* $\theta^{t+i-1} = a_{i1} + a_{i2}\theta + \cdots + a_{in}\theta^{n-1}$ *for* $i = 1, \ldots, n$, *and so obtain a matrix* $A = (a_{ij})$. *Then* $A = C_f^t$ *and* $f_t(x) = |xI - A|$.

III. Write $t = sp^a$, where s is prime to p. Then $\theta^t = (\theta^s)S^a$, where S is the automorphism $x \to x^p$. But then $f_t(x) = f_s(x)$. *It therefore suffices to take* t *prime to* p. Then there exists a primitive tth root of unity ω in an extension $\mathfrak{W}$ of $\mathfrak{K} = \mathfrak{F}_q(\theta)$, and we see that if $f(x) = (x - \theta_1) \cdots (x - \theta_n)$, where $\theta = \theta_1$, $\theta_2 = \theta_1^q, \ldots, \theta_n$ are in $\mathfrak{K}$, then $f(y)f(\omega y) \cdots f(\omega^{t-1}y) = (y - \theta_1)(\omega y - \theta_1) \cdots (\omega^{t-1}y - \theta_1) \cdots (y - \theta_n)(\omega y - \theta_n) \cdots (\omega^{t-1}y - \theta_n) = (y^t - \theta_1^t) \cdots (y^t - \theta_n^t)$. *Put* $y = x^{1/t}$ *and see that*

$$f_t(x) = f(x^{1/t})f(\omega x^{1/t}) \cdots f(\omega^{t-1}x^{1/t}) \,. \tag{67}$$

We are now ready to see which polynomials $f_t(x)$ are irreducible.

THEOREM 25. *Let* d *be the g.c.d. of* t *and* $q^n - 1$, *so that* $q^n - 1 = ed$. *Then* $f_t(x)$ *is irreducible over* $\mathfrak{F}_q$ *if and only if* e *does not divide* $q^m - 1$ *for any proper divisor* m *of* n.

For Theorem 1.23 states that if θ is a primitive element of the field $\mathfrak{F}_q(\theta)$ defined by a primitive polynomial $f(x)$, the period of θ^t is e. By Theorem 14 the degree of $\mathfrak{F}_q(\theta^t)$ is the least m such that e divides $q^m - 1$. Moreover, m must divide n. Hence $f_t(x)$ is irreducible if and only if e divides no $q^m - 1$ with m a *proper* divisor of n.

ILLUSTRATIVE EXAMPLE

Find the values of t for which $f_t(x)$ is irreducible if $q = 2$ and $n = 6$.

Solution. The integer $q^n - 1 = 2^6 - 1 = 63 = 3^2 \cdot 7$ and the nontrivial factors of 63 are $e = 3, 7, 9$, and 21. The proper divisors m of n are $m = 1, 2, 3$, and $q^m - 1 = 1, 3, 7$. It follows that, when $e = 3$ or 7, the corresponding polynomials are reducible. But then $f_t(x)$ is reducible for $0 < t < 63$ if and only if t is divisible by 9 or by 21. It follows that $f_t(x)$ is irreducible except when $t = 9, 18, 27, 36, 45, 54, 21, 42$.

EXERCISES

Determine the values of t for which $f_t(x)$ is irreducible in the following cases:

1. $q = 2, \quad n = 5$;
2. $q = 4, \quad n = 3$;
3. $q = 3, \quad n = 2$;
4. $q = 3, \quad n = 3$;
5. $q = 9, \quad n = 3$;
6. $q = 5, \quad n = 4$.

16. The cubing transformation. Let $f_t(x) = [g(x)]^r$, where $g(x)$ is irreducible in $\mathfrak{F}_q$ and the degree m of $g(x)$ divides $n = mr$. Then the mapping

$$T_c\colon \qquad f_t(x) \to f_{3t}(x)$$

of the set $\mathfrak{M}$ of all $f_t(x)$ into $\mathfrak{M}$ is called the *cubing transformation*. It maps $g(x)$ onto $T_c(g) = g_3(x)$, where $g_3(x)$ is the characteristic function of θ^{3t}

over $\mathfrak{F}_q$ considered as an element of $\mathfrak{F}_q(\theta)$, and $g(\theta^t) = 0$. Evidently, T_c is the consequence of the mapping

$$T: \qquad k = \theta^t \rightarrow k^3 = kT ,$$

of the multiplicative group $\mathfrak{K}^*$ of $\mathfrak{K} = \mathfrak{F}_q(\theta)$ into $\mathfrak{K}^*$.

It is now evident that

$$kT^a = k^{3^a} . \tag{68}$$

Then T_c is said to be a *periodic* transformation on $f_t(x)$, as well as on $g(x)$, if $T_c^\gamma[f_t(x)] = f_t(x)$ for a positive integer γ called the *period* of T_c. It will then be true that $g_\beta(x) = g(x)$, where $\beta = 3^\gamma$. Evidently, T_c is periodic on $f_t(x)$ if and only if there exist integers γ and s such that

$$(3^\gamma - q^s)t \equiv 0 \pmod{q^n - 1} . \tag{69}$$

However, k is a primitive eth root of unity, where $q^n - 1 = ed$ and d is the g.c.d. of t and $q^n - 1$. Then T_c is periodic if and only if there exist integers γ and s such that

$$3^\gamma \equiv q^s \pmod{e} . \tag{70}$$

Then 3 must be prime to e.

THEOREM 26. *Let* g(x) *be an irreducible polynomial of degree* m *over* $\mathfrak{F}_q$ *and let* g(x) *belong to* e. *Then the cubing transformation* $g(x) \rightarrow g_3(x)$ *is periodic if and only if* 3 *does not divide* e.

When 3 does not divide e, the images k^{3^a} under the cubing transformation all have period e and all define the same field. The corresponding polynomials $g_i(x)$ defined for $i = 3^a$ are then all irreducible polynomials of degree m belonging to e. We now study the irreducibility of $g_3(x)$ when 3 does divide e.

THEOREM 27. *Let* g(x) *be an irreducible polynomial of degree* m *over* $\mathfrak{F}_q$ *belonging to* $e = 3^\beta\epsilon$, *where* ϵ *is prime to* 3. *Then* $g_3(x)$ *is the square of an irreducible polynomial if and only if* $m = 2\mu$ *is even*, $\beta = 1$, *and* $q^\mu \equiv 1 \pmod{\epsilon}$. *The polynomial* $g_3(x)$ *is the cube of an irreducible polynomial if and only if* $\beta > 1$, $m = 3\mu$ *is divisible by* 3, *and* $q^\mu \equiv 1 \pmod{3^{\beta-1}\epsilon}$. *In all other cases* $g_3(x)$ *is irreducible.*

For let $g(k) = 0$, where k has period e. Then $g_3(x) = [h(x)]^\delta$, where $h(x)$ is the minimum function of k^3 over $\mathfrak{F}_q$. Thus the degree of $h(x)$ is the degree μ of $\mathfrak{F}_q(k^3)$ over $\mathfrak{F}_q$, and $m = \mu\delta$, where $\mathfrak{F}_q(k)$ has degree δ over $\mathfrak{F}_q(k^3)$. Evidently, $\delta \not> 3$, so that $\delta = 1$, 2, or 3. If $\delta = 2$, then m is even, $m = 2\mu$, $q^m \equiv 1 \pmod{e}$, $q^\mu \equiv 1 \pmod{3^{\beta-1}\epsilon}$, but $q^\mu \not\equiv 1 \pmod{e}$. Since $q^m - 1 = (q^\mu - 1)(q^\mu + 1)$, it follows that $q^\mu \equiv -1 \pmod{3}$, and so $\beta = 1$. Conversely, if $\beta = 1$, $m = 2\mu$, and $q^\mu \equiv 1 \pmod{\epsilon}$, the degree of $\mathfrak{F}_q(k^3)$ over $\mathfrak{F}_q$ is μ and $\delta = 2$. If $\delta = 3$, then $m = 3\mu$ and $q^\mu \equiv 1$

(mod $3^{\beta-1}\epsilon$). If $\beta = 1$, then $e = 3\epsilon$ and $q^\mu \not\equiv 1 \pmod{3\epsilon}$, since otherwise $\mathfrak{F}_q(k)$ would not have degree m over $\mathfrak{F}_q$. Hence $q^\mu \equiv 2 \pmod 3$ and $q^{2\mu} + q^\mu + 1 \equiv 4 + 2 + 1 \equiv 1 \pmod 3$, whence $q^m \equiv 2 \pmod 3$, a contradiction. Thus $\beta > 1$. Conversely, if $\beta > 1$, $m = 3$, and $q^\mu \equiv 1$ (mod $3^{\beta-1}\epsilon$), the degree of $\mathfrak{F}_q(k^3)$ over $\mathfrak{F}_q$ is μ, and so $\delta = 3$. The polynomial $g_3(x)$ is then clearly irreducible in all remaining cases, that is, when $\beta = 0$ or $\beta = 1$ but either m is odd or m is the even integer 2μ such that $q^\mu \not\equiv 1 \pmod{\epsilon}$, or $\beta > 1$ but either m is not divisible by 3 or $m = 3\mu$ and $q^\mu \not\equiv 1$ (mod $3^{\beta-1}\epsilon$).

The main advantage of the cubing transformation is that it is a relatively simple matter to compute $g_3(x)$ when $g(x)$ is given. The computations of $g_t(x)$ for other values of t are likely to be too laborious.

EXERCISES

1. Find the period of T_c when $q = 8$ and $e = 7$.
2. Find the period of T_c when $q = 16$ and $e = 5$.

17. Determination of primitive irreducible polynomials. L. E. Dickson (*Linear Groups and the Galois Theory*, pp. 35–42) has given a computational procedure for simultaneously determining all primitive irreducible polynomials of degree n over $\mathfrak{F}_q$ for n and q fixed. The method depends upon a formula for the product $\Lambda(x; q, n, e)$ of all distinct irreducible polynomials of degree n over $\mathfrak{F}_q$ belonging to e. Indeed, let

$$e = p_1^{\alpha_1} \cdots p_r^{\alpha_r}, \tag{71}$$

where the p_i are the distinct prime factors of e. Define $\Sigma = (p_1, \ldots, p_r)$ to be the set of primes p_i, $\Sigma_k = (p_{i_1}, \ldots, p_{i_k})$ to be any subset of k elements of Σ, and

$$\mu(\Sigma_0) = e, \ \mu(\Sigma_k) = \frac{e}{p_{i_1} \cdots p_{i_k}} \qquad (k = 1, \ldots, r). \tag{72}$$

Define

$$\{\mu\} = x^\mu - 1 \tag{73}$$

for all positive integers μ, and

$$\Omega_k(x) = \prod_{\Sigma_k \subseteq \Sigma} \{\mu(\Sigma_k)\}, \tag{74}$$

so that $\Omega_k(x)$ is a product of $\sigma_{r,k}$ factors, where $\sigma_{r,k}$ is the number of combinations of r elements k at a time. Then $\Omega_0(x) = x^e - 1$. The process of Section 6 can now be used and yields

$$\Lambda(x; q, m, e) = \frac{\Lambda_0(x)}{\Lambda_1(x)}, \tag{75}$$

where

(76) $$\Lambda_0(x) = \prod_{0 \leq 2k \leq r} \Omega_{2k}(x) ,$$

(77) $$\Lambda_1(x) = \prod_{1 \leq 2k+1 \leq r} \Omega_{2k+1}(x) .$$

We shall not give the details of the derivation. Evidently, $\Lambda(x; q, n, q^n - 1)$ is the product of the distinct primitive irreducible polynomials of degree n.

Dickson's method uses equation (75) as follows: We assume that

$$f(x) = x^n + a_1x^{n-1} + \cdots + a_n ,$$

where the a_i are in $\mathfrak{F}_q$ and are to be determined. The primitive irreducible polynomials are the polynomials $f_t(x)$, where t ranges over all integers less than $\tau = q^n - 1$ and prime to τ. Moreover,

$$f_t(x) = f_d(x)$$

if and only if θ^d is a conjugate of θ^t, that is,

$$d \equiv tq^s (\text{mod } \tau) .$$

Thus we may begin by enumerating those values of t which are prime to τ and give distinct values of $f_t(x)$ and $\Lambda(x; q, n, q^n - 1)$ is the product of these polynomials.

A method of using this result is to observe that $f(x)$ divides $\Lambda(x; q, n, q^n - 1)$, and so we may write

$$\Lambda(x; q, n, q^n - 1) = f(x)f_0(x) + f_1(x) ,$$

where the coefficients of $f_1(x)$ are polynomials in $a_1, \ldots, a_n$. Since $f_1(x)$ must be zero, the coefficients must be zero, and we solve the resulting equations for $a_1, \ldots, a_n$. A second procedure is the following: If t is prime to τ, there exists an integer s such that $ts \equiv 1 \pmod{\tau}$. Thus $f_t(x)$ and $f(x^s)$ have exactly the same roots, and it follows that $f(x^s)$ is a power of $f_t(x)$. This is of little use, but we observe that if

$$f(k^s) = 0 ,$$

then k is a primitive root of unity, $k^\tau = 1$. Hence $k^{1/2\tau} = -1$ if τ is even. It is frequently possible to express $f_t(x)$ in terms of $f(x^s)$ by the use of these relations and so to write $\Lambda(x; q, n, q^n - 1)$ as the product of polynomials involving the coefficients of $f(x)$ alone. The resulting equations then determine $f(x)$ as well as all the other primitive irreducible polynomials of degree n. The method is illustrated here.

ILLUSTRATIVE EXAMPLES

I. *a*) *Let* q = 3 *and* n = 2, so that $f(x) = x^2 + ax + b$ and $\tau = 8$. Then $f(x) = f_3(x)$ and $f_5(x) = f_{15}(x) = f_7(x)$. Thus

$$f_5(x)\, f(x) = \frac{x^8 - 1}{x^4 - 1} = x^4 + 1 .$$

We use $k^8 = 1$ and $k^4 = -1$ to see that $f(k^5) = k^{10} + ak^5 + b = k^2 + (-a)k + b$. But then $f_5(x) = x^2 - ax + b$ and $(x^2 + ax + b)(x^2 - ax + b) = x^4 + 1$. This yields $2b = a^2$ and $b^2 = 1$, and hence $b = -1$ and $a = 1$ or -1. Then

$$f(x) = x^2 + x - 1, \quad f_5(x) = x^2 - x - 1$$

are the two irreducible primitive quadratics over $\mathfrak{F}_3$.

b) (First alternative method). Write $x^2 = -ax - b$, $x^3 = -a(-ax - b) - bx = (a^2 - b)x + ab$, $x^4 = (b - a^2)(ax + b) + abx = b^2 + (2ab - a^3)x - a^2b = -1$. Hence $a(2b - a^2) = 0$, $-a^2b + b^2 = -1$, so $b^2 = 1$, as before.

c) (Second alternative method.) The equation $x^2 = -1$ has no root in $\mathfrak{F}_3$ and so defines a quadratic field $\mathfrak{F}_3(k)$, where k has period 4. Since $a^2 = 1$ for every element of $\mathfrak{F}_3$, one of the elements $k + 1$ or $k - 1$ must be primitive. Actually, $\theta = k - 1$ is primitive, since $\theta^2 = k$. Then $\theta^2 - \theta - 1 = 0$. Also $-\theta$ is primitive and yields $f_5(x) = x^2 + x - 1$.

II. Let $q = 5$ and $n = 2$. Then $\tau = 24$, and the $\phi(24) = 8$ integers t prime to τ and less than τ may be paired so that they yield the following pairs of conjugate primitive elements:

$$\theta, \theta^5; \quad \theta^7, \theta^{35} = \theta^{11}; \theta^{13}, \quad \theta^{65} = \theta^{17}; \quad \theta^{19}, \theta^{95} = \theta^{23} = \theta^{-1} .$$

We also observe that $\theta^{17} = (\theta^7)^{-1}$. Now

$$f(x)\, f_7(x)\, f_{17}(x)\, f_{23}(x) = \frac{x^{24} - 1}{x^{12} - 1} \cdot \frac{x^4 - 1}{x^8 - 1} = \frac{x^{12} + 1}{x^4 + 1} = x^8 - x^4 + 1 .$$

We use $x^{24} = 1$ and $x^{12} = -1$ to compute $f(x^{13}) = x^{26} + ax^{13} + b = x^2 - ax + b = f_{17}(x)$. Then $bf_7(x) = bx^2 - ax + 1$, and $bf_{23}(x) = bx^2 + ax + 1$, so that

$$(x^2 + ax + b)(x^2 - ax + b)(bx^2 + ax + 1)(bx^2 - ax + 1) = b^2(x^8 - x^4 - 1) .$$

We obtain $b^2 = -1$ and $2a^2 = b$, and this yields the quadratics

$$x^2 + x + 2, \quad x^2 - x + 2, \quad x^2 + 2x - 2, \quad x^2 - 2x - 2 .$$

This example may also be solved by dividing $x^8 - x^4 + 1$ by $x^2 + ax + b$, as in Example I*b*. It may also be solved as in I*c*, where $k^2 = 2$, $k^4 = 4 = -1$ in $\mathfrak{F}_5$, and k has period 8. Then $\rho = 1 + k$ has the property that $\rho^2 = 1 + 2k + k^2 = 3 + 2k$, $\rho^3 = (3 + 2k)(1 + k) = 3 + 4 + 5k = 2$, $(2\rho)^3 = 16 = 1$, and so 2ρ has period 3. But then $2\rho k = 2k(1 + k) = 2k + 4 = \theta$ has period 24. Also $(\theta - 4)^2 = \theta^2 - 8\theta + 16 = 4k^2 = 8$, $\theta^2 + 2\theta - 2 = 0$, and we have obtained $f(x) = x^2 + 2x - 2$. Since $\theta^7 = \theta\theta^6 = \theta(2\rho k)^6 = \theta 2^6 \cdot 4 \cdot 8 = 3\theta$, we have $(\theta^7)^2 = (3\theta)^2 = -(2 - 2\theta) = -2 - 3\theta = -2 - \theta^7$, and we obtain $f_7(x) = x^2 + x + 2$. The remaining polynomials are $3x^2 f_7(1/x) = 3(2x^2 + x + 1) = x^2 + 3x + 3 = x^2 - 2x - 2$ and $-3x^2 f(1/x) = -3(-2x^2 + 2x + 1) = x^2 - x + 2$.

III. Let $q = 3$ and $n = 4$. The quadratics $x^2 + x - 1$ and $x^2 - x - 1$ determine the irreducible quartics $x^4 + x^2 - 1$ and $x^4 - x^2 - 1$ belonging to the exponent 16 by Theorem 18, and any root k of either quartic defines the field $\mathfrak{F}_3(k)$ of degree 4 over $\mathfrak{F}_3$. Take $g = k^2 - k$, where $k^4 = k^2 + 1$. Then $k^8 = k^4 - k^2 + 1 = -1$ in $\mathfrak{F}_3$, $k^6 = k^4 + k^2 = 1 - k^2$, $k^{10} = -k^2$, $k^9 = -k$, $k^7 = k - k^3$, and $k^5 = k^3 + k$. Hence $g^5 = k^5(k - 1)^5 = k^5(k^5 + k^4 + k^3 - k^2 - k - 1) = -k^2 - k - 1 + k^3 - k + k^2 - 1 - k^3 - k = 1$. It follows that $\theta = gk$ is a primitive element of $\mathfrak{F}_3(k)$. But $\theta = k^3 - k^2$, $\theta^2 = k^4(k^2 + k + 1) = 1 - k^2 + k^3 + k + k^2 + 1 = k^3 + k - 1 = \theta + k^2 + k - 1$, $\theta^3 = k^6 - k^5 + k^4 - k^3 + k^2 - k^3 = 1 - k^2 - k^3 - k + k^2 + 1 - k^3 + k^2 - k^3 = -1 - k + k^2$, $\theta^3 = \theta^2 - \theta - 2k$, and $\theta^4 = \theta^3 - \theta^2 + k^4 - k^3 = \theta^3 - \theta^2 + (k^2 + 1 - k^3) = \theta^3 - \theta^2 - \theta + 1$. Thus we have obtained the primitive irreducible polynomial $f(x) = x^4 - x^3 + x^2 + x - 1$.

EXERCISES

1. Determine a primitive irreducible quartic over $\mathfrak{F}_5$.

2. By Theorem 14 and Appendix I the polynomial $x^6 + x^5 + x^4 + x^2 + x + 1$ is irreducible in $\mathfrak{F}_5$. Find a primitive irreducible polynomial.

3. Prove that the polynomial $x^p = x + \alpha$ is a primitive irreducible polynomial if and only if α is a primitive element of $\mathfrak{F}_p$ and a root of $y^p = y + 1$ belongs to $\sigma = (p^p - 1)(p - 1)^{-1}$. *Hint:* Show that the product of the roots of $x^p = x + \alpha$ is $\alpha = x^\sigma$ and put $x = \alpha y$.

4. Let θ be a root of one of the irreducible quadratics of Illustrative Example II, so that $x^3 - \theta$ is irreducible in $\mathfrak{F}_{25}$. Derive the corresponding irreducible polynomial of degree 6 over $\mathfrak{F}_5$.

5. Let $\theta^6 = 2\theta^3 + 2$, where we use one of the results of Exercise 4. Show that $\alpha_0 + \alpha_1\theta + \alpha_2\theta^2 + \alpha_3\theta^3 + \alpha_4\theta^4 + \alpha_5\theta^5$ is in $\mathfrak{F}_{125}$ if and only if $\alpha_0 = 0$, $\alpha_4 = 3\alpha_1 + 4\alpha_2$, and $\alpha_5 = 2\alpha_1 + 3\alpha_2$. Also prove that $\psi = \theta + \theta^2 + 2\theta^4$ is a primitive element of $\mathfrak{F}_{125}$ and that $\psi^3 = 2\psi + 3$ (due to E. H. Moore).

6. Prove that $x^5 = x - 1$ is irreducible in $\mathfrak{F}_3$.

7. Let $\theta^9 = \theta + 1$ over $\mathfrak{F}_2$. Show that θ belongs to 73 and that $\theta + \theta^4 + \theta^6 + \theta^7 + \theta^8$ belongs to 7. The product then belongs to $2^9 - 1$ and is therefore a primitive element of $\mathfrak{F}_3(\theta)$. Show, in fact, that the product is a root of $(x^{10} - 1)(x - 1)^{-1}$.

18. Miscellaneous results. In this concluding section of the theory of finite fields we shall present a number of known results without proof.

Our first results come from Dickson's *Linear Groups and the Galois Field Theory*, pages 44–71. We call an element α of $\mathfrak{F}_q$ a square or a non-square according as $\alpha = \beta^2$ or $\alpha \neq \beta^2$ for β in $\mathfrak{F}_q$. The concept is vacuous in $\mathfrak{F}_q$ unless q is odd. For odd q we have the following result:

THEOREM 28. *Let* q *be odd. Then the non-squares of* $\mathfrak{F}_q$ *are squares or non-squares in* $\mathfrak{F}_{q^m}$ *according as* m *is even or odd.*

We also have

THEOREM 29. *Let* d *be the g.c.d. of* m *and* $q - 1$. *Then there are* $(q - 1)d^{-1}$ *elements of* $\mathfrak{F}_q$ *which are the* m*th powers of elements of* $\mathfrak{F}_q$.

COROLLARY. *Every element of* $\mathfrak{F}_q$ *is the* m*th power of an element of* $\mathfrak{F}_q$ *if and only if* m *is prime to* $q - 1$.

Dickson considered the number of solutions of quadratic equations in $\mathfrak{F}_q$ and obtained the following results:

THEOREM 30. *Let* q *be odd and take* $\nu = 1$ *or* -1 *according as* $-\alpha\beta \neq 0$ *is or is not a square in* $\mathfrak{F}_q$. *Then the equation* $\alpha x^2 + \beta y^2 = \gamma$ *has* $q - \nu$ *solution vectors* (x, y) *in* $\mathfrak{F}_q$ *if* $\gamma \neq 0$ *and* $q + \nu(q - 1)$ *solution vectors if* $\gamma = 0$.

THEOREM 31. *Let* q *be odd and take* $\nu = 1$ *or* -1 *according as* $-\alpha_1 \cdots \alpha_{2m} \neq 0$ *is or is not a square in* $\mathfrak{F}_q$. *Then the equation* $\alpha_1 x_1^2 + \cdots + \alpha_{2m} x_{2m}^2 = \gamma$ *has* $q^{2m-1} - \nu q^{m-1}$ *solution vectors in* $\mathfrak{F}_q$ if $\gamma \neq 0$ *and* $q^{2m-1} + \nu(q^m - q^{m-1})$ *solution vectors in* $\mathfrak{F}_q$ *if* $\gamma = 0$.

THEOREM 32. *Let* q *be odd and put* $\omega = 1, -1,$ *or* 0 *according as* $(-1)^m \gamma \alpha_1 \cdots \alpha_{2m+1}$ *is a square, a non-square, or zero in* $\mathfrak{F}_q$, *where* $\alpha_1 \cdots \alpha_{2m+1} \neq 0$. *Then the equation* $\alpha_1 x_1^2 + \cdots + \alpha_{2m+1} x_{2m+1}^2 = \gamma$ *has* $q^{2m} + \omega q^m$ *solution vectors.*

A polynomial $f(x)$ with coefficients in $\mathfrak{F}_q$ determines a mapping

$$f: \qquad x \to f(x)$$

of $\mathfrak{F}_q$ into $\mathfrak{F}_q$. This mapping is *one to one onto* if the equation $f(x) = \alpha$ has a solution x in $\mathfrak{F}_q$ for every α of $\mathfrak{F}_q$. Each such polynomial defines what is called the *analytic representation* of the permutation f on the finite set $\mathfrak{F}_q$. The polynomial is called a *substitution polynomial* for $\mathfrak{F}_q$. Since

$$\xi^q = \xi$$

for every element of $\mathfrak{F}_q$, we may *limit our study to polynomials of degree at most* q − 1 *in what follows.*

THEOREM 33. *Two distinct polynomials define different permutations on* $\mathfrak{F}_q$.

For if $f(\xi) = g(\xi)$ for every ξ of $\mathfrak{F}_q$, the polynomial $f(x) - q(x)$ of degree at most $q - 1$ has q roots and must be zero.

THEOREM 34. *The polynomial* x^m *is a substitution polynomial for* $\mathfrak{F}_q$ *if and only if* m *is prime to* q − 1.

THEOREM 35. *The polynomial* $f(x) = 5x^5 + 5\alpha x^3 + \alpha^2 x$ *is a substitution polynomial for every* α *of* $\mathfrak{F}_q$ *if* $q = p^n$ *where* n *is odd and* $p = 5m + 2$ *or* $5m - 2$.

THEOREM 36. *Let* d *divide* $p^r - 1 = de$ *and* α *be an element of* $\mathfrak{F}_q$ *which is not the* d*th power of any element of* $\mathfrak{F}_q$. *Then* $x(x^d - \alpha)^e$ *is a substitution polynomial of* $\mathfrak{F}_q$.

THEOREM 37. *The polynomial*

$$\psi(x) = \sum_{i=1}^{m} \alpha_i x^{q(m-i)}$$

is a substitution polynomial for $\mathfrak{R} = \mathfrak{F}_r$, $r = q^m$, *if and only if* $x = 0$ *is the only solution in* $\mathfrak{R}$ *of* $\psi(x) = 0$. *The set of all permutations of this kind on* $\mathfrak{R}$ *is a group called the* Betti-Mathieu group.

In his paper entitled "Criteria for the Irreducibility of Functions in a Finite Field," *Bulletin of the American Mathematical Society*, XIII (1906–7), 1–8, L. E. Dickson derived the following results:

THEOREM 38. *A polynomial* f(x) *in* $\mathfrak{F}_q[x]$ *is irreducible when* q *is odd only if its discriminant is a square or a non-square according as the degree of* f(x) *is odd or even.*

THEOREM 39. *Let* q *be odd. Then a cubic has exactly one root in* $\mathfrak{F}_q$ *only if its discriminant is a non-square.*

THEOREM 40. *The cubic* $x^3 + \alpha x + \beta$ *is irreducible in* $\mathfrak{F}_q$, $q = p^n$, $p > 3$, *if and only if* $-4\alpha^3 - 27\beta^2$ *is a non-square* $81\mu^2$ *in* $\mathfrak{F}_q$ *and* $-\frac{1}{2}(-b + \mu\sqrt{-3})$ *is a non-cube in* $\mathfrak{F}_q(\sqrt{-3})$.

THEOREM 41. *Let* $f(x) = x^4 + ax^3 + bx^2 + cx + d$ *where* $c \neq \frac{1}{2}ab - \frac{1}{8}a^3$ *and* a, b, c, d *are in* $\mathfrak{F}_q$, $q = p^n$ *odd. Then* f(x) *is irreducible in* $\mathfrak{F}_q$ *if and only if* $(\frac{1}{2}b - \frac{1}{8}a^2)^2 - d$ *and* $\frac{5}{16}a^4 - a^2b + 16d$ *are non-squares.*

THEOREM 42. *Let* f(x) *be as in Theorem 41. Then* f(x) *is irreducible in* $\mathfrak{F}_q$ *if and only if the resolvent cubic has exactly one root* γ *in* $\mathfrak{F}_q$ *and* $\mathfrak{F}_q$ *and* $a^2 - 4b + 4\gamma$ *is a non-square.*

In the same volume (pp. 8–10) Dickson considered the Galois theory for finite fields. He did not obtain any of the modern results.

Dickson published a paper entitled "Invariants of Binary Forms under Modular Transformations," *Transactions of the American Mathematical Society*, VIII (1907), 205–32. He later studied binary forms over a modular field in a paper entitled "An Invariantive Investigation of Irreducible Binary Modular Forms," *Transactions of the American Mathematical Society*, XII (1911), 1–18, and general forms in the same volume, pages 75–98. In the latter paper he obtained the case mentioned of our Theorem 24.

In his paper entitled "On Triple Algebras and Ternary Cubic Forms," *Bulletin of the American Mathematical Society*, XIV (1907–8), 160–69, Dickson studied cubic forms over $\mathfrak{F}_q$. A form $f(x) = f(x_1, \ldots, x_n)$ is called a *null* form if there exists a non-zero vector $\xi = (\xi_1, \ldots, \xi_n)$ with coordinates ξ_i in $\mathfrak{F}_q$ such that $f(\xi) = 0$. He obtained the following results:

THEOREM 43. *Let* $f(x) = f(x_1, x_2, x_3)$ *be a ternary cubic over* $\mathfrak{F}_q$ *where* q *is odd. Then* $f(x)$ *is not a null form if and only if the Hessian of* $f(x)$ *is* $mf(x)$, *where* m *is in* $\mathfrak{F}_q$ *and* $f(x_1, x_1, 0)$ *is irreducible in* $\mathfrak{F}_q$.

THEOREM 44. *Let* $f(x) = ax_1^3 + bx_1^2x_2 + cx_1^2x_3 + dx_1x_2^2 + ex_1x_3^2 + fx_1x_2x_3 + gx_2^3 + hx_2^2x_3 + kx_2x_3^2 + tx_3^3$ *be a ternary cubic with coefficients in* $\mathfrak{F}_q$ *where* q *is odd, and let*

$$\delta = \begin{vmatrix} 3a & b & c \\ 2b & 2d & f \\ d & 3g & h \end{vmatrix}.$$

Then $f(x)$ *is not a null form if and only if* $f(x)$ *has a linear factor in* $\mathfrak{F}_{q^3}$, $f(y, 1, 0)$ *is irreducible in* $\mathfrak{F}_q$, *and* $\delta \neq 0$.

In the same volume (pp. 313–18) Dickson derived a formula for the number of distinct roots in $\mathfrak{F}_{q^m}$ of a homogeneous binary equation $f(x_1, x_2) = 0$ of degree r over $\mathfrak{F}_q$. Here two vectors (x_1, x_2) and (y_1, y_2) are said to be equal solutions if $(y_1, y_2) = k(x_1, x_2)$ for k in $\mathfrak{F}_{q^m}$.

In a paper entitled "Invariantive Reduction of Quadratic Forms over $\mathfrak{G}\mathfrak{F}(2^n)$," *American Journal of Mathematics*, XXX (1908), 263–81, Dickson gave some special results on quadratic forms over a finite field of characteristic 2.

In a paper entitled "On the Representation of Numbers by Modular Forms," *Bulletin of the American Mathematical Society*, XV (1908–9), 338–47, Dickson stated the following conjecture:

THEOREM 45. *Every form of degree* m *in* $m + 1$ *variables over a finite field is a null form.*

Dickson proved the theorem for $m = 2$ and 3. The general case of the theorem was proved by C. Chevalley, "Demonstration d'une hypothèse de M. Artin," *Hamburg Abhandlungen*, XI (1935), 73–75.

The following is a list of references to other papers on equations in several variables over a finite field.

1. ARTIN, E. "Quadratische Körper im Gebiete der höheren Kongruenzen," *Math. Zeitschr.*, XIX (1924), 230–31.
2. CARLITZ, L. "Some Applications of a Theorem of Chevalley," *Duke Math. Jour.*, XVIII (1951), 811–19.
3. ———. "Some Problems Involving Primitive Roots in a Finite Field," *Proc. Nat. Acad. Sci.*, XXXVIII (1952), 314–18.
4. CHOWLA, I. "On Waring's Problem (mod p)," *Proc. Nat. Acad. Sci. India Sec. A*, XIII (1943), 195–220.
5. CORNACCHIA, G. "Sulla congruenza $x^n + y^n \equiv z^n$ (mod p)," *Gior. di mat.*, XLVII (1909), 219–63.
6. DAVENPORT, H. "On the Distribution of Quadratic Residues (mod p)," *Jour. London Math. Soc.*, VI (1931), 49–54.
7. DAVENPORT, H., and HASSE, H. "Die Nullstellen der Kongruenzzetafunktionen in gewissen zyklischen Fallen," *Jour. f. Math.*, CLXXII (1935), 173–75.
8. DICKSON, L. E. "On the Last Theorem of Fermat," *Messenger of Math.*, ser. 2, XXXVIII (1908), 14–32.
9. ———. "On the Last Theorem of Fermat," *Quart. Jour. Math.*, XL (1908), 27–45.
10. ———. "On the Congruence $x^n + y^n + z^n \equiv 0$ (mod p)," *Amer. Math. Monthly*, XV (1908), 217–22.
11. ———. "On the Congruence $x^n + y^n + z^n \equiv 0$ (mod p)," *Jour. f. Math.*, CXXXV (1909), 134–42.
12. ———. "Lower Limit for the Number of Sets of Solutions of $x^e + y^e + z^e \equiv 0$ (mod p)," *ibid.*, pp. 181–88.
13. ———. "Cyclotomy and Trinomial Congruences," *Trans. Amer. Math. Soc.*, XXXVII (1935), 363–80, and XXXVIII, 187–200.
14. ———. "Congruences Involving Only eth Powers," *Acta Arith.*, I (1935), 161–67.
15. ———. "Cyclotomy, Higher Congruences, and Waring's Problem. I," *Amer. Jour. Math.*, LVII (1935), 391–424.
16. ———. "Cyclotomy, Higher Congruences, and Waring's Problem. II," *ibid.*, pp. 463–74.
17. FAIRCLOTH, O. B. "A Summary of New Results concerning the Solution of Equations in Finite Fields," *Proc. Nat. Acad. Sci.*, XXXVII (1951), 619–22.
18. FAIRCLOTH, O. B., and VANDIVER, H. S. "On the Multiplicative Properties of a Generalized Jacobi-Cauchy Cyclotomic Sum," *Proc. Math. Acad. Sci.*, XXXVI (1950), 144–51.
19. ———. "On Certain Diophantine Equations in Rings and Fields," *ibid.*, XXXVIII (1952), 52–57.

20. GEGENBAUER, L. "Ueber ein Theorem des Herrn Pépin," *Wien. Sitzungsber.*, II, XCV (1887), 838–42.
21. HARDY, G. H., and LITTLEWOOD, J. E. "The Number $\tau(k)$ in Waring's Problem," *Proc. London Math. Soc.*, ser. 2, XXVIII (1927), 526–28.
22. HUA, L. K., and MIN, S. "On the Number of Solutions of Certain Congruences," *Sci. Rept. Nat. Tsing Hua Univ.*, IV (1940), 113–33.
23. HUA, L. K., and VANDIVER, H. S. "On the Existence of Solutions of Certain Equations in a Finite Field," *Proc. Nat. Acad. Sci.*, XXXIV (1948), 258–63.
24. ———. "Characters over Certain Types of Rings with Applications to the Theory of Equations in a Finite Field," *ibid.*, XXXV (1949), 94–99.
25. ———. "On the Number of Solutions of Some Trinomial Equations in a Finite Field," *ibid.*, pp. 477–81.
26. ———. "On the Nature of the Solutions of Certain Equations in a Finite Field," *ibid.*, pp. 481–87.
27. HULL, R. "The Number of Solutions of Congruences Involving Only kth Powers," *Trans. Amer. Math. Soc.*, XXXIV (1932), 908–37.
28. HURWITZ, A. "Ueber die Kongruenz $ax^e + by^e + cz^e \equiv 0 \pmod{p}$," *Jour. f. Math.*, CXXXVI (1909), 272–92.
29. JACOBI, C. G. J. "Ueber die Kreistheilung und ihre Anwending auf die Zahlentheorie," *Jour. f. Math.*, XXX (1846), 181–82, or *Werke*, VI, 254–94. Berlin: Verlag von Georg Reimer, 1891.
30. KUMMER, E. E. "Ueber die Zerlegung der aus Wurzeln der Einheit gebildeten complexen Zahlen in ihre Primfactoren," *Jour. f. Math.*, XXXV (1847), 328–29.
31. ———. "Mémoire sur les nombres complexes composés de racines de l'unité et des nombres entiers," *Jour. de Math.*, ser. 1, XVI (1851), 377–498.
32. ———. "Ueber die Ergänzungesätze zu den allgemeinen Reciprocitätsgesetzen," *Jour. f. Math.*, XLIV (1852), 95–100.
33. LANDAU, E. *Vorlesungen über Zahlentheorie*, I, 296. Leipzig: Verlag von S. Hirzel, 1927.
34. LEGESGUE, M. "Recherches sur les nombres," *Jour. de Math.*, ser. 1, II (1837), 253–92.
35. ———. "Recherches sur les nombres," *ibid.*, ser. 1, III (1838), 113–45.
36. ———. "Demonstration de quelques formules d'un mémoire de M. Jacobi," *ibid.*, ser. 1, XIX (1854), 289–96.
37. LIBRI, G. *Mém. divers savants ac. sc. de l'institut de France* (*math.*), Vol. V (1838).
38. MIN, S. "On Systems of Algebraic Equations and Certain Multiple Exponential Sums," *Quart. Jour. Math.*, Oxford ser., XVIII (1947), 133–42.
39. MITCHELL, H. H. "On the Generalized Jacobi-Kummer Cyclotomic Functions," *Trans. Amer. Math. Soc.*, XVII (1916), 165–77.
40. ———. "On the Congruence $cx^a + 1 = dy^a$ in a Galois Field," *Ann. Math.*, ser. 2, XVIII (1917), 120–31.

41. Mordell, L. J. "The Number of Solutions of Some Congruences in Two Variables," *Math. Zeitschr.*, XXXVII (1933), 193–209.
42. Pellet, A. E. "Méthode nouvelle pour diviser le cercle en parties égales," *Comptes rendus* (Paris), XCIII (1881), 838–40.
43. ———. "Mémoire sur la théorie algébrique des équations," *Bull. Soc. math. de France*, XV (1886–87), 80–93.
44. Pépin, P. "Sur divers tentatives de démonstration du théorème de Fermat," *Comptes rendus* (Paris), XCI (1880), 366–68.
45. Piuma, C. M. "Interno ad una congruenza di modula primo," *Ann. di mat.*, ser. 2, XI (1882–83), 237–45.
46. Rédei, L. "Zur Theorie de Gleichungen in endlichen Körpern," *Acta Univ. Szeged*, Vol. XI (1946).
47. Schur, I. "Ueber die Kongruenz $x^m + y^m \equiv z^m \pmod{p}$," *Jahresber. Deutsch. math. Vereinigung*, XXV (1916), 114–17.
48. Schwarz, S. "On Waring's Problem for Finite Fields," *Quart. Jour. Math.*, Oxford ser. XIX (1948), 123–28.
49. ———. "On an Equation in Finite Fields," *ibid.*, pp. 160–63.
50. ———. "On Universal Forms in Finite Fields," *Casopis Pěst. Mat. Fys.*, LXXV (1950), 45–50.
51. Schwering, K. "Zur Theorie der arithmetischen Functionen, welche von Jacobi $\psi(\alpha)$ genannt werden," *Jour. f. Math.*, XCIII (1882), 334–37.
52. Tornheim, L. "Sums of nth Powers in Fields of Prime Characteristic," *Duke Math. Jour.*, IV (1938), 359–62.
53. Vandiver, H. S. "Some Theorems in Finite Field Theory with Applications to Fermat's Last Theorem," *Proc. Nat. Acad. Sci.*, XXX (1944), 362–67.
54. ———. "On Trinomial Congruences and Fermat's Last Theorem," *ibid.*, pp. 368–70.
55. ———. "New Types of Relations in Finite Field Theory," *ibid.*, XXXI (1945), 50–54.
56. ———. "On the Number of Solutions of Certain Non-homogeneous Trinomial Equations in a Finite Field," *ibid.*, pp. 170–75.
57. ———. "New Types of Relations in Finite Field Theory," *ibid.*, pp. 189–94.
58. ———. "On the Number of Solutions of Some General Types of Equations in a Finite Field," *ibid.*, XXXII (1946), 47–52.
59. ———. "On Classes of Diophantine Equations of Higher Degree Which Have No Solutions," *ibid.*, pp. 101–6.
60. ———. "Cyclotomy and Trinomial Equations in a Finite Field," *ibid.*, pp. 317–19.
61. ———. "On Some Special Trinomial Equations in a Finite Field," *ibid.*, pp. 320–26.
62. ———. "Limits for the Number of Solutions of Certain General Types of Equations in a Finite Field," *ibid.*, XXXIII (1947), 236–42.
63. ———. "Applications of Cyclotomy to the Theory of Non-homogeneous Equations in a Finite Field," *ibid.*, XXXIV (1948), 62–66.

64. ———. "Quadratic Relations Involving the Numbers of Solutions of Certain Types of Equations in a Finite Field," *ibid.*, XXXV (1949), 681–85.
65. ———. "On a Generalization of a Jacobi Exponential Sum Associated with Cyclotomy," *ibid.*, XXXVI (1950), 144–51.
66. WARNING, E. VON. "Bemerkung zur vorstehenden Arbeit von Herrn Chevalley," *Abhandl. a. d. math. Seminar d. Hamburg. Univ.*, XI (1936), 76–83.
67. WEIL, A., "Number of Solutions of Equations in Finite Fields," *Bull. Amer. Math. Soc.*, LV (1949), 497–508.
68. WHITEMAN, A. L. "Theorems Analogous to Jacobstahl's Theorem," *Duke Math. Jour.*, XVI (1949), 619–26.
69. ———. "Theorems on Quadratic Partitions," *Proc. Nat. Acad. Sci.*, XXXVI (1950), 60–66.
70. ———. "Finite Fourier Series and Cyclotomy," *ibid.*, XXXVII (1951), 373–78.

19. Historical notes. The major work on finite fields is L. E. Dickson's *Linear Groups and the Galois Theory* (Chicago, 1900). A historical account of the theory of finite fields appears in Dickson's *History of the Theory of Numbers*, I, 233–52.

Many of the early papers on finite fields present rather confused ideas on the subject. For example, Dickson found it necessary to state as late as 1903 that the congruence $x^q \equiv x \pmod q$ does not have as its solutions the elements of $\mathfrak{F}_q$ for $q = p^n > p$.

The theorem which states that $x^q = x$ in $\mathfrak{F}_q$ is due to E. Galois and appeared in his paper "Sur la théorie des nombres," *Bulletin des sciences mathématiques de M. Ferussac*, XIII (1830), 248. Many of the early papers consider only questions about the theorem on the existence of finite fields. Indeed, this theorem, now a trivial consequence of the theory of splitting fields, was called the chief theorem on the subject on page 239 of Dickson's *History*.

E. A. Moore proved that every finite field is a Galois field $\mathfrak{F}_q$ in the *Mathematical Papers of the Chicago Congress of 1893*, pages 200–226. Dickson gave an inductive proof of the existence of a finite field on page 19 of his *Linear Groups and the Galois Theory*.

Theorem 12 is essentially due to R. Dedekind, *Journal für Mathematik*, LIV (1857), 1–26.

The theorems of Sections 9, 10, and 11 on the determination of irreducible polynomials are due to Serret, *Cours d'algêbra supérieure*, Vol. II (1879). They were originally published in 1866.

We close our account with a mention of the tables of Bussey, which appear as Appendix III.

APPENDIX I

Table of Least Primitive Roots

The following table is a list of the least primitive roots δ modulo p for each odd prime $p < 500$. It also includes a list of the residues modulo p of $-\delta$ for those primitive roots δ such that $-\delta$ (mod p) is a minimum. The table is a portion of the table of A. Cunningham, H. J. Woodall, and T. G. Creak (*Proceedings of the London Mathematical Society*, XXI [1922], 343–58), where a list is given up to p = 25,409.

p	δ	$-\delta$	p	δ	$-\delta$	p	δ	$-\delta$	p	δ	$-\delta$
3.....	2	1	101...	2	2	229...	6	6	367...	6	2
5.....	2	2	103...	5	2	233...	3	3	373...	2	2
7.....	3	2	107...	2	3	239...	7	2	379...	2	4
11.....	2	3	109...	6	6	241...	7	7	383...	5	2
13.....	2	2	113...	3	3	251...	6	3	389...	2	2
17.....	3	3	127...	3	9	257...	3	3	397...	5	5
19.....	2	4	131...	2	3	263...	5	2	401...	3	3
23.....	5	2	137...	3	3	269...	2	2	409...	21	21
29.....	2	2	139...	2	4	271...	6	2	419...	2	3
31.....	3	7	149...	2	2	277...	5	5	421...	2	2
37.....	2	2	151...	6	5	281...	3	3	431...	7	5
41.....	6	6	157...	5	5	283...	3	6	433...	5	5
43.....	3	9	163...	2	4	293...	2	2	439...	15	5
47.....	5	2	167...	5	2	307...	5	7	443...	2	3
53.....	2	2	173...	2	2	311...	17	2	449...	3	3
59.....	2	3	179...	2	3	313...	10	10	457...	13	13
61.....	2	2	181...	2	2	317...	2	2	461...	2	2
67.....	2	4	191...	19	2	331...	3	5	463...	3	2
71.....	7	2	193...	5	5	337...	10	10	467...	2	3
73.....	5	5	197...	2	2	347...	2	3	479...	13	2
79.....	3	2	199...	3	2	349...	2	2	487...	3	2
83.....	2	3	211...	2	4	353...	3	3	491...	2	5
89.....	3	3	223...	3	9	359...	7	2	499...	7	5
97.....	5	5	227...	2	3						

APPENDIX II

Extract from Jacobi's Canon

Probably the first extensive table of primitive roots was that of C. G. J. Jacobi, *Canon arithmeticus* (Berlin, 1839). His tables gave the value of a primitive root δ (taken to be 10 very frequently) modulo p for each prime $p < 1{,}000$, and the index $\gamma(n)$ such that $0 \leq \gamma \leq p - 1$, and $n \equiv \delta^{\gamma} \pmod{p}$. The tables for $p = 5, 7, 11$, and 17 show how elaborate such tables can be and suffice for our purposes.

$p = 5$

γ	0	1	2	3	4	5	6	7	8	9	n	0	1	2	3	4	5	6	7	8	9
n		2	4	3	1						γ		4	1	3	2					

$p = 7$

γ	0	1	2	3	4	5	6	7	8	9	n	0	1	2	3	4	5	6	7	8	9
n		3	2	6	4	5	1				γ		6	2	1	4	5	3			

$p = 11$

γ	0	1	2	3	4	5	6	7	8	9	n	0	1	2	3	4	5	6	7	8	9
n		2	4	8	5	10	9	7	3	6	γ	0	10	1	8	2	4	9	7	3	6
1	1 [that is, $\gamma(1) = 10$]										1	5 [that is, $\gamma(10) = 5$]									

$p = 17$

γ	0	1	2	3	4	5	6	7	8	9	n	0	1	2	3	4	5	6	7	8	9
n		10	15	14	4	6	9	5	16	7	γ		16	10	11	4	7	5	9	14	6
1	2	3	13	11	8	12	1				1	1	13	15	12	3	2	8			

APPENDIX III

Bussey's Tables

These tables appear in two papers by W. H. Bussey entitled "Galois Field Tables for $p^n \leq 169$," *Bulletin of the American Mathematical Society*, XII (1905), 22–38, and "Galois Field Tables of Order Less than 1,000," *ibid.*, XVI (1909), 188–206. Each table is headed by a primitive irreducible polynomial $f(x)$ of degree n over $\mathfrak{F}_p$ for $q = p^n < 1,000$. Then $f(x)$ defines the field $\mathfrak{F}_q = \mathfrak{F}_p(\theta)$, where $f(\theta) = 0$ and θ is a primitive $(q - 1)$st root of unity. The table then presents the exponent ϵ in the expression

$$g(\theta) = a_0\theta^{n-1} + a_1\theta^{n-2} + \cdots + a_n = \theta^{\epsilon}$$

for each non-zero element $g(\theta)$ in $\mathfrak{F}_q$. We shall present only a few cases of these tables but shall present the complete list of the primitive irreducible polynomials obtained by Bussey.

$p = 2$: $x^3 - x - 1$; $x^4 - x - 1$; $x^5 - x^3 - x^2 - x - 1$; $x^6 - x - 1$; $x^7 - x - 1$; $x^8 - x^4 - x^3 - x^2 - 1$; $x^9 - x^8 - x^4 - x^3 - x^2 - x - 1$.

$p = 3$: $x^2 - x - 1$; $x^3 - x - 2$; $x^4 - 2x^3 - 2x^2 - x - 1$; $x^5 - x - 2$; $x^6 - x - 1$.

$p = 5$: $x^2 - 2x - 2$; $x^3 - 2x - 3$; $x^4 - x^3 - x - 2$.

$p = 7$: $x^2 - x - 4$; $x^3 - x - 5$.

$p = 11$: $x^2 - 4x - 9$.
$p = 13$: $x^2 - x - 11$.
$p = 17$: $x^2 - x - 14$.
$p = 19$: $x^2 - x - 17$.
$p = 23$: $x^2 - x - 16$.
$p = 29$: $x^2 - x - 26$.
$p = 31$: $x^2 - x - 19$.

We shall now present the Bussey tables for $p^n = 2^3$.

ϵ	a_0	a_1	a_2
1		1	0
2	1	0	0
3		1	1
4	1	1	0
5	1	1	1
6	1	0	1
7			1

ϵ	a_0	a_1	a_2
7			1
1		1	0
3		1	1
2	1	0	0
6	1	0	1
4	1	1	0
5	1	1	1

We shall give a few more examples of the results of the Bussey tables, presenting only the right-hand table.

$p^n = 3^2$

ϵ	a_0	a_1
8.		1
4.		2
1.	1	0
2.	1	1
7.	1	2
5.	2	0
3.	2	1
6.	2	2

$p^n = 2^4$

ϵ	a_0	a_1	a_2	a_3
15.				1
1.			1	0
4.			1	1
2.		1	0	0
8.		1	0	1
5.		1	1	0
10.		1	1	1
3.	1	0	0	0
14.	1	0	0	1
9.	1	0	1	0
7.	1	0	1	1
6.	1	1	0	0
13.	1	1	0	1
11.	1	1	1	0
12.	1	1	1	1

$p^n = 2^5$

ϵ	a_0	a_1	a_2	a_3	a_4
31. .					1
1. .				1	0
12. .				1	1
2. .			1	0	0
24. .			1	0	1
13. .			1	1	0
27. .			1	1	1
3. .		1	0	0	0
8. .		1	0	0	1
25. .		1	0	1	0
10. .		1	0	1	1
14. .		1	1	0	0
18. .	1	1	1	0	1
28. .		1	1	1	0
5. .		1	1	1	1
4. .	1	0	0	0	0
17. .	1	0	0	0	1
9. .	1	0	0	1	0
7. .	1	0	0	1	1
26. .	1	0	1	0	0
23. .	1	0	1	0	1
11. .	1	0	1	1	0
30. .	1	0	1	1	1
15. .	1	1	0	0	0
21. .	1	1	0	0	1
19. .	1	1	0	1	0
20. .	1	1	0	1	1
29. .	1	1	1	0	0
22. .	1	1	1	0	1
6. .	1	1	1	1	0
16. .	1	1	1	1	1

$p^n = 2^6$

ϵ	a_0	a_1	a_2	a_3	a_4	a_5
63. .						1
1. .					1	0
6. .					1	1
2. .				1	0	0
12. .				1	0	1
7. .				1	1	0
26. .				1	1	1
3. .			1	0	0	0
32. .			1	0	0	1
13. .			1	0	1	0
35. .			1	0	1	1
8. .			1	1	0	0
48. .			1	1	0	1
27. .			1	1	1	0
18. .			1	1	1	1
4. .		1	0	0	0	0
24. .		1	0	0	0	1
33. .		1	0	0	1	0
16. .		1	0	0	1	1
14. .		1	0	1	0	0
52. .		1	0	1	0	1
36. .		1	0	1	1	0
54. .		1	0	1	1	1
9. .		1	1	0	0	0
45. .		1	1	0	0	1
49. .		1	1	0	1	0
38. .		1	1	0	1	1
28. .		1	1	1	0	0
41. .		1	1	1	0	1
19. .		1	1	1	1	0
56. .		1	1	1	1	1
5. .	1	0	0	0	0	0
62. .	1	0	0	0	0	1
25. .	1	0	0	0	1	0
11. .	1	0	0	0	1	1
34. .	1	0	0	1	0	0
31. .	1	0	0	1	0	1
17. .	1	0	0	1	1	0
47. .	1	0	0	1	1	1
15. .	1	0	1	0	0	0
23. .	1	0	1	0	0	1
53. .	1	0	1	0	1	0
51. .	1	0	1	0	1	1
37. .	1	0	1	1	0	0
44. .	1	0	1	1	0	1
55. .	1	0	1	1	1	0
40. .	1	0	1	1	1	1
10. .	1	1	0	0	0	0
61. .	1	1	0	0	0	1
46. .	1	1	0	0	1	0
30. .	1	1	0	0	1	1
50. .	1	1	0	1	0	0
22. .	1	1	0	1	0	1
39. .	1	1	0	1	1	0
43. .	1	1	0	1	1	1
29. .	1	1	1	0	0	0
60. .	1	1	1	0	0	1
42. .	1	1	1	0	1	0
21. .	1	1	1	0	1	1
20. .	1	1	1	1	0	0
59. .	1	1	1	1	0	1
57. .	1	1	1	1	1	0
58. .	1	1	1	1	1	1

Irreducible Polynomials over $\mathfrak{F}_2$

The following tables are due to Richard Marsh. They are called the *octal* representations of the irreducible polynomials $f(x) = x^n + a_1x^{n-1} + \cdots + a_n$ over $\mathfrak{F}_2$ for $n \leq 9$. The list requires the adjunction of the reciprocal polynomial $x^nf(1/x)$ for each $f(x)$ represented, in order to obtain all irreducible polynomials of degree n. When $f(x) = x^nf(1/x)$, the star appears after the representation.

Since the coefficients $1, a_1, \ldots, a_n$ are either 0 or 1, each $f(x)$ may be represented by a sequence $b_1, \ldots, b_m$ of triples of coefficients, where $n = 3m - 1$, $3m - 2$, or $3m - 3$ and $b_1 = (100), (010), (001)$ in the respective cases. We number the triples as follows:

$$0 = (000), \quad 1 = (001), \quad 2 = (010), \quad 3 = (011),$$
$$4 = (100), \quad 5 = (101), \quad 6 = (110), \quad 7 = (111),$$

and may then represent $f(x)$ by a sequence $c_1, \ldots, c_m$, where $c_i = 0, 1, \ldots, 7$. The number e is the exponent to which $f(x)$ belongs. For example, 433 represents the coefficient sequence 100, 011, 011, and the polynomial $x^8 + x^4 + x^3 + x + 1$ belonging to $e = 51$. The tables of Marsh extend to $n = 13$, and we list only the primitive polynomials $x^{10} + x^3 + 1$ belonging to 1,023, $x^{11} + x^2 + 1$ belonging to 2,047, $x^{12} + x^6 + x^4 + x + 1$ belonging to 4,095, and $x^{13} + x^4 + x^3 + x + 1$ belonging to the prime 8,191.

n	$f(x)$	e	n	$f(x)$	e	n	$f(x)$	e
1.......	2		8.......	433	51	9......	1113	73
	3*	1		435	255		1131	511
2.......	7*	3		453	255		1137	511
3.......	13	7		455	255		1145	73
4.......	23	15		471*	17		1157	511
	37	5		477	85		1167	511
5.......	45	31		515	255		1175	511
	57	31		537	255		1207	511
	67	31		543	255		1225	511
6.......	103	63		567	85		1243	511
	111*	9		573	85		1257	511
	127	21		607	255		1267	511
	133	63		613	85		1275	511
	147	63		637	51		1317	511
7.......	207	all 27		717	255		1333	511
	211			727*	17		1423	511
	217		9.......	1003	73		1437	511
	235			1021	511		1473	511
	247			1027	73		1517	511
	253			1033	511		1533	511
	277			1055	511		1577	511
	313			1063	511		1617	511
	357							

Index